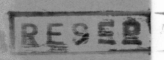
Monday, Tuesday,
Thursday and Friday
10 a.m. — 8 p.m.

Wednesday and Saturday
10 a.m. — 5 p.m.

FINES:—Fines for detention
will be charged according to
the bye-laws.

RENEWALS:—Period of loan
may be renewed if the book
is not required by another
borrower

**BOOKS DAMAGED OR
LOST:**—Readers are required
to take care of books issued
to them. Loss or damage
must be made good and the
value of books lost or
damaged will be charged.

**This book is due for return
on latest date stamped on
card.**

**PLEASE DO NOT REMOVE
CARD**—6d. fine will be
charged if lost.

LOCOMOTIVE PRACTICE AND PERFORMANCE IN THE TWENTIETH CENTURY

LOCOMOTIVE PRACTICE
AND PERFORMANCE
IN THE
TWENTIETH CENTURY

by
CECIL J. ALLEN
M.INST.T., A.I.LOCO.E.

CAMBRIDGE
W. HEFFER & SONS LTD

First Published	-	-	-	1949
Second Impression, revised		-	1950

Printed in Great Britain at the Works of
W. HEFFER & SONS LTD., CAMBRIDGE, ENGLAND

The late Sir Nigel Gresley with the Author on the trial trip of the "Coronation" streamline train, 1937. (*C. Smith.*)

∼ Foreword ∼

UNTIL now there has been no collation, in a published form, of the most outstanding performances of British locomotives on the track. From time to time these have been described in the "British Locomotive Practice and Performance" series of articles in *The Railway Magazine*, which have been appearing for nearly half-a-century, and which I have been privileged to conduct for some 40 years past. But the present generation, for the most part, does not possess the earlier volumes of this popular journal, so that to many younger students of the subject the great locomotive feats of the past remain no more than legendary.

The present book is designed to meet this need, by bringing together in one book all the most notable runs of the present century of which details are available. The majority of the "logs" so presented in Chapters 11 to 16 inclusive thus were printed first in *The Railway Magazine*, and I am indebted to the late Mr. J. A. Kay, Editor, for his agreement to their use in this book, and also for permission to reprint, from *The Railway Magazine Gradients of the British Main Line Railways*, the series of gradient profiles found on pp. 264 to 294, which make the description of these runs so much the more intelligible.

No time could be more suitable than the present for such a publication. The magnificent advance that was achieved in the quality of British locomotive performance during the years from 1932 to 1939, when a mile-a-minute standard of main line speed was established in all directions from London, was cruelly cut short by the Second World War, and because of indifferent coal, and track not yet fully restored to its pre-war condition of maintenance, many of the most brilliant achievements described in this book may remain unchallenged for many years to come. It therefore marks a milestone in British locomotive history.

For purposes of comparison, Chapter 17 gives details of the work of the highly competent modern locomotives on the mainland of Europe, particularly in France, and Chapter 18 a corresponding review of American locomotive performance. As regards the United States, it must be admitted that the amazingly high quality of the steam locomotive runs in that country that are described in Chapter 18 represent little more than normal everyday running over the routes concerned. We can teach our American friends nothing in the matter of high speed on rails.

In order that this volume may serve as a handbook to the whole subject of locomotive practice and performance, I have taken the opportunity to include a simple explanation of locomotive design, in order that the technical terms so often used in describing locomotive runs may be better understood by readers who have no more than an elementary acquaintance with these matters. Locomotive construction, maintenance, testing and handling, are covered in this survey.

The rapid advance in electric and diesel-electric traction on railways, the latter in particular, has made it necessary to include chapters on these forms of railway locomotion. So amazing has been the reception of the all-conquering diesel in the United States that within a measurable period of time steam locomotives may have disappeared entirely from express passenger trains in that country, unless they, in their turn, have to give place to an even more up-to-date competitor in the form of the gas turbine.

Finally, in response to requests from many readers of my "British Locomotive Practice and Performance" articles for information as to the best methods of train-timing, I have added a chapter dealing in detail with the subject, which I trust may prove useful to those who wish to perfect their practice of this most fascinating of journey occupations.

The attraction of this book owes much to the competence of the present-day motion picture experts, among whom I would mention especially Mr. F. E. Mackay, *doyen* of British express-train photographers, Canon Eric Treacy, Mr. Maurice W. Earley, and my good friends of Rail Photo Service in Boston, U.S.A., who put the whole of their vast collection of spectacular American train "shots" freely at my disposal. Acknowledgment is due also to the Public Relations Officers of British Railways for their assistance in the photographic realm. The ingenious sectional drawings by Mr. A. N. Wolstenholme are a further asset to the book.

Most valuable help has been given by various friends in the revision of the proofs, and in this connection I would accord grateful thanks to Mr. J. Pelham Maitland for his scrutiny of Chapters 1 to 10, Messrs. G. J. Aston, R. E. Charlewood and A. H. Holden for their work on Chapters 11 to 16, and to Mr. Basil K. Cooper for helpful advice on Chapter 19.

I would like to pay my warm tribute to the late Mr. Ernest W. Heffer, who commissioned the book and gave much kindly encouragement during its compilation, but never lived, unfortunately, to see its completion; to his successor, Mr. Reuben Heffer, and Mr. G. Newman, for their ready agreement to all the author's most extravagant requests; and especially to Mr. L. L. Asher, of the publishers' staff, to whose railway enthusiasm the book owes its inception, and whose pleasant company, as *cicerone* during many lunch-time perambulations of the byways of the beautiful town of Cambridge, will remain one of the pleasantest of recollections of the time during which this volume was in production.

Most of this book was written while there were still four independent railways in Great Britain. Their names often stray into its pages where, more properly, "Regional" titles should take their places. Personally, in common with many others who share equally in the fascination of a railway interest, I cannot but regret that the invigorating competition of the past is now at an end, and that eventually all the locomotive practice of the country is to be forced into a dull mould of rigid standardisation. Fortunately, many years must elapse before all the varied characteristics and lineaments of the past disappear from view, and nothing can extinguish the memories or the glories of the great achievements of byegone days, which this book has attempted to set on record.

CECIL J. ALLEN.

February, 1949.

~ Contents ~

Contents

– Index of Illustrations –

DEVELOPMENT: 1900–1925

THE steam locomotive to-day is fighting for its life. Half a century ago there came the first challenge to its supremacy on railways, in the form of electric traction. Such is the cost of electrification, however, that, as experience has proved, well-defined conditions are necessary before justification can be found for the expense involved—dense suburban traffic, for example, or the cheap power that can be obtained in mountainous country by hydro-electric means. In recent years, therefore, main-line railway electrification on an extensive scale has been confined chiefly to countries like Sweden, Switzerland, France, Germany, Italy, and others which have abundant resources of water power, whereas suburban electrification is found in and around all the world's greatest cities.

But now a second strong competitor has appeared on the scene, and in the United States, in particular, it is sweeping the railways like a prairie fire. This is diesel-electric propulsion, which makes possible all the advantages of electric traction, in practically continuous availability, without the cost of electrification, for each locomotive is its own self-contained power-station. Though the first diesels went into service no more than a quarter-of-a-century ago in North America, thousands of these locomotives are now in use, on high-speed passenger and long-distance freight trains, and, above all, as shunters. Over 90 per cent. of the production of the principal American locomotive building firms, for home use, is now going into diesel production.

In Great Britain, up to the taking over of the railways by the State, one principal use of diesel power had been in the smart diesel-mechanical passenger railcars of the Great Western Railway, and for another, all four British railways had made their first successful experiments with diesel-electric shunters, which thoroughly commend themselves as being able to work continuously for 24 hours a day, if necessary, without giving any trouble. In December, 1947, the London, Midland & Scottish Railway introduced the first British diesel-electric locomotives for fast passenger service—a significant development indeed—and the London & North Eastern and Southern Railways were evolving similar designs.

Until recent years, the use of oil as a fuel in British locomotives, whether in the fireboxes of steam engines, or in the cylinders of internal-combustion engines, has been ruled out as uneconomical in view of the fact that we have in Great Britain some of the finest steam coal in the world.   But the Second World War and its aftermath have changed the conditions greatly.   Coal in this country has risen in price to such an extent, while at the same time declining in both quantity and quality, as to bring the possible substitution of imported oil into a prominence never previously anticipated.   It is for this reason that about 90 British steam locomotives were fitted temporarily to burn oil instead of coal, and also that plans were made for the introduction here of diesel-electric locomotives for general service, as well as in shunting and marshalling yards.

Competition, of course, is always healthy, and the threat of these competitors has spurred those responsible for steam power to renewed attempts to increase the efficiency and the availability of the steam locomotive of traditional design.   For reasons explained in Chapters 3 and 5, the limitations within which a steam locomotive has to work, over railway tracks, have influenced design in such a way as to make it one of the most thermally inefficient of all applications of steam power, chiefly because of the heat and energy thrown to waste out of the chimney.   On the other hand, it would be difficult to imagine any other class of machine so extraordinarily flexible in its adaptation to the varied conditions of railway service, as, for example, one of the Class "5" 4-6-0 locomotives of the late L.M.S.R.,   equally at home on an express passenger train, travelling at speeds up to 90 m.p.h., or on a slow goods train, stopping everywhere to pick up or set out wagons.

Nevertheless, designers are doing their utmost to improve the steam locomotive in such a way that more heat units from the coal burned in the firebox may be turned into useful work, and also that it may spend a larger proportion of its time actually at the head of trains, and a smaller proportion standing still for servicing, maintenance and repair. To increase efficiency, there have been many developments in firebox design and other details affecting the generation of the steam, as also in steam passages, valves and valve-setting, blast-pipes and chimneys, and "front-end" design generally; to increase availability, locomotives are being fitted with rocking grates, self-cleaning smokeboxes, and other equipment intended to reduce the time that the locomotive needs to spend at the engine-shed for servicing.   With the constant improvements thus in progress, steam locomotive power may be expected to put up a good fight against its competitors on the railways for a long time to come.

As yet, of course, even steam locomotion is comparatively young. Barely a century and a half have elapsed since the Cornish mining engineer, Trevithick, associated in his mind the idea of the steam road carriage, first invented by Cugnot in 1770, with the iron plateways which had been in existence for a considerable time previously, enabling horses to pull considerably greater loads of minerals than they could drag over the rough roads of the period. So there emerged, in 1804, the first railway locomotive. Twenty-three years more were to pass before the first steam-operated public railway, between Stockton and Darlington, was opened for traffic, and it was not until 1829 that George Stephenson, with the locomotive that he named the *Rocket*, established steam rail transport on a firm footing. In the *Rocket* Stephenson, assisted by his son Robert, combined two principles—the multi-tubular boiler, first suggested by Henry Booth, and the use of the exhaust steam from the cylinders to provide draught for the fire—which still lie at the basis of normal steam locomotive design.

Into the development of the locomotive from the earliest years it is not necessary to go; many able historians have put the facts on record; and this present book is concerned alone with the locomotives of the Twentieth Century. But it is necessary to lay stress on the influence exerted on British locomotive practice, as we find it when the present century opened, by the matter of draught just mentioned.

Probably it is no exaggeration to say that the quality, the abundance and the cheapness of coal in Great Britain in no small measure impeded the development of the British steam locomotive in the first century of its history. By the year 1900 the locomotives of this country, in general, were of small dimensions and light weight in relation to the work that they were called upon to perform; they were of robust but very simple design; and the ratio of cylinder volume to firegrate area and heating surface was high.

Designers found that by working such engines with a late cut-off, the blast could be sharpened to any degree of fierceness necessary for the production of steam to meet the most extreme demands. Vociferous locomotive exhausts in those days, and showers of cinders pattering on carriage roofs, witnessed loudly to the fact that the locomotives were being "thrashed," and, moreover, to the fact that a considerable proportion of the fuel was being drawn through the tubes and thrown out of the chimneys in a condition only partially consumed. But what did it matter? Coal was cheap; and with the railway directorates of the period doubtless it was much to the credit of their Locomotive Superintendents that locomotives of such modest dimensions and cost—by comparison, say, with those in use on the mainland of Europe or in America—could be relied on to perform such prodigies of haulage and speed.

A second hampering influence in British locomotive design has been the absence in this country of any systematic method of training engine-crews. As compared, say, with France, where drivers require to serve for two years as fitters and to qualify as such before being permitted to drive, the British driver picks up his experience solely by what he sees during his years of cleaning and firing, with the help of knowledge acquired in Mutual Improvement classes (if he has availed himself of the excellent opportunities offered by the latter). This is no disparagement of an exceedingly fine body of men, many of whom become experts in the handling of their engines; but as seniority rather than merit is the normal basis of advancement, this expert knowledge is by no means as general as it might be. Moreover, as a result of the difficulty of getting many of the conservatively-minded drivers away from the older and more traditional methods of driving, design in Great Britain has always tended in the direction of simplicity, and away from any kind of complication.

The third limitation on British locomotive design has been that of the loading gauge, more restricted than that of most, if not all, the other principal countries in the world. This matter is gone into in more detail in Chapter 3; at this stage it is sufficient to say that these restrictions have been felt the most acutely, probably, in the development of locomotive boilers in this country, and in particular of fireboxes. But it was well after the opening of the Twentieth Century that designers in general began to feel themselves hampered in any serious degree by limitations of space.

At the beginning of the century, the reign of the 4-4-0 locomotive on express passenger service was almost universal. Single-driver locomotives, mostly of the 4-2-2 type, were still fairly extensively in use on the Midland, Great Northern, Great Western, and North Eastern lines; and new engines of this wheel arrangement were built as late as 1898 by the Great Northern and Great Eastern, and 1900 by the Midland and Great Central. But with the introduction of corridor trains and dining cars, trains by now were increasing in weight to such a degree that the maximum adhesion weight of 20 tons obtained with a single pair of driving wheels was rapidly becoming insufficient. The first Atlantic (4-4-2) locomotives had made their appearance on the Great Northern and Lancashire & Yorkshire Railways in 1898 and 1899 respectively, and the first express passenger 4-6-0 made its *début* on the North Eastern Railway in 1900.

Certain locomotive engineers at this period, however, were alive to the need for more efficient means of producing and using steam than those then current. In the first decade of the century two names came into prominence—those of H. A. Ivatt, then Locomotive Superintendent of the Great Northern, and G. J. Churchward, who succeeded to the corresponding office on the Great Western Railway in 1902. The latter was destined to have a greater influence on British locomotive practice in general than any other individual engineer in history; though it took a quarter of a century for the basic principles that he laid down at Swindon to come into use on the other railways of the country.

In the year 1902, Ivatt, who, as previously mentioned, had introduced an Atlantic design on the G.N.R. four years earlier, turned out a second edition of this in which, for the first time, advantage was taken of the wheel arrangement to mount behind the coupled wheels a wide firebox extending to the full width of the engine. This he combined with a boiler of the then unprecedented diameter of 5 ft. 6 in. Not only so, but he retained the relatively small cylinders, 18¾ in. diameter by 24 in. stroke, with which his previous Atlantics had been fitted. This was a complete reversal of the contemporary practice of mating cylinders of about 19 in. diameter and 26 in. stroke to a boiler with 1,000 sq. ft. less of heating surface and a considerably smaller firegrate. Thus Ivatt initiated on the Great Northern the "big engine" policy which was continued by his successor, H. N. Gresley—later Sir Nigel Gresley—and which proved of such inestimable benefit to the London & North Eastern Railway in later years. It was the policy of building locomotives with a reserve of power more than ample to cope with all abnormal as well as normal service conditions.

When Churchward took over the reins at Swindon, the first Great Western express passenger 4-6-0 had just been built, nominally to the designs of William Dean, though there is little doubt that Churchward, as second-in-command, was mainly responsible for the design. This engine, originally carrying the number 100, but later No. 2900, *William Dean*, was the first of a long series of G.W.R. 4-6-0 locomotives which in the main features of their design have changed but little from that day to this. No. 100 had cylinders of 18 in. diameter with the unusually long stroke of 30 in., 6 ft. 8 in. driving wheels, a working pressure of of 200 lb. per sq. in., piston-valves in place of slide-valves, and, above all, long-travel valves which made it possible to work the engine with an early cut-off, and so to make the maximum use of the expansive properties of the steam.

By this time, compound locomotive working in France had made great strides, and the performances of the de Glehn four-cylinder compound express engines, particularly on the Northern Railway of France, were attracting a good deal of attention. In 1903 and 1905, therefore, three locomotives of this type were built for the G.W.R. by a well-known French firm in Belfort, to be tried against Churchward's engines, both of the 4-6-0 and 4-4-2 types, for Churchward had built a number of Atlantics identical with the 4-6-0s in all respects other than the number of coupled wheels. Lengthy comparative trials proved that Churchward, as a result of his methods of front-end design, was obtaining much the same overall thermal efficiency with simple expansion as the French were with compounding, and with two exceptions, no change in Churchward policy resulted from the working of the French engines on British metals.

One exception was the use of four cylinders, though still with simple expansion, instead of two; the other concerned the working pressure. As then customary in France, the French compounds carried boilers pressed to 227 lb. per. sq. in.; and for the purposes of comparison, Churchward fitted his engines with 225 lb. boilers, a record pressure in Great Britain at that time. The higher pressure, coupled with the Churchward valve-setting, unusually large steam and exhaust ports, and early cut-off working, added still further to the efficiency of his engines, and from that time onwards became standard Great Western practice with the larger locomotives. This was at a time when working pressures on other British railways seldom exceeded 180 lb. per sq. in., and often were no higher than 160 lb.

The next important development in British locomotive practice was the introduction of superheating. As far back as 1899 Sir John Aspinall had fitted one of his Lancashire & Yorkshire Atlantics with a smokebox superheater which proved quite efficient, but it was not until a German engineer, Wilhelm Schmidt, of Cassel, had perfected his high temperature superheater, that the full advantages of super-heating on locomotives became apparent. The first Schmidt patents were tried out in Germany from 1898 onwards, and by 1905 the later and more successful type of Schmidt superheater began to come into general use in Europe. In Great Britain the first trial was again on the L. & Y.R., where George Hughes fitted a couple of his goods engines with the equipment late in 1906. But it was Earle Marsh, of the London, Brighton & South Coast, who was destined to publicise, in a striking way, the benefits of superheated steam.

In the autumn of 1907 Earle Marsh had turned out of Brighton Works a new type of 4-4-2 tank engine with driving wheels of 6 ft. 9 in. diameter, and 19 in. by 26 in. cylinders, for express passenger service. In the following year five more of these engines were built, in which the designer incorporated the Schmidt superheating equipment, at the same time enlarging the diameter of his cylinders to 21 in. Ultimately seven of the non-superheated tanks were on test against ten fitted with superheaters. But the most spectacular trial was one arranged with the London & North Western Railway in the working of the "Sunny South Express" between Rugby and Brighton.

For the month of November, 1909, it was arranged that Brighton tank No. 23 should run the train through over the 132 miles from Brighton to Rugby, returning on the following day; and that the opposite working should be undertaken by the London & North Western non-superheated "Precursor" class 4-4-0 No. 7, *Titan*. The 75-ton Brighton engine had a tank capacity no greater than 2,110 gallons and no apparatus for picking up water *en route*; yet day after day she would run the 90 miles between East Croydon and Rugby without tank replenishment, including the 77¼-mile non-stop run between Willesden Junction and Rugby, with a 235-ton train, at a scheduled average of 53 m.p.h. Moreover, the two-day round trip of 264 miles was completed on one heaped-up bunkerful of coal, about 3¼ tons all told. Average consumption was thus 27 lb. of coal and 22 gallons of water per mile. No more convincing exhibition than this could have been given of the advantages of superheating; from the efficiency point of view the Brighton tank was an easy winner.

The immediate result of this exchange working, so far as the London & North Western was concerned, was the production at Crewe in 1910 of the first "George the Fifth" class 4-4-0 engines, a superheated development of the "Precursors." As in the days of Webb, the L.N.W.R. was still building the smallest locomotives which would cope with the demands of its operating authorities, and the "George the Fifth" engines, amazing though their performances certainly were in relation to their 60 tons of weight, were no exception to the rule. The excellence of their work was due in part to very accurate valve-setting, in which the suppliers of the superheaters are believed to have had some say; but even so, with the heaviest loads and fastest trains, long cut-offs and heavy coal consumption were inevitable. By now 400-ton trains were becoming common, together with start-to-stop average speeds of 52 to 55 m.p.h., and the tax on locomotive power was increasing rapidly.

The next locomotive event of importance was the appearance on L.N.W.R. metals, in 1910, of the Great Western Churchward four-cylinder 4-6-0 *Polar Star*, in exchange for which the North Western sent an "Experiment" class 4-6-0, *Worcestershire*, over to the G.W.R. But between the 66-ton non-superheated L.N.W.R. 4-6-0, with its 6 ft. 3 in. driving wheels and 180 lb. pressure, and the G.W.R. 6 ft. 8 in. 4-6-0 with 225 lb. pressure and all the Churchward refinements of design, there was so utter a disparity that the result of the trials was a foregone conclusion. The Great Western engine made light of all its North Western tasks; the North Western 4-6-0, after a gallant fight against hopeless odds, returned to Crewe in a badly strained condition.

In the "Prince of Wales" 4-6-0 engines, Bowen Cooke supplied the L.N.W.R. in 1912 with a superheated version of the "Experiments" which was a considerable improvement on its predecessors; the real upshot of the G.W.R.-L.N.W.R. exchange, however, was the appearance, in 1913, of the Bowen Cooke four-cylinder 4-6-0 "Claughton" class. Yet even in this new L.N.W.R. design none of the lessons of the exchange appeared to have been learned; the engines were under-boilered, and the steam distribution arrangements in general were unchanged. As a result, the performance of these much larger engines showed little or no advance on that of the "George the Fifth" 4-4-0s and "Prince of Wales" 4-6-0s.

In the decade from 1910 onwards, the First World War held up new locomotive developments, and the principal advance made was that brought about by superheating. The performance of numerous loco-motive classes was greatly improved, and in some cases almost completely transformed, by the addition of superheating equipment. Churchward of the Great Western Railway maintained that none of the heat energy put into the superheating of the steam should be thrown to waste out of the chimney, and contented himself with what was little more than steam drying; with the carefully selected Welsh coal supplied to his engines, his theory worked out well enough on his own system. Elesewhere, however, a higher temperature of superheat was found to be desirable; and with the decline in the quality of British fuel in later years, even the G.W.R. had to modify its policy in the same direction.

At first, with the introduction of superheating, which made it possible to increase both the volume of the steam, and the range of expansion, without fear of condensation, and so to enlarge cylinders, there was a tendency among locomotive designers to reduce the boiler pressures (with a view to economy in boiler maintenance), thus main-taining tractive efforts unchanged. But this reversal of the trend of rising pressures was only temporary, and in later years both working pressures and superheat temperatures (the latter by the installation of progressively bigger superheaters) have been increasing to the highest practicable limits, as development along these lines, coupled with proper front-end design in general, is found to provide the surest road towards increased thermal efficiency.

Among the locomotive types transformed by superheating were the famous Ivatt Atlantics of the Great Northern Railway. His first superheated version of this class, built in 1910, had the cylinders enlarged in diameter from 18¾ to 20 in., while still retaining the short stroke of 24 in., but the working pressure was brought down from 175 to 160 lb. per sq. in. In later years, the original pressure was restored, and these locomotives then entered upon the more notable stage of their careers, which reached their zenith, perhaps, in the working of the moderately-weighted and very fast Pullman services between London and Leeds from the middle 1920's to the middle 1930's.

All three partners in the East Coast Route—the Great Northern, North Eastern and North British Railways—had standardised the 4-4-2 wheel arrangement for their principal express passenger workings, while the Great Western, London & North Western, Caledonian, and London & South Western were depending on 4-6-0 and 4-4-0 designs. The Midland Railway, which specialised in a frequent express train service of relatively light trains, used nothing more powerful than 4-4-0 locomotives in express passenger service, and continued to do so until after entering the London, Midland & Scottish group in 1923. Similarly with its freight services, the Midland depended still on 0-6-0 locomotives long after most of the other principal lines had turned to 0-8-0 and 2-8-0 designs. The South Eastern & Chatham was another company which used 4-4-0 locomotives exclusively for passenger service until after the grouping. In both the latter cases, restrictions in maximum permissible locomotive weight because of weak underline bridges on main routes played a major part in this locomotive limitation.

Another development of note during this decade was that of multi-cylinder propulsion. Apart from compound locomotives, and one or two experimental engines, the use of more cylinders than two was confined to the four-cylinder express engines of the London & South Western (first introduced by Drummond in 1897), Great Western (Churchward, 1906), and Lancashire & Yorkshire (Hughes, 1909) Railways. Then Raven, of the North Eastern Railway, in 1910, built his first three-cylinder design—a 4-6-2 mineral tank—following this in 1911 with a three-cylinder Atlantic express engine. Not only did these locomotives prove the forerunners of a number of North Eastern three-cylinder classes, but they foreshadowed what was to become, under Sir Nigel Gresley, the general standard of construction for the London & North Eastern Railway, including express passenger, mixed traffic, freight, and tank classes.

In 1911 Gresley took over the reins of control from Ivatt at Doncaster Works. It was not until 1920 that his first three-cylinder mixed traffic engine—G.N.R. No. 1000, a 2-6-0, which afterwards became the L.N.E.R. Class "K3"—emerged from Doncaster Works.

Two years later there followed No. 1470, *Great Northern*, his first Pacific. Actually Churchward of the Great Western had built a four-cylinder Pacific—No. 111, *The Great Bear*—as far back as 1908; but the chassis designs of Churchward were not the equal of his boilers and front-ends, and No. 111 showed so incurable a tendency to leave the track that eventually the engine was rebuilt as a 4-6-0. By contrast, the Gresley Pacific and its successors were destined to become some of the most famous locomotives that this country has yet known, and to be expanded to a class of well over one hundred engines.

2

DEVELOPMENT: 1925—1947

IN 1925 there occurred in Great Britain an event which had a considerable influence on subsequent British locomotive practice, and in it the Gresley Pacific design was concerned. At the Wembley Exhibition of 1924 one of these engines, London & North Eastern Railway No. 4472, *Flying Scotsman*, was exhibited alongside No. 4073, *Caerphilly Castle*, of the Great Western Railway, which had been turned out of Swindon Works to the designs of C. B. Collett, the successor of Churchward, in the preceding year. Notwithstanding the fact that the L.N.E.R. locomotive was considerably the bigger and heavier of the two, the G.W.R. advertised their exhibit as being "the most powerful express passenger engine in Great Britain." This, on a tractive effort basis, they were entitled to do, for the G.W.R. locomotive, with its 225 lb. pressure, had a nominal tractive effort of 31,625 lb., whereas that of the L.N.E.R. Pacific was 29,835 lb. The upshot was a challenge from Gresley to the Great Western authorities to prove their contention on the road.

This challenge was accepted, and in May, 1925, G.W.R. "Castle" 4-6-0 No. 4079, *Pendennis Castle*, went over to the L.N.E.R. for a fortnight's comparative trials between Kings Cross and Doncaster, and L.N.E.R. Pacific No. 4474, *Victor Wild*, ran over the G.W.R. between Paddington and Plymouth, for the second week on the "Cornish Riviera Limited" express in each direction. The results were remarkable. The "Castles," 80 tons in weight (without tender), as compared with the 92 tons of the Pacifics, made slightly better times than the Pacifics, on an average coal consumption which was 3·7 lb. per mile less over L.N.E.R. metals with Yorkshire coal, and 6 lb. per mile less with Welsh coal on the G.W.R. runs.

This was by no means to disparage the performance of the Gresley engines. Many observers considered that the feat of the L.N.E.R. driver Pibworth in working the down "Cornish Riviera" to time after no more than a week's acquaintance with the unusual characteristics of the Paddington-Plymouth road, and with downhill speeds, over the constant curvature of the route, limited by the longer wheelbase of his engine (35 ft. 9 in. as compared with the 27 ft. 3 in. of the "Castle") was the finest piece of locomotive handling in the tests. Moreover, his fireman, Birkwood, was bringing his coal consumption down steadily as he became more accustomed to the Great Western line; with the up "Limited" there was a fall from 50·9 to 40·4 lb. per mile on the three consecutive up journeys.

But with all such qualifications, the superiority of the Swindon principles of design initiated by Churchward was now beyond dispute. Gresley was too big a man to refrain from taking action through his personal prestige being at stake. After successful experiments had been made with one of the "A1" Pacifics, in which the valve-setting was altered to permit of early cut-off working, No. 4480, *Enterprise*, was rebuilt in 1927 with a boiler carrying 220 lb. pressure (instead of the previous 180 lb.), a maximum valve travel, in full gear, of 5¾ in. as compared with 4 9/16 in., and a considerably larger superheater, with 43 elements as compared with the previous 32. Thus began the "A3" class of Gresley Pacifics, and the changes in Gresley policy so introduced became permanent from that time onwards.

Meantime, in 1926, another locomotive exchange had taken place in which a Great Western "Castle" was concerned. This was the loan to the London, Midland & Scottish Railway, in that year, of No. 5000, *Launceston Castle*, which made a number of journeys between London, Crewe and Carlisle. Sir Henry Fowler, who was Chief Mechanical Engineer of the Midland Railway at the time of the grouping, and had assumed the same L.M.S.R. office in 1925, was a man of advanced ideas. In 1923 he had completed the design of a three-cylinder compound 4-6-0, on the lines of the Midland 4-4-0 compounds; and in 1926 he followed this with a 4-6-2 four-cylinder compound design of considerable note, based largely on the successful Pacific compounds of the Northern Railway of France, and with 240 lb. per sq. in. steam pressure.

It is a thousand pities that neither of these engines was ever built; they might have helped in solving the problem as to whether a compound locomotive, built within the narrow restrictions of the British loading gauge, but with modern refinements in valve-setting and front-end design generally, could compete in overall thermal efficiency with the best contemporary British designs, such as the Great Western 4-6-0 engines. Unfortunately, however, Fowler had neither the unrestricted sway of Gresley on the L.N.E.R., nor the combined control of locomotive building and operation, as Churchward and Collett had on the G.W.R. at Swindon. The opposition of the L.M.S.R. operating authorities, steeped as they were in the "small engine" tradition of the London & North Western and Midland Railways, was such that these enterprising Fowler designs went no further than the drawing-board stage.

But augmented L.M.S.R. locomotive power was needed urgently, and it was in these conditions that the loan of *Launceston Castle* was obtained from the G.W.R. for trial purposes. On L.M.S.R. metals the triumph of the Great Western engine was more pronounced than on the L.N.E.R., for the "Castle" had no other design of anything like equal merit with which to compete. With her imperturbable driver, William Young (who also drove *Pendennis Castle* on the L.N.E.R. the previous year), the engine showed an easy mastery over every allotted task, and broke every record that had been made in the L.M.S.R. dynamometer car up to that time. The upshot of these trials was the emergence of the L.M.S.R. "Royal Scot" 4-6-0 class in 1927.

It should be mentioned here that in 1926 R.E.L. Maunsell, Chief Mechanical Engineer of the Southern Railway, had produced his four-cylinder 4-6-0 "Lord Nelson" design. Nominally this class, with a tractive effort of 33,500 lb., was even more powerful than the Great Western "Castles"; but the tractive force formula takes no account of the capacity of the boiler to raise sufficient steam to make it effective; and although the "Castle" design is known to have been studied in the evolution of the "Lord Nelsons," the average performance of the latter, in their original condition, was not the equal of that of the "Castles." In view of the speed with which the L.M.S.R. "Royal Scot" design had to be got out (for twelve months only were available, from the decision to build, in which to produce the completed engines), the "Lord Nelson" drawings were loaned to the L.M.S.R., and controversy arose in later years as to whether the "Royal Scot" was actually based on the "Lord Nelson" design.

Certainly there were many close similarities, but the L.M.S.R. has made it clear that the major influence on the design, in regard to high boiler pressure (250 lb. per sq. in.), simple expansion, and long-lap, long-travel valve-motion, was the performance of *Launceston Castle* on L.M.S.R. metals. From the Southern engines, the principal features copied were the firebox design and proportions, and the use of steel stays. The L.M.S.R. thus joined the L.N.E.R. in adopting the features of Swindon practice which had the strongest influence in increasing thermal efficiency and in facilitating the maintenance of high speeds continuously in hard steaming conditions. Maunsell of the Southern had taken a similar step considerably earlier, in his Mogul (2-6-0) design first built in 1917 for the South Eastern & Chatham Railway.

The year 1927 also witnessed the production of the Great Western "King" 4-6-0 class. Most locomotive designers would have preferred to mount this 89-ton locomotive on a 4-6-2 rather than a 4-6-0 chassis, but with recollections, no doubt, of the difficulties experienced with *The Great Bear*, C. B. Collett decided to stick to the 4-6-0 wheel arrangement. Like the L.M.S.R. "Royal Scots," in the G.W.R. "Kings" the working pressure was stepped up to 250 lb. per sq. in., and with driving wheels slightly smaller than those of the "Castles," the tractive effort of the "Kings" rose to the then unprecedented figure of 40,300 lb. Magnificent though the work of the "Kings" has been, it cannot be said that in all respects the latter has been so successful a design as the "Castles," and this doubtless helps to explain why no more than thirty of the former have been built.

The next British locomotive event of note was the appointment as Chief Mechanical Engineer, London Midland & Scottish Railway, of Mr. W. A. Stanier (later Sir William Stanier), who until then had been Assistant Chief Mechanical Engineer of the Great Western Railway at Swindon. With him, Swindon practice in general was transferred to the L.M.S.R., including taper boilers without steam-domes, steam-drying instead of high temperature superheat, and various other characteristic features of Great Western locomotive design. But not all these changes were to be permanent.

Reversion to high temperature superheat soon became necessary, for without G.W.R. Welsh coal many of the engines were soon in trouble with steaming; and before long steam domes also reappeared. But with these minor modifications, the change of direction was all to the good. In 1933 the first Stanier Pacific—No. 6200, *The Princess Royal*—took the rails, dimensionally almost exactly equal to a Great Western "King" in all respects other than the provision of a far larger boiler and firebox. The year 1934 saw the emergence of the first Stanier 4-6-0s of the "Jubilee" three-cylinder type, for express passenger work. and the 6 ft. Class "5" type, for mixed traffic. The latter, of which over 800 have now been built, have proved the most competent and versatile engines of their type that the country has ever seen, adaptable equally, as already mentioned in Chapter 1, to the haulage of heavy freight trains and of express passenger trains at speeds up to 90 m.p.h. New 2-6-4 and 2-6-2 modifications of existing Fowler tank engines of the same wheel arrangement, and a new 2-8-0 freight design, soon followed.

By the year 1932 the tide of main-line train acceleration in Great Britain had set in strongly, especially on the L.N.E.R. and L.M.S.R., and locomotives capable of even higher speeds were now being called for. In time for the inauguration, at the end of September, 1935, of Britain's first streamlined express—the L.N.E.R. "Silver Jubilee"— Gresley designed and built the first of his "A4" streamlined modifications of the "A3" Pacifics. The "A4" has proved one of the most outstanding designs in British locomotive history. As set out in detail in Chapter 14, engines of this class have attained what is believed to be the world's record maximum speed with steam—126 m.p.h.—and have exceeded 100 m.p.h. on many occasions; one has run 43 miles continuously at an average of 100 m.p.h. with a 235-ton train; and at the other end of the load scale an "A4" has covered 25 level miles with a 730-ton train at a mean speed of 76 m.p.h. For in addition to working the streamline trains, which eventually numbered three, with exemplary reliability and accurate timekeeping, these engines have always shared in the working of the fast and heavy main-line expresses, in which they have shown themselves definitely superior to their "A1" and "A3" predecessors.

One particularly notable Gresley design was his Class "P2" three-cylinder 2-8-2 for service between Edinburgh and Aberdeen, where most of the starts from intermediate stops, and recoveries from service slacks, have to be made up unusually steep inclines, so that ample tractive power and adequate adhesion are both needed with heavy trains. Some trouble, both with overheated bearings and with disturbance of the sharply curved permanent way over this section, was experienced with these engines, but apart from this they did fine work, and made unnecessary a good deal of the double-heading of trains previously needed. Yet after Gresley's death, on the grounds of excessive costs of maintenance, his successor converted them all to 4-6-2 engines, reducing their adhesion weight by nearly one-quarter in consequence.

One cannot help thinking that a more far-sighted measure would have been to find means of curing the troubles, and so of justifying this bold experiment. For the time must come (as already it has done in other countries) when eight-coupled locomotives will be needed in Great Britain to provide sufficient adhesion for heavy express passenger work. The liability to slipping of most of the British Pacific designs, when starting from rest, leaves little doubt that in this country tractive effort is beginning to outstrip adhesion weight. It might be added that one of Gresley's last designs, before his untimely death, was a very large 4-8-2 express engine with three 21 in. × 28 in. cylinders, 250 lb. pressure, 80 tons adhesion out of a total engine weight of 115 tons (175 tons with tender), and 6 ft. 8 in. driving wheels for high-speed work. It was intended to begin work on these engines immediately after the war; but, most unhappily, the designer's death intervened.

It should be remarked here that Gresley was responsible for many other designs during his *régime* as Chief Mechanical Engineer of the L.N.E.R., all with three cylinders and his patent derived motion for the inside cylinder. These included the 4-4-0 "Shires" and "Hunts" for intermediate passenger work; the "Sandringham" or "B17" class, initially for the Great Eastern Section, with its weight restrictions; several 2-8-0 tender freight and 2-6-2 tank classes; and, in 1936, the unique and highly successful "V2" 2-6-2 engines of the "Green Arrow" series, theoretically a mixed traffic design with 6 ft. 2 in. driving wheels, but actually used on many of the fastest and heaviest main-line duties, as, for example, the "Yorkshire Pullman" on its pre-war mile-a-minute runs between Kings Cross and Doncaster. When Sir Nigel Gresley died in harness, in 1941, he left a profound impression on London & North Eastern locomotive practice, and few would dispute that he ranks as one of the most distinguished and large-minded locomotive engineers that Great Britain has ever known.

With the introduction of the "Coronation Scot" streamline train by the L.M.S.R. in 1937, Stanier brought out a modified version of his Pacific design, fully streamlined, to work the train. This modification has been built since in both streamlined and non-streamlined versions, but the streamlining has now been removed from those engines which carried it as having been of but limited practical value as compared with the difficulty and expense that it added to normal maintenance. These later Stanier Pacifics also have collected some very notable performance records, as set out in Chapter 12, including indicated horse-power outputs of well over 3,000, the highest in British locomotive history. This became the standard L.M.S.R. type for the principal main-line duties.

On the Southern Railway the most outstanding locomotive design introduced by Maunsell after his "Lord Nelson" 4-6-0s of 1926 was, with little doubt, his three-cylinder "Schools" 4-4-0 class of 1930. The need for these engines arose from the difficulty of working the Tonbridge and Hastings line, with its scant clearances and very severe gradients. A 4-4-0 design was evolved, therefore, as nearly as possible the equal of a 4-6-0 in all respects but adhesion. This involved the imposition of no less than 25 tons of the engine's 67-ton weight on the bogie. Easily the most powerful 4-4-0 locomotives in the country, the Southern "Schools" have given an extremely good account of themselves. As may be seen in Chapter 16, they have proved themselves all but the equals in tractive capacity of the 81-ton 4-6-0 "King Arthurs," and have been able to keep time with trains of up to 15 bogie vehicles on the fast Waterloo and Bournemouth schedules.

In 1937, Mr. O. V. Bulleid succeeded to the position of Chief Mechanical Engineer, Southern Railway, and from then onwards the most outstanding developments in British locomotive practice have been under his direction. Until then Mr. Bulleid had been Personal Assistant to Sir Nigel Gresley on the L.N.E.R., but there is little Gresley influence to be seen in the former's Southern Railway designs, which are remarkably original in almost every respect. Chief among them are the Pacifics of the "Merchant Navy" and "West Country" series, which incorporate such novelties in Great Britain as the first use of a working pressure as high as 280 lb. per sq. in.; the designer's patent radial valve-motion, chain-driven and completely enclosed, with the inside connecting-rod, crosshead, slide-bar and crank-pin, in an oil-bath; thermic syphons to improve the firebox circulation; a steel firebox almost completely welded, instead of riveted; and special assistance for the fireman in the shape of a power-operated firedoor.

It is evidence of the modern improvement in front-end design that these locomotives, despite the fact of driving wheels of more than 6 ft. 2 in. diameter, run with the utmost freedom at speeds of 80 m.p.h. and over on level track, so making possible almost unlimited recovery of lost time, while equally they are able to tackle loads of a magnitude previously unknown over the heavy gradients west of Salisbury and elsewhere. Another notable Bulleid design, which has attracted a good deal of attention because of its unconventional, and, indeed, bizarre, appearance, is the "Q1" 0-6-0, the most powerful British type yet to be mounted on three axles, and the first 0-6-0 to carry 230 lb. pressure and to exert a tractive force of 30,000 lb. The curious appearance referred to was dictated both by the desire to reduce weight, so as to increase to the maximum extent possible the radius of action of these locomotives, and also to economise in the use of steel.

Throughout all this later period of British locomotive history, certain changes have been more or less general. Working pressures have been rising, until few locomotives are now being built with a less pressure than 200 lb., and three types are running with 280 lb. pressure. With the radical improvement in front-end design, which means that locomotives can get rid of their exhaust with much more freedom than before, driving wheels tend to be reduced in diameter, as in this way, without sacrifice of speed, the locomotives can be made adaptable to a wider range of duties. Of this development the 6 ft. 2 in. driving wheels of the Southern and the final series of London & North Eastern Pacifics, as well as the L.N.E.R. "V2" 2-6-2 engines, are an illustration, as all of these take part in the fastest passenger as well as freight duties.

Also, in connection with exhaust, the effect of the researches of certain French locomotive engineers is seen over here in the Kylchap and similar exhaust arrangements, with an elongated double chimney, fitted to certain L.M.S.R. and L.N.E.R. engines, or the Lemaître multiple-jet exhaust, with large-diameter chimney, introduced by the Southern Railway. In every possible way steam-flow has been improved by the elimination of sharp angles in steam passages, enlargement of steam-pipes, and so on; of this, external evidence is seen on all modern locomotives in the direct outside steam-pipes from the smokebox to the cylinders. Running-plates are now raised high above the wheels, in order to expose the motion more fully and thus to facilitate examination and maintenance, and also to provide better ventilation for axleboxes and motion details, so checking the tendency for bearings to overheat.

In addition to evolving new locomotive types, during the past quarter of a century much has been done in the rebuilding and modernisation of older types, in such a way as to increase, not merely their span of life, but also their power and efficiency. Some such rebuildings have been so complete as virtually to be "replacements" rather than the "renewals" as which they figure in the accounts; but in many cases the major replacement has been that of the boiler, and much of the material in the remainder of the locomotive, such as wheels and motion, has remained. Among the most notable of such reconstructions is that of the "Royal Scot" 4-6-0 locomotives of the late L.M.S.R. with taper boilers, double exhaust pipes and chimneys, and other modifications, transforming them into one of the most capable and efficient 4-6-0 classes in the country. A beginning has been made with a similar transformation of the "Patriot" series of 4-6-0s of Class "5XP," and the "Jubilee" 4-6-0s will receive similar attention later, bringing all three classes into one uniform standard Class "6" 4-6-0 of the highest competence.

Scant reference has been made in the present or the preceding chapter to freight and tank locomotives, but this is because the main trend in British design has been set by the express passenger classes. The period of independent railways has ended with the 2-8-0 wheel arrangement standard for heavy freight service on the L.M.S.R., L.N.E.R., and G.W.R., and with mixed traffic 4-6-0 and 2-6-0 classes taking a considerable share, especially in the working of fast freight trains, on these three railways and the Southern also. The L.N.E.R., as already mentioned, also built a 2-6-2 type extensively for fast freight working. For the lighter freight tasks all four groups continued to make use, on a very considerable scale, of 0-6-0 locomotives.

As to tank locomotives, the desire to enlarge tank and bunker capacity, and so to increase the length of run between the replenishment of supplies, resulted in the building by the L.M.S.R., L.N.E.R., and G.W.R. of large numbers of 2-6-2 tanks, in place of the earlier 0-6-2, 2-4-2 and 0-4-4 types; many larger 2-6-4 tanks have come into use on the L.M.S.R. also, and a similar L.N.E.R. design is being built in large numbers. Shunting has been conducted mainly by 0-6-0 tanks, with 0-8-0, 2-8-0, 4-8-0 and other bigger engines for the more onerous marshalling yard assignments. Great Britain continues to be the only country in the world which builds tank locomotives extensively.

In concluding this chapter, a word is necessary as to various attempts which have been made to break away in this country from the traditional in locomotive design, though with little measurable result. Among them have been the substitution of turbine or turbo-electric propulsion for cylinders and reciprocating motion. Two designs only have had any successful trials on British railways, and in both cases on the L.M.S.R. In 1926 and 1927 a locomotive built in accordance with the Swedish Ljüngstrom patents by Beyer Peacock & Company was tried for some time over the Midland Division; it had geared turbines, a condensing plant, a working pressure of 285 lb. per sq. in., a length of 74 ft. and a weight of 144 tons. No difficulty was experienced in keeping time on the schedules then in force, but nothing was heard later as to whether sufficient economies had been effected in running to justify the high constructional cost.

In 1935 the L.M.S.R. introduced a turbine locomotive of its own design, No. 6202, uniform in all respects with the first series of Stanier Pacifics save for having turbine drive. This engine also has handled successfully some of the heaviest and fastest trains, but without the assistance of a condensing plant the coal consumption has been heavier than of the sister Pacifics of normal design, and in addition there have been many breakdowns in service. The Pennsylvania Railroad of the United States has experimented unsuccessfully with an immense turbine-driven locomotive of the 6-8-6 wheel arrangement and the Chesapeake & Ohio has under test a vast steam turbine-electric unit.

In 1929, when experiments were in progress on the Continent with super-pressure locomotives, in an attempt to utilise the expansive properties of steam at a considerably higher pressure and temperature than ever previously, two such locomotives appeared in Great Britain. Both were designed for compound propulsion. One, on the L.N.E.R., was a large four-cylinder 4-6-4 compound, No. 10000, with a Yarrow marine water-tube boiler in place of the normal locomotive-type boiler, generating steam at 450 lb. per sq. in. The other, on the L.M.S.R., was a 4-6-0, No. 6399, *Fury*, in general dimensions uniform with the "Royal Scot" engines, but with a super-pressure boiler of special design generating at 900 lb. per sq. in. Similar super-pressure boilers, making steam at up to 1,000 lb. per sq. in., had been on trial on locomotives in several European countries and in Canada.

The L.N.E.R. engine made a number of fairly satisfactory runs, including one on the non-stop "Flying Scotsman" between London and Edinburgh; but the steaming was uncertain and the costs of maintenance were excessive. After some years, therefore, No. 10000 was rebuilt as a streamlined three-cylinder simple 4-6-4 with an ordinary boiler, since when she has done some very fine work. On the L.M.S.R., *Fury*, unfortunately, was the cause of a fatal accident, due to the bursting of a high pressure steam tube, and eventually this engine also was rebuilt as No. 6170, *British Legion*, the first of the taper boiler "Royal Scots."

And now, with the nationalisation of the railways, the days of independent locomotive designing have come to an end on British railways. While for some time, doubtless, there will be a measure of interest in watching the trial of many locomotive classes over routes other than those for which they were designed originally, this interest is bound progressively to diminish as the whole of the locomotives in the country gradually are reduced in variety to relatively few standard types. Moreover, ultimately there will no longer be any competition in performance or efficiency between the designs of different railways, and a valuable spur to progress will have been lost.

The appointment to the Railway Executive, British Railways, of Mr. R. A. Riddles, a Vice-President of the L.M.S.R., as the member in charge of all matters relating to rolling stock, with L.M.S.R. technical experts as his chief assistants, foreshadows the adoption in large measure of the L.M.S.R. standards of design laid down by Sir William Stanier, and based in part at least on the Churchward principles of the G.W.R. Doubtless this choice was almost inevitable, in view of the fact that the L.M.S.R. and G.W.R., up to the time of nationalisation, had proceeded further with standardisation of motive power than the remaining British railways.

In concluding this historical review, it should be added that developments in other motive power realms, which have produced such highly efficient units as the modern electric and diesel-electric locomotives, are dealt with in Chapters 19 and 20. Meanwhile, for the benefit of those to whom some of the technical terms used in these opening chapters are unfamiliar, it is necessary to explain the general principles of steam locomotive design.

3

DESIGN—WHEELS AND WHEEL ARRANGEMENTS

THE steam locomotive is a complete and self-contained power-station on wheels. It is designed to work within severe limitations of space and weight, and these limitations have been largely responsible for settling the traditional lines along which locomotive design has developed. British pioneers, in giving to the world the idea of railway transport, were farseeing, but not enough; they did not leave round their tracks sufficient room to meet future needs. Overline bridges, tunnels, platforms and other lineside structures, all combine to restrict the size of rolling stock. The profiles reproduced on p. 22 show that 13 ft. 6 in. above rail, in the best conditions, is the maximum to which the British locomotive designer may build, and 9 ft. 6 in. is the maximum width; so that proper clearance may be maintained on curves, actual heights and widths of 13 ft. 4 in. and 9 ft. respectively are seldom exceeded. Within these narrow limits the designer must contrive to-day to produce machines capable of exerting over 3,000 horsepower.

As the locomotive cannot be expanded any further in a vertical or a transverse direction, the only expansion still possible is longitudinal. This means that in the larger engines, in addition to the wheels needed for the transmission of power to the track, "idle" wheels are required to help in distributing the total tonnage over as great a length of track as possible. Morever, the locomotive has to travel over curved as well as straight lines, and the more lengthy the chassis, so much the greater are the problems involved in making it sufficiently flexible for smooth running in all conditions.

In Great Britain, except in subsidiary lines and sidings, the sharpest curves are about 500 ft. (7½ chains) radius, and the maximum weight permitted on any one locomotive axle is 22½ tons. The most powerful classes, such as the L.M.S.R., L.N.E.R. and S.R. Pacifics, or the G.W.R. "Kings," carry from 60 to 67½ tons on their three coupled axles. But on many secondary and branch lines the track and bridges are not sufficiently strong to carry such weights, and for this reason every railway has restrictions as to the routes over which its bigger and heavier locomotives may be allowed to work. On some of the smallest branches one or two of the lightest types only may be permitted. Various secondary and branch routes also have not the full clearances of height and width that obtain on the main lines, and thus impose further restrictions.

This is why the ubiquitous L.M.S.R. Class "5" locomotives, built for mixed passenger and freight work, were designed with a maximum height above rail no greater than 12 ft. 8 in., a maximum width of 8 ft. 7¾ in., a weight on the coupled wheels of 53 tons, and a total engine weight of 70½ tons only, so that this handy design might have the widest possible range of action all over the L.M.S.R. system. The Great Western Railway has given an outward indication of its route restrictions by means of coloured and lettered discs on the cab sides above the engine number-plate.

In most other countries loading gauge limits are less drastic. In the United States, for example, the headroom generally available makes it possible to build up to 15 ft. 6 in. above rail level, and up to 10 ft. 9 in. in width; axle-loads exceeding 30 tons also are common. As we shall see later, the Americans, using to the fullest degree the

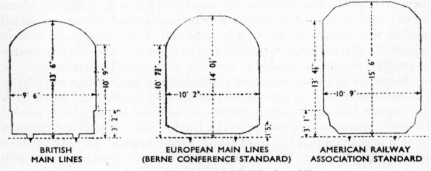

BRITISH   EUROPEAN MAIN LINES   AMERICAN RAILWAY
MAIN LINES   (BERNE CONFERENCE STANDARD)   ASSOCIATION STANDARD

Fig. I. TYPICAL LOADING GAUGES

space at their command, have developed mammoth steam locomotives which multiply by two and even three the weight, the size, and the power of the biggest locomotives in Britain, although the American track gauge of 4 ft. 8½ in. is identical with our own. On the mainland of Europe, also, though axle-loading does not exceed the British standard, the loading gauge dimensions are more generous. The Berne Conference standard for European main lines allows 14 ft. 0½ in. in height and 10 ft. 2 in. in width for rolling stock. Russia enjoys the distinction of having the largest construction gauge in the world; in the U.S.S.R., locomotives may be built up to a maximum height of 17 ft. British, European and American loading gauges are compared in Fig. 1.

As already indicated, the wheels carrying a locomotive are divided into two groups—wheels used to transmit to the rails the power developed in the cylinders, and wheels whose sole function is to help in distributing the weight of the locomotive over the track. The former are distinguished readily from the latter by the coupling rods which cause a group of adjacent pairs of wheels to move in unison. Coupling arises from the necessity to obtain sufficient adhesion, or grip, between the driving wheels and the rails. Adhesion can be, and is, artificially increased by the use of sand, dropped on the rails in front of the driving wheels or blown right under them by a steam jet; but even so the adhesion at times may be insufficient. Then the wheels will slip round violently without obtaining a grip, a phenomenon seen and heard chiefly when a train is starting away from rest.

The earliest British passenger locomotives, even down to the time of the renowned "eight-footers" of Patrick Stirling's design on the one-time Great Northern Railway, had one pair of single driving wheels only, in this particular case of the large diameter of 8 ft. 1½ in., and with 18 tons of the engine's weight resting on them. But the constantly increasing demands on locomotive power resulting from faster and heavier trains made more adhesion weight essential. First, two pairs of driving wheels of equal diameter were coupled together, to make a "four-coupled" (four wheels coupled) engine. From that we have passed to six-coupled designs, but even the 60 to 67½ tons of adhesion weight of the largest British passenger engines is now being outstripped by the power that they develop, as their addiction to severe slipping when starting, unless most carefully handled, bears witness. In North America and elsewhere, eight-coupled locomotives for some time past have been standard for the heaviest passenger duties, and a number of locomotive classes are provided with small "booster" engines, as described in Chapter 4, to give auxiliary power on starting.

For long distance freight service, reliance in Great Britain is placed principally on eight-coupled designs, but elsewhere ten-coupled freight locomotives are common, and twelve-coupled designs are not unknown. The Russians, indeed, have evolved a freight class with no fewer than seven axles coupled; these engines are of the 4-14-4 type, and are used for coal haulage in the Donetz basin. But when it comes to power development on this scale, the general preference to-day is to divide the coupled wheels into two groups, each with its own cylinders and motion, in what are known as "articulated" and similar designs; these are described later.

In earlier days it was thought that the coupling of wheels together would seriously affect the capacity of a locomotive for high speed, but this fear has proved to be without foundation. To some extent, increase in the number of wheels coupled and in the length of coupling rods does increase the loss of power by mechanical friction, but at the same time the highest speeds on record with steam have been made by six-coupled locomotives, and in particular the 126 m.p.h. attained by the L.N.E.R. Pacific engine *Mallard* in 1938. In the United States even eight-coupled locomotives on the Union Pacific and other lines have been run at 100 m.p.h. and over, as described in Chapter 18.

The arrangement of the wheels carrying a locomotive, in relation to the work which it is designed to perform, is of considerable importance. A simple means has been devised, therefore, to define the way in which the wheels are divided up under the locomotive chassis, or the "wheel arrangement." In Great Britain and North America the Whyte notation is used. This consists of three numbers, with the number of coupled wheels in the centre, and the carrying or "idle" wheels ahead of or behind the coupled wheels to left and right respectively of the central figure. A "Merchant Navy" or "West Country" Pacific of the Southern Region, for example, has six-coupled wheels, with a four-wheel truck at the leading end, and a two-wheel truck under the firebox and cab; these engines, therefore, are of the 4-6-2 type. In this notation no account is taken of the tender, which is a separate vehicle.

On the mainland of Europe, the notation is in axles instead of wheels, so that the Whyte 4-6-2 becomes 2-3-1. On French railways the wheel arrangement may form a part of the locomotive number; No. 231-602, for example, indicates engine No. 602 of the 2-3-1 (or 4-6-2) type. Elsewhere letters are used for the coupled wheels instead of numbers—"B" for four-coupled, "C" for six-coupled, "D" for eight-coupled, "E" for ten-coupled driving wheels, and so on—and with this notation 4-6-2 or 2-3-1 becomes 2-C-1. This helps to explain the method used by the late Southern Railway in numbering its "Merchant Navy" and "West Country" locomotives, though the S.R. numeration varied from the customary practice in that both leading and trailing carrying axles were shown ahead of the coupled wheels, 2-C-1 becoming 21C. Both these Pacific classes thus had 21C prefixed to their numbers; the "Merchant Navy" numbers ran from 21C1 to 21C20, and the "West Country" numbers began at 21C101—that is to say, Nos. 1 to 20 and from 101 upwards of the 21C type.

In the Whyte and other notations, provision must be made for the absence of carrying wheels ahead of or behind the coupled wheels, and this is done by the use of a cipher instead of a number. All the express passenger classes of the late Great Western Railway, such as the "Kings," for instance, have a four-wheel leading bogie truck and six-coupled driving wheels, but no idle wheels at the firebox end; this wheel arrangement, therefore, is 4-6-0. There are numerous classes of freight and tank locomotives having the 0-6-0 and 0-8-0 wheel arrangement, in which all the wheels are coupled wheels.

In all countries the leading bogie is a characteristic feature of locomotives used for fast passenger and freight work. It is a four-wheel truck, pivoted under the smokebox of the engine; this is free to swing about its pivot, and also, within narrow and strictly controlled limits, to move laterally by sliding. The bogie enables the locomotive smoothly and easily to enter and traverse the curves in the track. Many of the latest American main-line designs have bogies at both the leading and trailing ends of the engine, such as the "Hudson" or 4-6-4 type used so largely on the New York Central System, or the immense 4-8-4 locomotives which now handle the fastest and heaviest steam-hauled services on a number of American railways. The Pennsylvania Railroad has introduced, in its "T1" class, a variant of the 4-8-4 in which the driving wheels are divided into two groups of four, each with its own cylinders and motion, so making a 4-4-4-4 type locomotive; this is not, however, one of the articulated types mentioned later.

Many other classes, such as the L.N.E.R. "Green Arrow" 2-6-2 locomotives used for both express passenger and fast freight service, have a single axle at the leading end, carried in what is known as a pony truck, and with freedom of lateral movement which gives it an action somewhat similar to that of a bogie. Also the trailing axles of 4-6-2, 2-6-2 and similar designs are usually provided with a limited freedom to slide in a transverse direction, so that the whole wheelbase of the locomotive may adjust itself readily to the curves. Another precaution adopted with locomotives which have a number of axles coupled is to thin the flanges of the middle pair or pairs of coupled wheels, or even to omit them altogether, so that the tendency to derailment on sharp curves may be minimised.

References previously made to locomotives of the "Pacific" type are a reminder that certain of the most familiar arrangements of wheels have nicknames attaching to them. These names, chiefly of American origin, include "Pacific" for the 4-6-2, "Atlantic" for the 4-4-2, "Mountain" for the 4-8-2, "Mikado" for the 2-8-2, "Prairie" for the 2-6-2, "Mogul" for the 2-6-0, and so on. A list of wheel arrangements in use in Great Britain is given in Table 1, and the principal American wheel arrangements and their nicknames appear in Table 2.

Another method of classification which has been used to some extent is that of names. The Great Western Railway, for example, has had its "King," "Castle," "Hall," "Manor," and "Grange" 4-6-0 classes, each class uniformly named and with its own standard characteristics. In recent years, there have been some departures from the

"Castle" sequence of names, but this has been the only variation. Generally speaking, the naming of engines is to provide a public attraction, rather than for any technical reason.

We must now devote some attention to the principle of articulation, by which exceptional locomotive power is developed without undue concentration of weight. In effect, the articulated locomotive consists of two independent engines supplied with steam from a single boiler. In order that the lengthy machine so produced may be flexible enough to traverse curves without difficulty, arrangements must be made for each chassis to have a limited turning movement independently of the

TABLE I

BRITISH LOCOMOTIVE WHEEL ARRANGEMENTS

Wheel Arrangement	Tender Engines		Tank Engines	
	Duty	Owning Railway§	Duty	Owning Railway§
2-8-8-2†*	—	—	Banking	L.N.E.R.
2-8-2	—	—	Freight	G.W.R.
4-8-0	—	—	Shunting	L.N.E.R., S.R.
0-8-4	—	—	Shunting	L.M.S.R., L.N.E.R.
2-8-0	Freight	L.M.S.R., L.N.E.R., G.W.R., S.R.	Freight	G.W.R.
0-8-2	—	—	Shunting	L.M.S.R.
0-8-0	—	—	Shunting	L.M.S.R., L.N.E.R., S.R.
2-6-6-2†	—	—	Freight	L.M.S.R.
4-6-4	Passenger	L.N.E.R.*	—	—
4-6-2	Passenger, Freight	L.M.S.R., L.N.E.R., S.R.	Passenger, Freight	L.M.S.R., L.N.E.R., S.R.
2-6-4	—	—	Passenger, Freight	L.M.S.R., L.N.E.R., S.R.
2-6-2	Passenger, Freight	L.N.E.R.	Passenger	L.M.S.R., L.N.E.R., G.W.R.
4-6-0	Passenger, Freight	L.M.S.R., L.N.E.R., G.W.R., S.R.	—	—
0-6-4	—	—	Passenger	S.R.
2-6-0	Passenger, Freight	L.M.S.R., L.N.E.R., G.W.R., S.R.	—	—
0-6-2	—	—	Passenger, Freight	L.M.S.R., L.N.E.R., G.W.R., S.R
0-6-0	Freight	L.M.S.R., L.N.E.R., G.W.R., S.R.	Shunting	L.M.S.R., L.N.E.R., G.W.R., S.R
4-4-4	—	—	Passenger	L.N.E.R.
4-4-2	Passenger	L.N.E.R., S.R.	Passenger	S.R.
4-4-0	Passenger	L.M.S.R., L.N.E.R., G.W.R., S.R.	—	—
0-4-4	—	—	Passenger	L.M.S.R., L.N.E.R., S.R.
2-4-2	—	—	Passenger	L.M.S.R., L.N.E.R.
2-4-0	Passenger	L.M.S.R.,‡ L.N.E.R.‡	Passenger	G.W.R.,‡ S.R.‡
0-4-2	Passenger, Freight	S.R.‡	Passenger	L.M.S.R.,‡ G.W.R., S.R.‡
0-4-0	—	—	Shunting	L.M.S.R. L.N.E.R., G.W.R., S.R.

† Articulated   * One only of this type   ‡ Obsolescent classes   § Pre-nationalisation

other. A common arrangement, therefore, is to carry the boiler centrally on a girder frame, and to transmit its weight to the two chassis through large pivots; flexible joints are arranged in the piping which carries the live steam from the boiler to the cylinders, and the exhaust steam from the cylinders to the chimney.

The earliest articulation in Great Britain was that of Fairlie, and examples of it could be seen until recently in the quaint little locomotives which worked over the Festiniog Railway, in North Wales. This line, with a gauge no wider than 1 ft. 11½ in., had much sharp curvature, and the utmost flexibility of engine wheelbase was therefore necessary. Two four-wheel bogies, each with its own cylinders and motion supported the two ends of the engine, of which the Whyte notation was 0-4-0 + 0-4-0, usually contracted to 0-4-4-0. The most curious feature of the Festiniog "double-enders" was that double boilers were provided, with one central firebox and chimneys at the outer end of each barrel.

Since the Fairlie patents there have developed the well-known Garratt or Beyer-Garratt locomotives, designed and built by the firm of Beyer Peacock & Company, in Manchester, and now in service on railways in all parts of the world. The "Garratt" has a boiler of large diameter—often larger, indeed, than could be accommodated within loading gauge limits immediately above the cylinders and motion—carried on a heavy girder frame between the two chassis. In the larger Garratt designs, the chassis may be some distance apart, and the weight of the locomotive is thus distributed over a considerable length of the track. This method of construction has been of the greatest value in many British Dominions and Colonies, for it has made possible the building of powerful power units to run over tracks of relatively light construction.

In some of the modern Garratt locomotives the distribution of weight and flexibility that have been obtained by careful design are remarkable indeed. The 4-8-2-2-8-4 of the South African Railways, illustrated in Plate 21, for example, though with a total wheelbase of 80 ft. 10 in. and a total weight in working order of 185 tons, has no rigid wheelbase of greater length than 13 ft. 4½ in., nor any axle-load heavier than 15 tons. It is therefore permitted to travel freely over narrow gauge tracks of 3 ft. 6 in., laid with light rails of 60 lb. per yard, and with very sharp curvature.

It was for the same reason that the London Midland & Scottish Railway, in 1927, introduced the first of a series of 33 Garratt locomotives of the 2-6-6-2 type, for working heavy coal traffic between Toton concentration sidings, near Nottingham, and the Brent sidings at Cricklewood, London. At that time the bridgework on the Midland main line restricted freight workings to 0-6-0 locomotives, which had to be used in pairs, and the adoption of the Garratt design thus offered considerable economies.

These L.M.S.R. Garratts were preceded by a considerably larger 2-8-8-2 locomotive, No. 2395, which the London & North Eastern Railway obtained in 1925 from Beyer Peacock & Company for banking coal trains up the 1 in 40 of the Worsborough incline, near Barnsley. The 2-8-8-2, since renumbered 9999, with its total weight of 178 tons, its wheelbase of 79 ft. 1 in., and its tractive effort of 72,940 lb., is easily the largest, heaviest and most powerful locomotive in Great Britain. It does the work of two 2-8-0 tender locomotives that were required previously for the same duty. Yet no single axle-load of this monster exceeds 18¼ tons.

It should be remarked that a Garratt is in reality an outsize in tank locomotives, for it carries its coal and water supplies on its own main frames, instead of requiring a separate tender. In the L.N.E.R. 2-8-8-2, water, to a total of 5,000 gallons, is carried in tanks mounted above the two chassis, and 7 tons of coal in a bunker above the water-tank at the cab end. The L.M.S.R. 2-6-6-2 Garratts have curious-looking circular coal bunkers, which are arranged by mechanical means to rotate while the engine is in motion, and so to cause the coal to slide downwards towards the fireman, in order that his work of bringing the coal forward may be lightened.

An endless variety of Garratt designs has been evolved for overseas service, and in many of the biggest the number of axles has been deliberately multiplied, in order to bring axle-loads down to the limits that the tracks of their prospective owners will safely carry. So the 2-6-6-2 and 2-8-8-2 designs have expanded to 2-6-2 + 2-6-2 and 2-8-2 + 2-8-2 (that is, a pair of 2-6-2 or 2-8-2 chassis back to back); also there are 4-6-2 + 2-6-4, 4-8-2 + 2-8-4, and even 4-8-4 + 4-8-4 designs now at work.

In North America the development of articulation during recent years has been on a very extensive scale. But because of the more ample loading gauge, and the massive permanent way of modern main lines in the United States, the evolution has been of a somewhat different nature. The rear chassis of the American articulated loco-motive is integral with the main frames of the engine, and only the front chassis has pivotal action; moreover the boiler is carried above both chassis instead of between them.

The first articulated locomotives in the United States used compound propulsion (in which, as described in Chapter 4, the steam is used twice, direct from the boiler in high-pressure cylinders, and then for a second stage of expansion in low-pressure cylinders), and were built under the Mallet patents. The most unusual of these Mallet compounds was the "Triplex" design on the Erie Railroad, built in 1914, in which there were six cylinders, two high-pressure and four low-pressure. The high-pressure cylinders drove the middle set of eight-coupled wheels; two low-pressure cylinders drove the leading 2-8-0 chassis; and the remaining pair drove a 0-8-2 chassis which carried the tender. The full notation of this extraordinary machine was thus 2-8-0 + 0-8-0 + 0-8-2, or, in brief, 2-8-8-8-2.

The name Mallet still sticks to American articulation, although most modern articulated locomotives in the United States are of simple expansion types, using high-pressure steam in all four cylinders. They include the largest and most powerful locomotives in the world. Pride of place is taken by the so-called "Big Boy" class on the Union Pacific Railroad, of the 4-8-8-4 type, which with their 14-wheel tenders weigh no less than 540 tons in running trim—over *three times* the weight of any British Pacific locomotive with its tender, and precisely three times the weight of the L.N.E.R. 2-8-8-2 Garratt. Each of the Union Pacific 4-8-8-4s exerts a tractive force of 135,375 lb., and on test one of them has developed an indicated horsepower of 7,000. The total wheelbase of engine and tender is 117 ft. 7 in., and a turntable 120 ft. in length is needed to turn them. Other articulated American varieties include the 2-8-8-4, 4-8-8-2, 4-6-6-4, and 2-6-6-6, the last-named a design of the Chesapeake & Ohio Railroad, which has a six-wheel bogie at the rear end of the engine to support the large and heavy firebox.

In the steam locomotive the general method of propulsion is to develop the power of the steam in cylinders; this power is then applied to the driving wheels either by means of cranked axles, or crankpins on the wheels themselves; and the wheels transmit the power to

TABLE 2

PRINCIPAL AMERICAN LOCOMOTIVE WHEEL ARRANGEMENTS

Wheel Arrangement	Nickname	No of Tender Wheels	Duty
4-4-0	American	8	Passenger*
4-4-2	Atlantic	8	Passenger*
2-6-0	Mogul	8	Passenger, Freight*
4-6-0	Ten-wheel	8	Passenger*
2-6-2	Prairie	8	Passenger*
4-6-2	Pacific	8	Passenger
4-6-4	Hudson	12	Passenger
0-8-0	Eight-wheel	8	Shunting
2-8-0	Consolidation	8	Freight, Shunting
2-8-2	Mikado	8	Freight
4-8-2	Mountain	8 or 12	Passenger, Freight
2-8-4	Berkshire	12	Freight
4-8-4	Northern, &c.	12, 14, 16	Passenger, Freight
2-10-0	Decapod	8	Freight
4-10-0	Mastodon	8	Freight*
2-10-2	Santa Fe	12	Freight
4-10-2	Overland, &c.	12	Passenger, Freight†
2-10-4	Texas	12	Passenger, Freight†
4-12-2	Union Pacific	12 or 14	Freight†
4-14-4	Soviet	12	Freight‡

NON-ARTICULATED TYPES			
4-4-4-4	—	16	Passenger§
4-4-6-4	—	16	Freight§

ARTICULATED TYPES			
2-6-6-2	—	12	Freight
4-6-6-4	—	12 or 14	Passenger, Freight
2-6-6-6	—	12	Freight‖
4-8-8-2	—	12	Passenger, Freight
2-8-8-4	—	12	Freight
4-8-8-4	—	12 or 14	Passenger, Freight

* Obsolescent.   † For mountain routes.
‡ U.S.S.R. only, coal trains in Donetz basin.
§ Pennsylvania R.R. only.   ‖ Chesapeake & Ohio R.R. only.

the rails. As we have seen already, the grip or adhesion of a single pair of driving wheels on the rails no longer is sufficient to match the cylinder power of the modern locomotive, and additional wheels, there-fore, are coupled to the driving wheels proper to increase the adhesion.

But the coupling of the driving wheels of the locomotive is not the only factor connected with the wheels that influences power development. Driving wheel diameter has a direct bearing on the power that can be developed at the rail. Increasing the diameter reduces the tractive effort; reducing the diameter increases it in the same proportion. On the other hand, at any given speed the rate at which the rotating parts are in motion decreases as driving wheel diameter is increased, and *vice versa*. Consequently, where maximum tractive power is desired, and speed is the less important consideration, smaller driving wheels are used; for express passenger work, on the other hand, wheels of larger diameter are desirable.

In earlier days, far bigger driving wheels were a common feature of express engines. The famous Patrick Stirling "single-drivers" of the one-time Great Northern Railway (of which one is still to be seen in the Railway Museum at York) had 8 ft. $1\frac{1}{2}$ in. driving wheels. Those of the London & North Western engine *Cornwall*, now preserved at Crewe Works, London Midland Region, were 8 ft. 6 in. in diameter. The Bristol & Exeter Railway, which became a part of the Great Western, had its unique Pearson 4-2-4 tank locomotives, with 9 ft. driving wheels. In 1838 an engine was built for the G.W.R., the *Hurricane*, which had drivers no less than 10 ft. diameter, carried in a 2-2-2 frame independently of the six-wheel chassis on which the boiler was mounted, but a total failure because of inadequate adhesion.

Steady growth in the size of boilers, however, began to rule out wheels of such extravagant size, for the height above rail both of the axles and of the wheels themselves restricted boiler development too severely. Also the demands for increased tractive power made it necessary to bring the size of driving wheels within reasonable limits. Moreover, improvements in valves, valve-motions, and "front-end" design generally, by facilitating the release of the spent steam at the end of the piston-stroke and so reducing the cushioning effect of back-pressure on the pistons, completely changed the problem of piston speed.

As a result, designers have been able, by using driving wheels of relatively small diameter, to combine a high tractive effort with a capacity for high speed which in earlier years would have been thought impossible in such conditions. While the highest speed ever reached with steam power—the 126 m.p.h. of the L.N.E.R. Pacific *Mallard*—was attained with 6 ft. 8 in. driving wheels, L.M.S.R. 4-6-0 "mixed traffic" locomotives of the numerous Class "5," with 6 ft. wheels, have been timed at speeds of 90 m.p.h. and slightly over, and the same company's 2-6-4 tanks, with 5 ft. 9 in. wheels, at over 80 m.p.h. Incidentally, at 126 m.p.h. the pistons of *Mallard* were making all but nine return strokes in each cylinder *every second*; with 6 ft. wheels at 90 m.p.h. the figure is exactly seven return strokes per second.

To-day the tendency is to build, in increasing numbers, "general purpose" locomotives, which can be used at will in both passenger and freight service. In days gone by, "mixed traffic" was the more general term, but it indicated a class of engine used for the most part on freight trains; if such engines were rostered to take passenger trains, these were generally stopping or excursion trains, or other services not requiring much in the way of speed. But the general purpose loco-motive of to-day, for reasons set out in the last two paragraphs, has a much wider radius of action.

For example, as mentioned in Chapter 2, Mr. O. V. Bulleid, Chief Mechanical Engineer of the late Southern Railway, in designing his "Merchant Navy" and "West Country" Pacifics with driving wheels no bigger than 6 ft. 2 in. diameter, kept fully in view the future demand for speeds of 90 to 95 m.p.h., though the engines are regarded as being in the "general purpose" category. On the late London & North Eastern Railway the fine 2-6-2 locomotives of Class "V2," designed by the late Sir Nigel Gresley, despite their 6 ft. 2 in. driving wheels have shared all the express passenger haulage since the outbreak of war in 1939 on equal terms with the 6 ft. 8 in. Pacifics, and quite successfully, while also devoting much of their time to freight working. In the United States the 4-8-4 locomotives which are being built in such large numbers to-day, with driving wheels of 6 ft. to 6 ft. 3 in. diameter, are all regarded as "general purpose" engines and used accordingly.

The great advantage of locomotives of this "maid-of-all-work" type, of course, is that their working day can be filled up with any kind of service. In one direction they will haul, it may be, a fast passenger express; then, instead of wasting time waiting for another train of the same description on which to return to the starting point, they will come back on the next available freight service. Much modern "control" working is expressly designed to make the maximum possible use in this way of all locomotives during the hours that they are in steam and on the road.

For purely express passenger service, the diameter of driving wheel most favoured is between 6 ft. and 6 ft. 9 in. The "Claud Hamilton" (Class "D16") 4-4-0 locomotives of the late L.N.E.R. are a reminder that on the old Great Eastern Railway 7 ft. was the general driving wheel diameter of four-coupled locomotives; the one-time Lancashire & Yorkshire Railway went even further with 7 ft. 3 in. With general purpose or mixed traffic locomotives from 5 ft. 8 in. to 6 ft. 2 in. is the diameter most favoured; for the larger passenger tank locomotives 5 ft. 3 in. to 5 ft. 9 in.; for heavy freight locomotives 4 ft. 6 in. to 4 ft. 9 in.; and for shunting tanks about the same figure.

Driving wheel diameter plays a part in the calculation of what is known as the "tractive effort" of a locomotive. Tractive effort has some value for purposes of comparison, as an indication of maximum possible power output, but too much reliance must not be placed on tractive effort figures, for they take no account of the steam-raising capacity of the boiler. The tractive effort calculation is based on the volume of the cylinders, the diameter of the driving wheels, and the working pressure of the boiler. It is customary to allow for a certain loss of pressure between the boiler and the cylinders; the proportion of the working pressure used in the calculation, therefore, is usually 85 per cent.

The tractive effort of a two-cylinder locomotive is obtained by the formula $\dfrac{d^2 \times s \times p}{D}$, where $d =$ the diameter of the cylinders, $s =$ the piston stroke, $D =$ the diameter of the driving wheels (all in inches), and $p = 85$ per cent. of the working pressure. For a three-cylinder simple locomotive the result must be multiplied by 1·5, and for a four-cylinder simple by 2. For a compound locomotive, in which, as described in Chapter 4, the steam is carried through a second stage of expansion, a more complicated formula is necessary. The tractive efforts and leading dimensions of the principal British passenger, freight, and tank locomotive classes are set out in Tables 3, 4 and 5.

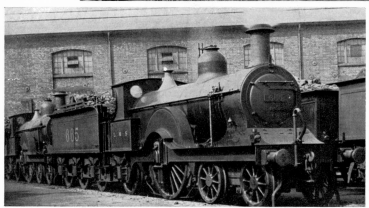

1.   A Great Western Dean 7 ft. 8 in. 4-2-2 at full speed with a down West of England express passing Uphill Junction, Weston-super-Mare.   (*R. G. Sellon.*)

2.   Great Northern Stirling 8 ft. 1½ in. 4-2-2 No. 1 leaves York Railway Museum for a commemoration run in 1938.   (*M. W. Earley.*)

3.   Two of the graceful Johnson 7 ft. 6 in. 4-2-2s of the Midland Railway at Kentish Town shed in 1924.   (*H. C. Casserley.*)

THE PAST ERA OF THE SINGLE-WHEELER

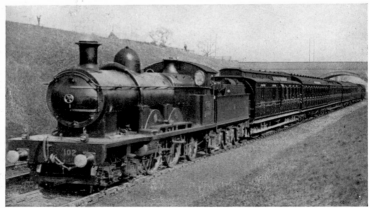

4. One of the last London & North Western Webb compounds—a 4-cylinder 4-4-0 on an up Birmingham two-hour express near Kenton. (*F. E. Mackay.*)

5. The most numerous compound class ever built in Britain—a Midland 3-cylinder 4-4-0 on a down Leeds express near Mill Hill. (*F. R. Hebron.*)

6. French 4-cylinder compound 4-4-2 *La France* of the Great Western Railway hauling a down Birmingham two-hour express. (*F. E. Mackay.*)

COMPOUND LOCOMOTIVES IN GREAT BRITAIN

7. An Ivatt 4-4-2 of the Great Northern Railway, later L.N.E.R. Class "C1," near Grantham with an up Leeds express. (*M. W. Earley.*)

8. A Raven 3-cylinder 4-4-2 of the North Eastern Railway, later L.N.E.R. Class "C7," at speed with an Edinburgh-London express. (*Rail Photo Service, Boston, Mass., H. W. Pontin.*)

THE ATLANTIC ERA ON THE EAST COAST ROUTE

9. The famous 4-6-0 *Cardean* of the Caledonian Railway, passing Rockcliffe with the 2 p.m. from Glasgow to Euston.   (*F. E. Mackay*.)

10.   One of the original Churchward 2-cylinder 4-6-0s, *Stanford Court*, at Sonning, heading an up Cheltenham express.   (*M. W. Earley*.)

4-6-0 DESIGNS THAT HAVE MADE BRITISH LOCOMOTIVE HISTORY

11.   A Gresley Pacific of the original Class "A1," *Pretty Polly*, with a down Newcastle express, climbing the 1 in 200 to Potter's Bar, L.N.E.R.   (*Canon E. Treacy.*)

12.   The most outstanding of all Swindon products—a "Castle" 4-cylinder 4-6-0 of the G.W.R., *Winchester Castle*, at speed in Sonning cutting with an up Bristol express.   (*M. W. Earley.*)

PROTAGONISTS OF THE HISTORIC 1925 LOCOMOTIVE EXCHANGE

13. Ministry of Supply 2-8-0 locomotive, built during the Second World War, in action near Hatfield, Eastern Region. (*F. R. Hebron.*)

14. London Midland Region standard Class "8" 2-8-0, in winter near Keighley, with small snowplough attached to buffer-beam. (*Canon E. Treacy.*)

STANDARD BRITISH HEAVY FREIGHT TYPES

15. A 3-cylinder Class "K3" 2-6-0 heads a fast freight train. The only British type with parallel boiler as large as 6 ft. diameter. (*Canon E. Treacy.*)

16. A 3-cylinder Class "V2" 2-6-2 at speed with a semi-fast passenger train. (*Canon E. Treacy.*)

"GENERAL PURPOSE" CLASSES, EASTERN REGION

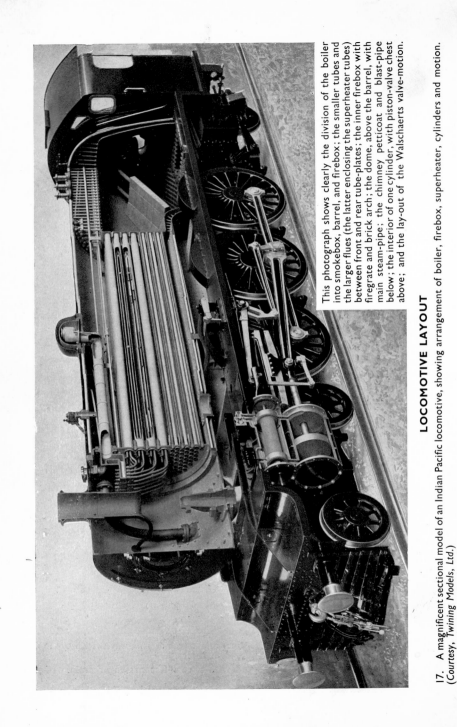

LOCOMOTIVE LAYOUT

This photograph shows clearly the division of the boiler into smokebox, barrel, and firebox; the smaller tubes and the larger flues (the latter enclosing the superheater tubes) between front and rear tube-plates; the inner firebox with firegrate and brick arch; the dome, above the barrel, with main steam-pipe; the chimney petticoat and blast-pipe below; the interior of one cylinder, with piston-valve chest above; and the lay-out of the Walschaerts valve-motion.

17. A magnificent sectional model of an Indian Pacific locomotive, showing arrangement of boiler, firebox, superheater, cylinders and motion. (Courtesy, Twining Models, Ltd.)

— 4 —

DESIGN—CYLINDERS AND MOTION

FROM the earliest days of the steam locomotive, the traditional method of propulsion has been by means of reciprocating motion— cylinders with pistons acting on cranked driving axles, or on crank- pins in driving wheels, through the medium of piston-rods, crossheads and connecting-rods. Admission of steam to the cylinders, and release of the spent steam at the end of the stroke, have been through sliding valves of various types, arranged in valve-chests attached to the cylinders. The vast majority of steam locomotives are so designed; it is in a minority of cases only that lifting, or poppet, valves have replaced the previous slide-valves or piston-valves, and that, as mentioned in Chapter 2, the first attempts have been made to do away altogether with reciprocating motion by the use of steam turbines.

It is obvious that in any locomotive using cylinders for propulsion, at least two cylinders are necessary. With a single cylinder it would be impossible to re-start the locomotive if it came to rest with the piston in such a position that the exhaust port only was uncovered. For the same reason, in any two-cylinder engine the cranks are arranged, not in line, but at right-angles to one another. Even so, it is possible for a locomotive to stop with its valves in such a position that it cannot start in forward gear, for the port openings will not admit sufficient steam. In such conditions the driver must reverse his engine; hence the phenomenon, often observed by travellers, of trains setting back slightly before a start is made, with the loud accompaniment of steam released directly from the cylinders by the cylinder cocks, and shooting out from beneath the buffer-beam, which must be done before the driver can reverse again into forward gear and get his train away.

In past years, opinion was divided among locomotive engineers as to whether cylinders should be mounted outside the main frames of the engine or between them. The outside position has the advantage of accessibility; the inside position concentrates the disturbing forces, set up by the action of the reciprocating motion, nearer to the centre-line of the engine, and so makes for smoother riding. By the beginning of the present century, inside cylinders had become the standard practice on most British railways, and had helped to establish the neatness of outline that for so long was a characteristic of the British locomotive. Since then, however, the advantage of accessibility, both for inspection and repairs, has gained the upper hand, and except for the smaller types used in shunting, almost all new locomotives have outside cylinders.

The disturbing forces to which reference has just been made are the subject of special attention in the design of a locomotive, which for this reason requires to be "balanced." At speed, the rotation of heavy moving parts would cause dangerous oscillation were they not counterbalanced. When the connecting-rod, crank and coupling-rod approach the top of their throw, they tend to lift the adjacent driving wheels off the rails; and as they approach the bottom of their throw, a stress is produced, known as "hammer-blow," which is equivalent to a sudden and heavy impact on the rail. Counterbalance is therefore applied by means of weights in the driving wheel rims; in these balance-weights there are cavities, into which molten lead is run in exactly the right quantity to produce the balance required.

True balance is verified by means of a balancing machine at the locomotive works; in this the driving wheels are spun round at speed, complete with driving axle, cranks or crank-pins, and connecting-rod big-ends, and weight is added until the wheels are running in perfect truth. A certain proportion also of the forces developed by the reciprocating motion is balanced in many locomotives, though this requires to be done with great care, or oscillation-producing stresses of another kind may be set up. As yet there is not complete agreement among locomotive engineers concerning the precise degree to which balancing of the reciprocating parts should be carried out, and the matter is complicated by various developments that have taken place in recent years in the number and arrangement of cylinders, as described in the next paragraph. Reference is made to this matter also in Chapter 8.

In the course of time, tractive power demands have grown on such a scale that in Great Britain it is no longer possible to mount two cylinders of adequate size, either in the space between the frames, or (within the limited confines of the loading gauge) in the space available outside the frames. With all the larger engines, therefore, it has become the practice to divide up the total cylinder volume into three or four equal parts, instead of using two cylinders only. If three cylinders are used, one is located between the frames and the two others are outside. Three-cylinder engines have their cranks set at 120° to one another, dividing the circle up into three equal parts; for this reason it is easy to distinguish three-cylinder engines when running, for they exhaust six times to every revolution of the driving wheels.

Four-cylinder engines, on the other hand, have two of their cylinders between the frames, and the other two outside. Normally the four cranks are set at right-angles, dividing up the circle into four equal

TABLE 3

BRITISH EXPRESS LOCOMOTIVES—LEADING DIMENSIONS

Wheel Arrange-ment	Rail-way§	Type and Class	Cylinders No.	Cylinders Dia.	Cylinders Stroke	Driving Wheels Dia.	Heating Surface Tubes	Heating Surface Fire-box	Heating Surface Super-heater	Heating Surface Total	Fire-grate Area	Working Pressure	Tractive Effort*	Engine Wheel-base	Weight Adhesion	Weight Engine	No. of Wheels	Tender Coal	Tender Water	Tender Weight†	Engine & Tender Weight†	Engine & Tender Length Overall
				in.	in.	ft. in.	sq. ft.	sq. ft.	sq. ft.	sq. ft.	sq. ft.	lb./sq. in.	lb.	ft. in.	tons	tons		tons	gallons	tons	tons	ft. in.
4-6-2	L.M.S.R.	"Duchess" ("7P")	4	16½	28	6 9	2,577	230	830‖	3,637	50·0	250	40,000	37 0	67·0	105·3	6	10	4,000	56·4	161·6	73 10
,,	,,	"Princess Royal" ("7P")‡ ..	4	16¼	28	6 6	2,299	217	598	3,007	45·0	250	40,300	37 9	67·5	104·5	6	10	4,000	54·7	159·2	74 4
,,	L.N.E.R.	Streamlined ("A4") ..	3	18½	26	6 8	2,345	231	749	3,325	41·3	250	35,455	35 9	66·0	103·0	8	8	5,000	64·9	167·9	71 0
,,	,,	Post-war ("A1") ..	3	19	26	6 8	2,216	245	680	3,141	50·0	250	37,395	36 3	66·0	104·1	8	9	5,000	60·4	164·5	73 0
,,	,,	Super-Pacific ("A3") ..	3	19	26	6 8	2,477	215	635	3,327	41·3	220	32,910	35 9	66·2	96·3	8	8	5,000	57·0	154·2	70 5
,,	,,	General Purpose ("A2") ..	3	19	26	6 2	2,216	245	680	3,141	50·0	250	40,430	36 11	66·0	101·5	8	9	5,000	60·4	161·9	72 10
,,	,,	"Flying Scotsman" ("A10")	3	20	26	6 8	2,715	215	525	3,455	41·3	180	29,835	35 9	60·0	92·5	8	8	5,000	56·3	148·8	70 5
,,	S.R.	"Merchant Navy" ("MN")	3	18	24	6 2	2,176	275	822	3,273	48·5	280	37,500	36 9	63·0	94·8	6	5	5,000	50·0	142·5	69 8
,,	,,	"West Country" ("WC") ..	3	16⅜	24	6 2	1,869	253	545	2,667	38·3	280	31,005	35 6	56·3	86·0	6	5	4,500	42·6	128·6	67 5
4-6-0	G.W.R.	"King"	4	16¼	28	6 6	2,007	194	289	2,490	34·3	250	40,300	29 5	67·5	89·0	6	6	4,000	46·7	135·7	68 2
,,	,,	"Castle"	4	16	26	6 8½	1,858	163	262	2,283	29·4	225	31,625	27 3	58·9	79·9	6	6	4,000	46·7	126·6	65 2
,,	,,	"Star"	4	15	26	6 8½	1,686	155	263	2,104	27·1	225	27,800	27 3	55·4	75·6	6	6	3,500	40·0	115·6	64 2
,,	,,	"Saint"	2	18½	30	6 8½	1,686	155	263	2,104	27·1	225	24,395	27 1	54·8	72·0	6	6	3,500	40·0	112·0	63 0
,,	,,	"County"	2	18½	30	6 3	1,545	169	265	1,979	28·8	280	32,580	27 3	59·1	76·9	6	7	4,000	49·0	125·9	63 0
,,	L.M.S.R.	Rebuilt "Royal Scot" ("6P")	3	18	26	6 9	1,655	195	420	2,270	31·3	250	33,150	27 6	61·0	83·0	6	9	4,000	54·6	137·6	64 11
,,	,,	"Royal Scot" ("6P") ..	3	18	26	6 9	1,892	189	399	2,480	31·2	250	33,150	27 6	62·5	84·9	6	9	4,000	54·6	139·5	65 3
,,	,,	"Jubilee" ("5XP")	3	17	26	6 9	1,460	181	307	1,948	31·0	225	26,610	27 7	60·0	79·6	6	9	4,000	54·6	134·2	64 9
,,	L.N.E.R.	"Sandringham" ("B17") ..	3	17½	26	6 8	1,508	168	344	2,020	27·5	200	25,380	27 9	54·4	77·3	6	7½	4,200	52·5	129·8	62 2
,,	,,	Ex-G.E.R. (Rebuilt "B12") ..	2	20	28	6 6	1,405	154	315	1,874	31·0	180	21,970	28 6	48·1	69·5	6	4	3,670	39·3	108·8	57 9
,,	S.R.	"Lord Nelson" ("LN") ..	4	16½	26	6 7	1,795	194	376	2,365	33·0	220	33,500	29 6	62·0	83·5	8	5	5,000	56·7	140·2	69 10
,,	,,	"King Arthur" ("N15") ..	2	20½	28	6 7	1,716	162	337	2,215	30·0	200	25,320	27 6	60·0	81·0	8	5	5,000	57·5	138·5	66 5
4-4-2	L.N.E.R.	Ex-G.N.R. ("C1")	2	20	24	6 8	1,824	141	568	2,533	31·0	170	17,340	26 4	40·0	69·6	6	6½	3,500	43·1	112·7	57 10
,,	,,	Ex-N.E.R. ("C7")	3	16½	26	6 10	1,673	185	437	2,295	27·0	175	19,300	29 6	40·8	79·3	6	5½	4,125	46·6	125·9	63 8
4-4-0	L.M.S.R.	Compound ("4P")	3	{(1) 19 (2) 21}	26	6 9	1,169	147	291	1,607	28·4	200	22,650	24 3	39·2	61·7	6	5½	3,500	42·7	104·4	56 8
,,	,,	Standard ("2P")	2	19	26	6 9	1,034	124	252	1,410	21·1	180	17,730	22 9	35·0	54·1	6	4	3,500	41·2	95·3	54 4
,,	L.N.E.R.	"Shire" ("D49")	3	17	26	6 8	1,226	172	272	1,670	26·0	180	21,555	24 11	42·0	65·6	6	7½	4,200	52·0	117·6	58 9
,,	,,	"Claud Hamilton" ("D16")	2	19	26	7 0	1,304	126	204	1,634	21·0	180	17,095	23 6	36·5	55·9	6	5	3,450	39·3	95·2	53 2
,,	,,	"Director" ("D11") ..	2	20	26	6 9	1,388	155	209	1,752	26·5	180	19,645	25 3	39·8	61·2	6	6	4,000	48·3	109·5	59 0
,,	S.R.	"Schools" ("V")	3	16½	26	6 7	1,604	162	283	2,049	28·3	220	25,130	25 6	42·0	67·1	6	5	4,000	42·4	109·5	58 10
,,	,,	Ex-S.E. & C.R. ("L1") ..	2	19½	26	6 8	1,252	155	235	1,642	22·5	180	18,910	24 4	37·6	57·8	6	5	3,500	40·5	98·3	56 8
,,	,,	Ex-L.S.W.R. ("D15") ..	2	20	26	6 7	1,140	144	252	1,536	27·0	180	20,100	24 9	39·9	61·6	8	5	4,000	44·8	106·4	59 2

* At 85 per cent. working pressure † In full working order ‡ Streamlined locomotives of this series weighed 108·1 tons, or 164·5 tons with tender
§ Railway owning locomotive before nationalisation ‖ Nos. 46256 and 46257, 979 sq. ft.

parts; in consequence the exhaust puffs are thrown out in pairs, and the exhaust sounds the same as that of a two-cylinder engine. With the "Lord Nelson" 4-6-0 engines of the late Southern Railway, which have four cylinders, the experiment was tried of advancing two of the cranks by 135°, so evening out the torque by giving eight impulses to every revolution of the driving wheels. This and similar experiments elsewhere have resulted in small economies both in coal consumption and maintenance, but have proved a slight handicap in starting as compared with the more normal four-cylinder arrangement. The balancing problem in three-cylinder and four-cylinder engines is greatly simplified, as the crank arrangement is largely self-balancing. In the Southern "Merchant Navy" and "West Country" Pacifics, reciprocating balance is dispensed with entirely.

Locomotive engineers differ in their opinions as to how the cylinders of three-cylinder and four-cylinder engines should best be disposed. To have all the cylinders in line across the engine has considerable advantages in simplifying the steam passages and the layout of the front end generally; but unless very short connecting-rods are used (which are objectionable because of the angular position that they take up at the top and bottom of their throw), the inside cylinders are faced with the obstacle of the leading coupled axle if it is desired that they should drive the middle coupled axle with connecting-rods of reasonable length.

With his three-cylinder six-coupled engines, Gresley got over this difficulty by raising and sharply inclining his middle cylinders, so that the crossheads and connecting-rods clear the leading coupled axle, and and all cylinders drive the middle coupled axle. In all the four-cylinder designs of the late Great Western Railway, on the other hand, the cylinders are staggered, the inside cylinders, projecting well ahead of the smokebox, driving the leading pair of coupled wheels, and the outside cylinders, in rear of the smokebox, the middle pair. This "divided drive," as it is called, has an advantage in that all the work developed in the cylinders of a powerful locomotive is not concentrated on a single axle.

Another multi-cylinder arrangement is known as "compounding." The term "compound" is in contrast to the "simple" use of steam direct from the boiler in cylinders of equal size. Compound propulsion is designed to divide the expansion, by which the steam does the major part of its work, into two stages. The steam is taken from the boiler direct into one or two "high pressure" cylinders; from there, after one stage of expansion, it passes into a reservoir known as a "receiver," and from the latter into two "low-pressure" cylinders of larger diameter,

TABLE 4

BRITISH GENERAL PURPOSE AND FREIGHT LOCOMOTIVES—LEADING DIMENSIONS

Wheel Arrangement	Railway‖	Type and Class	Cylinders No.	Cylinders Dia.	Cylinders Stroke	Driving Wheels, Dia.	Heating Surface Tubes	Heating Surface Fire-box	Heating Surface Super-heater	Heating Surface Total	Fire-grate Area	Working Pressure	Tractive Effort*	Engine Wheel-base	Weight Adhesion	Weight Engine	Tender No. of Wheels	Tender Coal	Tender Water	Tender Weight†	Engine & Tender Weight†	Engine & Tender Length Overall
				in.	in.	ft. in.	sq. ft.	sq. ft.	sq. ft.	sq. ft.	sq. ft.	lb.sq. in.	lb.	ft. in.	tons	tons		tons	gallons	tons	tons	ft. in.
2-6-6-2	L.M.S.R.	Garratt (articulated) ..	4	18½	26	5 3	1,954	183	500	2,637	44·5	190	45,620	25 9‡	122·1	155·5	—	9	4,500	—	155·5	87 11
2-6-2	L.N.E.R.	"Green Arrow" ("V2")	3	18½	26	6 2	2,216	215	680	3,111	41·3	220	33,730	33 8	65·6	93·1	6	7½	4,200	51·0	144·1	66 5
4-6-0	,,	"Antelope" ("B1") ..	2	20	26	6 2	1,493	168	344	2,005	27·9	225	26,880	28 0	52·5	71·2	6	7½	4,200	52·0	123·2	61 7
,,	L.M.S.R.	Standard ("5") ..	2	18½	28	6 0	1,479	171	359	2,009	28·7	225	25,455	27 2	53·2	72·1	6	9	4,000	53·7	125·8	63 8
,,	G.W.R.	"Hall"	2	18½	30	6 0	1,583	155	295	2,033	27·1	225	27,275	27 1	56·5	75·8	6	6	4,000	47·3	123·1	63 0
,,	,,	"Grange"	2	18½	30	5 8	1,686	155	263	2,104	27·1	225	28,875	27 1	55·2	74·0	6	6	3,500	40·0	114·0	63 0
,,	,,	"Manor"	2	18	30	5 8	1,286	140	190	1,616	22·1	225	27,340	27 1	50·4	68·9	6	6	3,500	40·0	108·9	61 9
,,	S.R.	*Ex*-L.S.W.R. ("S15") ..	2	20½	28	5 7	1,716	162	337	2,215	28·0	200	29,860	26 8	59·3	79·3	8	5	5,000	56·4	135·7	65 7
2-6-0	L.N.E.R.	Standard ("K3") ..	3	18½	26	5 8	1,719	182	407	2,308	28·0	180	30,030	25 2	60·9	72·6	6	7½	4,200	51·0	123·6	59 6
,,	L.M.S.R.	Standard ("4") ..	2	21	26	5 6	1,345	160	307	1,812	27·5	180	26,580	27 5	56·2	66·0	6	5	3,500	42·2	108·2	59 4
,,	,,	Light ("4")	2	17½	26	5 3	1,090	131	231	1,221	23·0	225	24,255	24 1	49·6	59·1	6	4	3,500	40·3	99·4	55 11
,,	,,	Light ("2")	2	16	24	5 0	925	101	134	1,160	17·5	200	17,400	22 3	38·9	47·1	6	4	3,000	37·2	84·3	53 2
,,	G.W.R.	Standard ("4300") ..	2	18½	30	5 8	1,349	129	192	1,670	20·6	225	25,670	23 6	54·3	65·3	6	6	3,500	40·0	105·3	58 7
,,	S.R.	Three-cylinder ("U1")	3	16	28	6 0	1,391	135	285	1,811	25·0	200	25,385	23 10	54·7	65·3	6	5	4,000	42·4	107·7	57 9
,,	,,	Two-cylinder ("N") ..	2	19	28	5 6	1,391	135	285	1,811	25·0	200	26,040	24 4	52·2	61·2	6	5	4,000	42·4	103·6	57 9
2-8-0	G.W.R.	Mixed Traffic ("4700")	2	19	30	5 8	2,062	170	290	2,522	30·3	225	30,460	29 3	73·4	82·0	6	6	4,000	46·7	128·7	66 4
,,	,,	Standard ("2800") ..	2	18½	30	4 7½	1,686	155	263	2,104	27·1	225	35,380	25 7	67·5	76·3	6	6	3,500	40·0	116·3	63 3
,,	L.N.E.R.	,, ("O2") ..	3	18½	26	4 8	1,869	164	430	2,463	27·5	180	36,470	27 2	69·4	78·6	6	7½	4,200	51·5	103·1	63 3
,,	,,	*Ex*-G.C.R. ("O4") ..	2	21	26	4 8	1,349	154	242	1,745	26·2	180	31,325	25 5	66·2	73·2	6	6	4,000	48·3	121·5	61 9
,,	L.M.S.R.	Standard ("8F") ..	2	18½	28	4 8½	1,479	171	230	1,880	28·7	225	32,440	26 0	63·1	72·1	6	9	4,000	53·7	125·8	63 1
2-8-0	M.O.S.§	War Design	2	19	28	4 8½	1,512	168	311	1,991	28·6	225	34,215	24 10	61·3	70·3	8	9	5,000	55·5	125·8	63 6
0-8-0	L.M.S.R.	Standard ("7F") ..	2	19	26	4 8½	1,434	150	353	1,937	23·6	200	29,745	18 3	60·8	60·8	6	4	3,500	41·2	102·0	56 1
0-6-0	,,	,, ("4F") ..	2	20	26	5 3	1,033	124	253	1,410	21·1	175	24,555	16 6	48·8	48·8	6	4	3,500	41·2	90·0	52 0
,,	L.N.E.R.	,, ("J39") ..	2	20	26	5 2	1,226	172	272	1,670	26·0	180	25,665	17 0	57·9	57·9	6	7½	4,200	52·5	110·4	55 8
,,	,,	*Ex*-G.E.R. ("J20") ..	2	20	28	4 11	1,466	143	202	1,811	26·5	180	29,045	18 10	54·8	54·8	6	5	3,500	38·2	93·0	54 6
,,	S.R.	Standard ("Q1") ..	2	19	26	5 1	1,472	170	218	1,860	27·0	230	30,000	16 6	51·3	51·3	6	5	3,700	38·0	89·3	54 11
,,	,,	,, ("Q") ..	2	19	26	5 1	1,125	122	185	1,432	21·9	200	26,155	16 6	49·5	49·5	6	5	3,500	40·5	90·0	53 10
,,	G.W.R.	,, ("2251") ..	2	17½	24	5 2	1,069	102	76	1,247	17·4	200	20,155	15 6	43·4	43·4	6	5	3,000	36·8	80·2	53 8

* At 85 per cent. working pressure † In full working order ‡ Each chassis §Ministry of Supply design; many acquired by British Railways since the War ‖ Pre-nationalisation

in which the expansion is completed. In any simple locomotive, each cylinder is being alternately heated and cooled by the fall in temperature which accompanies a considerable range of expansion; with compound expansion, the temperature reduction in each cylinder is lessened, and this is an advantage from the thermal efficiency point of view.

There are three reasons why locomotive compounding has never made much progress in Great Britain. One is the ingrained British dislike of complication; a second has been the inherent defects of various systems of compounding tried in this country, notably that of Webb on the one-time London & North Western Railway. The third is the difficulty of compressing within British loading gauge limits low-pressure cylinders of sufficiently large diameter to match the steam-producing capacity of the modern boiler. One British compound design alone can claim to have been really successful, and that is the three-cylinder 4-4-0 class first introduced on the then Midland Railway in 1902, and later multiplied by the L.M.S.R. to a total of 240 engines.

In the Midland compounds, the expansions in the high- and low-pressure cylinders are linked with one another in a fixed ratio, and the driver has but one expansion gear to control. A regulator of ingenious design is provided; when the regulator handle is opened through a small arc, high-pressure steam passes direct through a small port to the low-pressure cylinders, in order to provide auxiliary power on starting (when the power developed in the single high-pressure cylinder alone would be inadequate); but as soon as the engine is well under way, the driver opens the regulator wide, and full compound working begins.

It is in France that compounding has reached its maximum development, in common with the technical development of the steam locomotive in every particular, for in this realm the French have no superiors. The modern French locomotive is a very complicated machine, but the training of French drivers is such as to enable them to make the most of such complications as independent cut-offs for high-pressure and low-pressure cylinders, the maintenance of correct receiver pressures (by admitting steam direct from the boiler, as required, to the low-pressure receiver), and so on. There are financial inducements to French engine-crews, also, to encourage the most efficient use of the locomotives in their charge, and as a result the French have developed steam locomotives which have established some of the most remarkable overall thermal efficiency records in locomotive history.

The reference just made to "cut-off" brings us to the means by which steam enters and leaves the cylinders. Valves are provided to uncover, at precisely the right moment, the steam port at the beginning of the stroke, and the exhaust port at the end of it. Moreover, the driver must be provided with means for varying the point, in the stroke of the piston in the cylinder, at which the supply of live steam to the cylinder is cut off, and expansion begins. The distance that the piston has travelled along the cylinder when the steam supply is thus cut off, proportioned to the total piston stroke, is called the percentage of cut-off, and is often quoted in descriptions of locomotive performance.

Until comparatively recent years, valves were exclusively of sliding types. The term "slide-valve," however, is applied to a certain type only—a flat valve, shaped like a ⌂. At its most extreme movement in either direction, the valve uncovers the steam port of the cylinder, at each end alternately, and admits steam; while the exhaust steam makes it way through the same ports through the interior of the ⌂, as the latter uncovers the port openings. The solid sliding portions of the valve are made wider than the port openings by a small width known as "lap"; this has an important influence on the locomotive working, and the greater the amount of lap, so much the greater must be the travel of the valve in order that the ports may be fully uncovered.

The main disadvantage of the older slide-valve is the pressure of the steam on the back of the valve; the friction so caused increases wear and tear. For this reason, in the past the introduction of modern short cut-off working, which is explained later, was objected to by many locomotive engineers because it could not be provided for apart from longer valve-travels, which in their turn increased the cost of maintaining valves and valve-motions. While some improvement of working was secured by the use of various types of "balanced" slide-valve, a much better solution of the difficulty was found in the piston-valve.

Like the slide-valve proper, the piston-valve does its work with a sliding motion; as it consists of two circular heads fixed on a spindle, however, it cannot, as the slide-valve, be forced down on to its seat by the steam pressure, but is perfectly balanced. Also, in view of the circular form of the piston-valve, the ports can be made larger in area than those of a slide-valve, so assisting the flow of the steam. There are two main types of piston-valve, those with outside and those with inside admission. In the former, admission of steam to the cylinder is from outside the two heads or pistons of the valve; in the latter, which is the type more favoured, steam is admitted to the valve chamber between the two pistons.

At times water gets trapped in engine cylinders, particularly when "priming" is going on— that is, the carrying down of water through the main steam-pipe, with the steam. Priming may result from over-filling the boiler, or from "foaming" in the boiler due to the presence in the water of compounds used in water-softening, or from other causes; and there is danger in such conditions of the pistons knocking out the cylinder-ends. If a driver realises that there is this risk, he can open his cylinder-cocks, and the water is ejected, with great force and much accompanying steam, through small pipes under the buffer-beam. In an engine fitted with slide-valves, the valves can be forced off their seats by this excessive pressure, so that the necessary relief is provided, but not so with piston-valves.

Special means are provided, therefore, for giving relief automatically when necessary. One way of releasing trapped water is by fitting automatic valves, which open under excessive pressure of water, but remain closed by springs against the maximum steam pressure; piston-valves have also been used which themselves incorporate some method of release, but some of these designs have given trouble by permitting steam leakages. In the same connection, provision has to be made for relieving the partial vacuum caused in the steam-chest by the pumping action of pistons in empty cylinders when an engine is running without steam, and especially at high speed. For this purpose anti-vacuum or bypass valves are fitted to many locomotives.

A still more modern type of valve used in steam locomotives is the poppet-valve, of which a number of different types are in use—the Lentz and the Caprotti in Great Britain, Germany and Italy, the Cossart in France and the Franklin in the United States. The poppet-valve does its work by lifting to uncover the steam or exhaust ports, and falling to close them, as in the internal-combustion engine. These valves are designed to give a more precise timing of the valve events than is possible with piston-valves, and so to improve steam distribution; they can be worked by an ordinary valve-motion or by oscillating or rotary cams (Fig. 4). With cams, however, it is not easy to provide for the gradual variations in cut-off which alone make it possible to work a steam locomotive with a maximum of efficiency. The most extensive application of poppet-valves to locomotives in Great Britain has been that of Lentz valves to the "Hunt" class 4-4-0s of the late L.N.E.R.; in the United States the most successful gear of this kind has been the Franklin, used on the notable "T1" class 4-4-4-4 locomotives of the Pennsylvania Railroad. Further trial is being made by the London Midland Region, British Railways, of Caprotti valves on some of its latest Class "5" 4-6-0 locomotives.

The characteristic movement of slide-valves and piston-valves is imparted by the valve-motion, the working of which is directly under

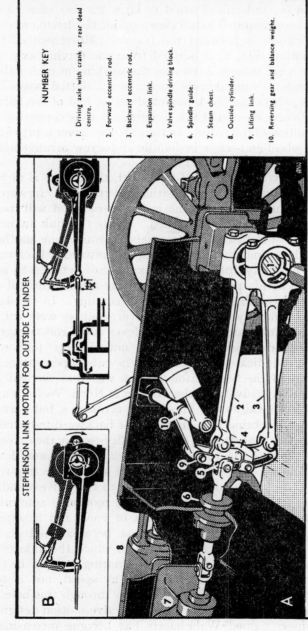

NUMBER KEY

1. Driving axle with crank at rear dead centre.
2. Forward eccentric rod.
3. Backward eccentric rod.
4. Expansion link.
5. Valve spindle driving block.
6. Spindle guide.
7. Steam chest.
8. Outside cylinder.
9. Lifting link.
10. Reversing gear and balance weight.

STEPHENSON LINK MOTION FOR OUTSIDE CYLINDER

Drawing "A". Gear set in almost full forward position with block (5) at top of expansion link slot. Valve spindle takes its timing from top, or forward eccentric rod (2) and its travel from a combination of the movements of both rods.

Inset "B". Full backward gear. Wheel crank at rear dead centre. Valve spindle timing is taken from lower, or backward eccentric rod (3).

Inset "C". Full backward gear showing maximum valve travel (x). Steam admitted to front end of cylinder; rear end exhausting. Valve travel reduces as block (5) is brought towards centre of slot in rocking expansion link by operation of reversing gear (10).

Fig. 2. STEPHENSON LINK MOTION

the driver's control. In Great Britain for many years the Stephenson link-motion held sway, and still is fitted to large number of engines. Occasionally it has been mounted in full view, outside the driving wheels, but the normal location is between the frames. Movement of the Stephenson link-motion (Fig. 2) is derived from the driving axle, on which four eccentrics are mounted, two for the working of each valve. The two eccentric rods are hinged in the two ends of a slotted expansion link, in which there works the block mounted on the end of the valve-spindle, and the circular motion of the eccentrics is thus converted to the reciprocating motion of the valve. In the cab, the driver is provided with a lever, or a wheel-and-screw or handle-and-screw arrangement, for moving the expansion link up and down.

When the link is at the bottom of its travel, the engine is in full forward gear, and the valves are in position for travelling forwards; when the link is at the top, the engine is in reverse, and will move backwards on the regulator being opened. With the link in mid-position, the motions of the two eccentric rods neutralise one another, and the valve-spindle is almost stationary. In full forward or backward gear, the cut-off is normally limited to a maximum of between 85 and 65 per cent.; between this position and mid-gear are all the cut-off variations that are at the driver's command in running. In the days when reversing was generally effected by a lever, notches were cut at intervals in the quadrant-plate in which the lever catch-rod engaged; from this came the characteristic expresssion "notching up" (or some-times "linking up") to indicate a reduction in the cut-off percentage.

An early variant of the Stephenson motion was that devised by David Joy, and used extensively on the London & North Western and Lancashire & Yorkshire Railways. This has no eccentrics, but derives its motion from the connecting-rod. Forward or backward movement is determined by the angle at which a curved guide is set by the driver's reversing wheel in the cab. In this guide a block slides up and down with the upward and downward movement of the connecting-rod, through a system of linkage which is connected to the valve-spindle, and gives the latter its desired motion. The Joy motion is admirable in action, from the steam distribution point of view, but a serious disadvantage is that the connecting-rod must be weakened at its weakest point by drilling it to receive the pin to which the linkage of the gear is attached. Owing to the high alternating stresses in the connecting-rod when an engine is travelling at speed, not a few connecting-rods of engines so drilled have broken through this hole.

Since the beginning of the present century, a valve-motion designed by a Belgian engineer named Walschaerts has become increasingly

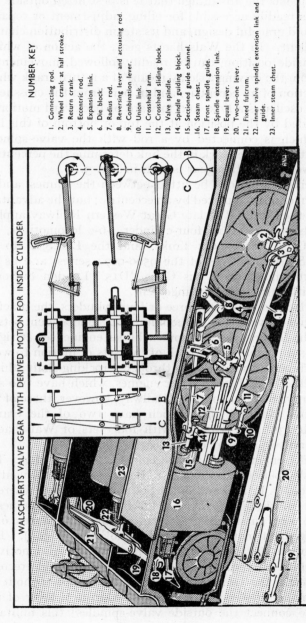

NUMBER KEY

1. Connecting rod.
2. Wheel crank at half stroke.
3. Return crank.
4. Eccentric rod.
5. Expansion link.
6. Die block.
7. Radius rod.
8. Reversing lever and actuating rod.
9. Combination lever.
10. Union link.
11. Crosshead arm.
12. Crosshead sliding block.
13. Valve spindle.
14. Spindle guiding block.
15. Sectioned guide channel.
16. Steam chest.
17. Front spindle guide.
18. Spindle extension guide.
19. Equal lever.
20. Two-to-one lever.
21. Fixed fulcrum.
22. Inner valve spindle extension link and guide.
23. Inner steam chest.

WALSCHAERTS VALVE GEAR WITH DERIVED MOTION FOR INSIDE CYLINDER

The main drawing shows the layout of components when set in backward gear. The outside valves derive their movement from the combined actions of the crosshead and the expansion link. The timing and length of the valve stroke depends on the position of the die block in the expansion link which is oscillated by the return crank. The inside cylinder valves are actuated by the outside valve spindles through the 2 to 1 gear.

Inset is shown the motion, simplified, in full forward gear. Shaded areas are the ranges of movement of the combination levers and the expansion links. Imaginary movement of the left-hand (lower) engine crank through 120° to "B" and then to "C" alters the attitude of the 2 to 1 levers as shown.

Fig. 3. WALSCHAERTS VALVE-MOTION (WITH GRESLEY DERIVED MOTION FOR INSIDE CYLINDER OF THREE-CYLINDER LOCOMOTIVES)

popular, and is now fitted to the great majority of new British locomotive designs.   It has the advantage that it is best fitted outside the
engine, where it is readily accessible for oiling, adjustment or repairs;
also it is of light and graceful design, and its steam distribution characteristics are excellent.   In the Walschaerts gear, the action of which,
because of its outside position, can be readily followed, movement is
derived in part from the driving axle by means of a return crank which
performs the function of an eccentric, and in part from the crosshead.
The return crank oscillates a link, and forward or backward motion of
the engine is decided by the position at the top or bottom of this link
of a die-block which is connected by a rod with the valve-spindle.
Intermediate positions of the block in the link determine the percentage
of cut-off.   The working of this gear is seen in Fig. 3.

The Walschaerts motion can be fitted between the frames, and in
this case the return crank is replaced by an eccentric; but the advantage
of accessibility is then lost.   The late Great Western Railway applied
inside Walschaerts gear to all its four-cylinder 4-6-0 locomotives, the
L.N.E.R. to its Class "N7" 0-6-2 tanks, and the L.M.S.R. to its
inside-cylinder 0-8-0 locomotives of the 9500-9674 series, and as far
back as 1912 Drummond fitted his Class "D15" London & South
Western 4-4-0s with this motion arrangement.

In the case of locomotives with three or four cylinders, the practice
of locomotive engineers varies as to the number of independent sets of
valve-motion.   The four cranks of a four-cylinder engine, set at right-
angles, make it a simple matter for each of two sets of motion to work
one piston-valve directly, and a second through a rocking-shaft; this is
the practice on all G.W.R. four-cylinder engines, which have two sets
of valve-motion only.   On the Southern Railway, however, those of the
four-cylinder "Lord Nelson" class which have two of the cranks
advanced through 135° are provided with four sets of Walschaerts
gear, two inside and two outside, one for each cylinder.

In three-cylinder engines the problem is less easy of solution.   The
late Sir Nigel Gresley perfected an ingenious derived gear (the invention
actually was that of Mr. H. Holcroft of the Southern Railway), whereby
the motion of the inside piston-valve of his three-cylinder engines is
derived from the two outside Walschaerts motions by means of a
2 to 1 lever arrangement mounted below the smokebox (Fig. 3).   But
although this motion has been fitted to hundreds of locomotives,
including some which have made the country's most notable records
for speed with steam, the Gresley derived motion is not without its
defects.   Chief among these is the amount of whip in a lever of the
length required to connect the outside valve-spindles; this militates

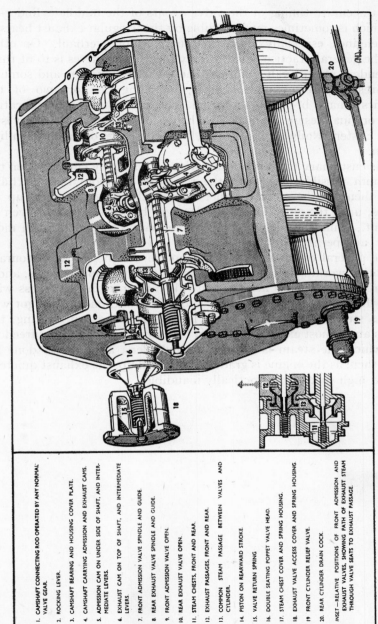

Fig. 4. ROTARY CAM POPPET-VALVE MOTION

1. CAMSHAFT CONNECTING ROD OPERATED BY ANY NORMAL VALVE GEAR.

2. ROCKING LEVER.

3. CAMSHAFT BEARING AND HOUSING COVER PLATE.

4. CAMSHAFT CARRYING ADMISSION AND EXHAUST CAMS.

5. ADMISSION CAM ON UNDER SIDE OF SHAFT, AND INTERMEDIATE LEVERS.

6. EXHAUST CAM ON TOP OF SHAFT, AND INTERMEDIATE LEVERS

7. FRONT ADMISSION VALVE SPINDLE AND GUIDE.

8. REAR EXHAUST VALVE SPINDLE AND GUIDE.

9. FRONT ADMISSION VALVE OPEN.

10. REAR EXHAUST VALVE OPEN.

11. STEAM CHESTS, FRONT AND REAR.

12. EXHAUST PASSAGES, FRONT AND REAR.

13. COMMON STEAM PASSAGE BETWEEN VALVES AND CYLINDER.

14. PISTON ON REARWARD STROKE.

15. VALVE RETURN SPRING.

16. DOUBLE SEATING POPPET VALVE HEAD.

17. STEAM CHEST COVER AND SPRING HOUSING.

18. EXHAUST VALVE ACCESS COVER AND SPRING HOUSING.

19. FRONT CYLINDER RELIEF VALVE.

20. REAR CYLINDER DRAIN COCK.

INSET—RELATIVE POSITIONS OF FRONT ADMISSION AND EXHAUST VALVES, SHOWING PATH OF EXHAUST STEAM THROUGH VALVE SEATS TO EXHAUST PASSAGE.

against accurate timing of the valve events of the middle cylinder—a fact which is sometimes made audible by the irregular exhaust beats of these engines, especially when they are due for overhaul. On other lines the general practice with three-cylinder locomotives is to fit three independent sets of valve-motion, one for each cylinder, and some of the Gresley three-cylinder engines, including one or two of the "Pacifics," have been rebuilt by his successor with this modification of the original design. All the L.N.E.R. three-cylinder locomotives of North Eastern Railway origin, also, have three sets of Stephenson link motion.

It is customary to start a locomotive on a lengthy cut-off, often the maximum possible, and with the regulator no more than partially open; then, as the engine gathers speed, the driver notches up by degrees, until the cut-off has been brought back to 25, 20, or even 15 per cent., while the regulator meantime has been opened much more widely, and perhaps to full.

The general object of many locomotive designers is to encourage locomotive working with wide open regulator and short cut-offs, and a measure of the success achieved in this matter is the quietness with which the modern locomotive sets about its work, once it has got well into its stride. When the cut-off is lengthened, as on starting, the sudden and almost explosive exhaust beats are a witness to the freedom with which the steam is leaving the cylinders, after it has done its work; then, as the engine is gradually notched up, the exhaust quietens until at high speed it is practically inaudible.

5

DESIGN—THE BOILER AND THE STEAM

ON a thermal basis, the steam locomotive of traditional design has had the doubtful distinction in the past of being one of the most inefficient, if not the most inefficient, of all machines in which steam provides the motive power. This bald statement, however, requires a great deal of qualification. Design has always been circumscribed by the specialised conditions in which the locomotive has to work, and, above all, the limitations on design imposed by the loading gauge. But improvements in design during recent years have made it possible for the locomotive to pull up no small proportion of the leeway in overall thermal efficiency.

The British locomotive, as we have seen in Chapter 3, must not exceed 13 ft. 4 in. in height above rail, nor 9 ft. in width; moreover, the maximum weight permitted on any one pair of wheels, in the best main-line track conditions, is 22½ tons. The boiler must be lifted high enough to clear the driving wheels, and to allow ample room for the development of the firebox, and thus is cramped in its cross-sectional dimensions. While the boiler must be long enough to extract the maximum possible proportion of the heat developed by the consumption of the fuel on the firegrate, and to transfer that heat to the water for steam-raising, at the same time it is limited in length by the length of the locomotive chassis. As a result, the locomotive boiler must be able to produce steam more rapidly than any other type of boiler of comparable size.

First of all, therefore, the designer must arrange for a supply of air to the firebox in sufficient volume to provide oxygen for rapid consumption of the fuel; the matter of draught is all-important. He must then design his boiler in such a way as to permit the most rapid transfer of heat possible between the hot gases produced by combustion and the water surrounding the fire and filling the boiler barrel. Finally, it is essential that no more energy shall be thrown away, either in the form of hot gases from the fire incompletely used, or of steam insufficiently expanded, than is lost unavoidably by reason of the characteristic working arrangement of the steam locomotive.

Chapter 1 mentioned how George Stephenson, as far back in locomotive history as his famous *Rocket* of 1829, first combined in a locomotive the use of a multi-tubular boiler with that of exhaust steam to furnish draught. From his day, while the actual design of the boiler has improved out of all knowledge, these basic principles of locomotive design have remained unchanged. Considerable loss of heat energy is involved in throwing away through the chimney both heat direct from the fire and steam which is still at a pressure higher than atmospheric; but this is the penalty imposed by the restricted conditions described in the first paragraph. The alternative would be to use live steam to provide forced draught, and in all probability this would prove less economical still.

The boiler is divided into three main parts—the firebox, the barrel, and the smokebox. Of these the firebox, adjacent to the driver's cab, is in two parts—the inner firebox, which contains the fire, and the outer firebox, which surrounds it. Between the walls of the inner and outer fireboxes is the boiler water. At the base of the firebox is the steel foundation ring, which extends round the firebox and to which the inner and outer shells are riveted. The opening for the firehole door, in the cab, is sometimes formed by a similar and smaller ring; or the plates are flanged and riveted. The top of the inner firebox is known as the "crown," and from this level the two "legs," enclosing the water and formed of the sides of the inner and outer fireboxes, extend downwards to the foundation ring, to which they are firmly secured. Hundreds of staybolts are used to maintain the correct distance apart of inner and outer fireboxes, against the pressure of the steam between them. Staybolts of a flexible type are popular, as they provide for a certain amount of movement resulting from the effects of expansion and contraction of the boiler.

Fireboxes are of various shapes. The L.N.E.R. has specialised in round-topped fireboxes, of which, as their name implies, the upper part of the outer firebox is an arc of a circle, of the same radius as the boiler barrel. The L.M.S.R. and G.W.R., on the other hand, have preferred the Belpaire firebox. The earliest Belpaire fireboxes were square in shape, but the later tendency, on the G.W.R. and L.M.S.R., has been a wedge-shaped box, largest in cross-section at the front end, and then tapering inwards on each side and downwards on top, towards the cab. It is held that the Belpaire box, in which both outer and inner fireboxes have flat tops and sides, simplifies the problem of staying as compared with the round-topped firebox, of which the circular outer firebox must be stayed to the flat top of the inner box, but actually this is a debatable point. There is also the wide firebox, as used on the Pacifics of the late L.M.S., L.N.E. and Southern Railways, which spreads outwards at the base and rests across the main frames, instead of narrowing at the base to drop between them. The L.M.S.R. type of wide firebox is a combination of this type with the Belpaire square-topped box.

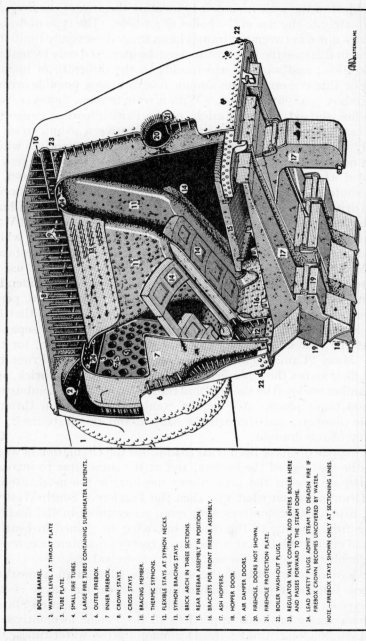

Fig. 5. FIREBOX SECTION OF SOUTHERN REGION PACIFIC LOCOMOTIVE, SHOWING OUTER AND INNER FIREBOXES, STAYING, THERMIC SYPHONS, ROCKING GRATE AND ASH HOPPERS

1 BOILER BARREL.
2 WATER LEVEL AT THROAT PLATE
3 TUBE PLATE.
4 SMALL FIRE TUBES
5 LARGE FIRE TUBES CONTAINING SUPERHEATER ELEMENTS.
6 OUTER FIREBOX.
7 INNER FIREBOX.
8 CROWN STAYS.
9 CROSS STAYS
10 BRACING MEMBER.
11 THERMIC SYPHONS.
12 FLEXIBLE STAYS AT SYPHON NECKS.
13 SYPHON BRACING STAYS.
14 BRICK ARCH IN THREE SECTIONS.
15 REAR FIREBAR ASSEMBLY IN POSITION.
16 BRACKETS FOR FRONT FIREBAR ASSEMBLY.
17 ASH HOPPERS.
18 HOPPER DOOR.
19 AIR DAMPER DOORS.
20 FIREHOLE DOORS NOT SHOWN.
21 FIREHOLE PROTECTION PLATE.
22 BOILER WASH-OUT PLUGS.
23 REGULATOR VALVE CONTROL ROD ENTERS BOILER HERE AND PASSES FORWARD TO THE STEAM DOME.
24 LEAD SAFETY PLUGS ADMIT STEAM TO DEADEN FIRE IF FIREBOX CROWN BECOMES UNCOVERED BY WATER.

NOTE.—FIREBOX STAYS SHOWN ONLY AT SECTIONING LINES.

The object of the wide firebox is to increase the area of the firegrate proportionately to the size of the boiler as a whole. The type of firebox which drops down between the frames has a firegrate severely limited in width, and in this case the firegrate area can be increased only by making the firebox long and narrow, which adds to the difficulty of manual firing. For this reason, the maximum firegrate area possible with a narrow firebox is about 30 sq. ft. With a wide firebox, however, notwithstanding the extreme limitations of the British loading gauge the designer is able to increase his firegrate area to between 40 and 50 sq. ft. Obviously the wide firebox can be installed only on locomotives which have one or more carrying axles with small diameter wheels in rear of the coupled wheels; it can be used, that is to say, on 4-6-2, 2-6-2, or 4-4-2 locomotives, but not on a 4-6-0 or a 2-8-0, unless the last-mentioned has small driving wheels and a high-pitched boiler, as the American-built 2-8-0s which worked on British railways during the Second World War.

In the United States, particularly on the Reading Railway, which serves the anthracite coalfields of Pennsylvania, very large fireboxes of the Wootten type were developed on locomotives for the use of anthracite. These capacious fireboxes not only were of considerable length, but were so bulky in width that it became customary to perch the driver's cab on the boiler barrel, ahead of the firebox (so that his look-out ahead might not be restricted), and to provide a separate shelter at the rear of the firebox, in the usual cab position, for the fireman. Many "Camelbacks," as they were known, are still running.

Extending across the inner firebox there is an arch of firebrick, and in the chamber enclosed by the arch and the firebox walls the combustion of the fuel takes place. Air for the combustion is drawn through adjustable dampers, and through the ashpan and the grate itself, by the agency of the draught.

Many expedients have been tried to improve the circulation of water between the two legs of the firebox, and at the same time to increase the heating surface in the area where the heat is the most intense. Dugald Drummond, on what was then the London & South Western Railway, fitted his locomotives with cross water-tubes in the firebox, extending from one leg to the other; but what he gained in heating surface and circulation he lost in increased costs of maintenance, owing to the difficulty of keeping the water-tubes from leakage.

A modern development of the same idea (though in a measure anticipated by the firebox "mid-feathers" of earlier days) is the thermic syphon, which has a considerable vogue in the United States, and in this country has been applied to all the Pacific locomotives of the Southern Region. Unlike the Drummond cross water-tubes, the

TABLE 5

BRITISH TANK LOCOMOTIVES—LEADING DIMENSIONS

Wheel Arrange-ment	Railway§	Type and Class	Cylinders			Driving Wheels Dia.	Heating Surface				Fire-grate Area	Working Pressure	Tractive Effort*	Coupled Wheel-base	Adhesion Weight	Capacity		Total Weight†	Length Overall
			No.	Dia.	Stroke		Tubes	Fire-box	Super-heater	Total						Coal	Water		
				in	in.	ft. in.	sq. ft.	sq. ft.	sq. ft.	sq. ft.	sq. ft.	lb./sq. in.	lb.	ft. in.	tons	tons	gallons	tons	ft. in.
2-6-4	L.M.S.R.	Passenger ("4P" three-cyl.)	3	16	26	5 9	1,126	139	185	1,450	26·7	200	24,600	16 6	57·0	3½	2,000	92·4	47 3
,,	,,	,, ("4P" two-cyl.) ..	2	19⅝	26	5 9	1,223	143	245	1,611	26·7	200	24,670	16 6	51·7	3½	2,000	87·9	47 3
,,	L.N.E.R.	,, Standard ("L1") ..	2	20	26	5 2	1,198	139	284	1,621	24·7	225	32,080	13 6	59·0	4½	2,630	89·5	43 4
,,	S.R.	Freight Standard ("W") ..	3	16½	28	5 6	1,391	135	285	1,811	25·0	200	29,450	15 0	57·2	3½	2,000	90·7	44 0
4-6-2	L.N.E.R.	Passenger Ex-G.C.R. ("A5")	2	20	26	5 7	1,139	141	178	1,458	21·0	180	23,745	13 0	54·0	4¼	2,280	85·9	43 0
,,	,,	,, Ex-N.E.R. ("A8")	3	16½	26	5 9	961	124	194	1,279	23·0	175	22,940	13 0	52·3	4	2,000	86·9	42 6
,,	S.R.	Freight Ex-L.S.W.R. ("H16")	2	21	28	5 7	1,267	139	252	1,658	27·0	180	28,200	15 0	59·0	3½	2,000	96·4	46 0
4-4-2	,,	Passenger Ex-L.B.S.C. ("I3")	2	21	26	6 7½	1,126	120	254	1,500	23·4	180	22,100	8 9	38·0	3	2,110	76·0	40 11
2-6-2	G.W.R.	,, "6100"	2	18	30	5 8	1,145	122	82	1,349	20·4	225	27,340	14 9	52·7	4	2,000	78·5	41 0
,,	,,	,, "3100"	2	18½	30	5 3	1,349	129	192	1,670	20·6	225	31,170	14 9	57·3	3½	2,000	81·5	41 0
,,	,,	,, "4575"	2	17	24	4 7½	992	94	78	1,164	16·6	200	21,250	11 6	46·3	3¾	1,300	61·0	36 5
,,	L.M.S.R.	,, Standard ("3P") ..	2	17½	26	5 3	996	111	145	1,252	19·2	200	21,485	16 6	46·5	3	1,500	71·3	42 0
,,	,,	,, Standard ("2P")	2	16	24	5 0	925	101	134	1,160	17·5	200	17,400	13 9	39·2	3	1,350	63·2	38 10
,,	L.N.E.R.	,, Standard ("V1") ..	3	16	26	5 8	1,198	127	284	1,609	22·1	180	22,464	16 3	57·2	4	2,000	84·0	42 0
0-6-2	,,	,, Ex-G.N.R. ("N2")	2	19	26	5 8	880	118	207	1,205	19·0	170	19,945	16 3	56·8	4	2,000	71·5	38 0
,,	,,	,, Ex-G.E.R. ("N7")	2	18	24	4 10	858	110	134	1,102	17·7	180	20,510	16 3	51·1	3¼	1,600	64·9	34 11
0-4-4	S.R.	,, Ex-L.S.W.R. ("M7")	2	18½	26	5 7	1,067	124	—	1,191	20·4	175	19,750	7 6	35·2	3	1,300	60·2	36 3
2-8-2	G.W.R.	Mineral "7200"	2	19	30	4 7½	1,349	129	192	1,670	20·6	200	33,170	20 0	72·8	6	2,500	92·6	44 10
2-8-0	,,	,, "5205"	2	19	30	4 7½	1,349	129	192	1,670	20·6	200	33,170	20 0	72·5	4	1,800	82·1	40 9
4-8-0	S.R.	Shunting Ex-L.S.W.R. ("G16")	2	22	28	5 1	1,267	139	252	1,658	27·0	180	34,000	18 0	72·9	3½	2,000	95·1	42 10
0-8-0	,,	,, Standard ("Z") ..	3	16	28	4 8	1,173	106	—	1,279	18·6	180	29,375	17 6	71·6	3	1,500	71·6	39 4
,,	L.N.E.R.	,, Standard ("Q1") ..	2	19	26	4 8	1,068	141	—	1,209	23·6	180	25,645	17 1	69·9	4½	1,500	69·9	36 0
0-6-0	,,	,, Standard ("J50") ..	2	18½	26	4 8	1,016	103	—	1,119	16·3	175	23,635	16 3	58·2	4¾	1,520	58·2	33 0
,,	G.W.R.	,, Pannier ("5700")	2	17½	24	4 7½	1,013	102	—	1,115	15·3	200	22,515	15 6	49·0	3¼	1,200	49·0	31 2
,,	L.M.S.R.	,, Standard ("3F") ..	2	18	26	4 7	968	97	—	1,065	16·0	160	20,830	16 6	49·5	2¼	1,200	49·5	31 5
,,	,,	,, Standard ("2F") ..	2	17	22	3 11	923	85	—	1,008	14·5	160	18,400	9 6	43·6	1½	1,000	43·6	27 6
,,	S.R.	,, Ex-L.B.S.C. ("A1/X")	2	12	20	4 0	433	56	—	489	10·0	150	7,600	12 0	28·3	1	500	28·3	26 1
,,	‡M.O.S.	,, War Design ..	2	18	26	4 3	873	87	—	960	16·8	170	23,870	11 0	48·2	2¼	1,200	48·2	30 4

* At 85 per cent. working pressure † In full working order ‡ Ministry of Supply design; many acquired by British Railways since the War § Pre-nationalisation

thermic syphon, of which two or more are usually fitted, extends longitudinally from the firebox front. Each syphon in shape is like a "Y," with the stem bent round at the bottom end, in the form of a tube, and the space between the arms of the "Y" flattened out to form a narrow triangular water space (Fig. 5).

The bent end of the tube communicates, through the bottom of the firebox tubeplate, with the water in the lower part of the barrel; the upper part of the triangular water space has an exit through a long narrow slot in the firebox crown. Water thus passes from the boiler, by syphonic action, to the upper part of the firebox, heated intensely as it moves through the narrow upper part of the syphon, with its flat sides. The remarkable steaming capacity of the Southern "Merchant Navy" and "West Country" class locomotives is probably due in no small measure to the use of this device.

Another modern detail of firebox equipment is the rocking grate. A bugbear of the fireman, especially on long continuous runs, is the formation of clinker on the firegrate; and as the quality of the coal deteriorates, so the tendency to clinker increases. Hitherto in Great Britain, the quality of coal supplied to locomotives has been such that no special precautions against clinkering have been regarded as necessary; but the rapid decline in quality caused by war conditions from 1939 onwards has hastened the introduction, on the late L.M.S. and Southern Railways, of the rocking type of firegrate which for long past has been a standard feature of locomotive construction in North America and elsewhere. In the latter countries, firegrates are of such large size that power assistance (usually a steam cylinder) is necessary for rocking them; but the British installations are manually operated.

The firebars, which are larger than the normal type, are arranged transversely, and pivot on two lugs in such a way that they can be rocked backwards and forwards. Gentle rocking is enough to break up the clinker, and to get rid of the ash into the ashpan below. Also, as the grate is divided into two sections or more, and one only is rocked at a time, by raking the fire on to one of these sections, and tilting the other to its extreme position, the larger pieces of clinker can be pushed bodily, with the ash, through the spaces between the bars into the ashpan.

These operations can be performed while the engine is in motion, and the choking of the firegrate with clinker, which adversely affects the steaming, can thus be avoided; moreover, the intelligent use of rocking grates on the road means less labour and time spent in cleaning or dropping fires when the engine reaches the shed. More massive firebars are needed than usual, but this is an advantage, as they do not distort so readily under the influence of heat, and so have a longer life. Many engines on the late L.N.E.R. and elsewhere, also, have been equipped with a "drop grate," which is a portion of the firegrate fitted with a tilting appliance, for use in dropping the fire only. On the Southern Bulleid Pacifics there is a combination of rocking and drop grate with a triple ashpan and self-cleaning hopper (Fig. 5).

The central portion of the boiler is the barrel, which extends from the firebox to the smokebox, and is firmly shut off from both by stout tubeplates, usually of steel at the smokebox end, and copper at the firebox end of the barrel. Each tubeplate is pierced by hundreds of circular holes, to receive the ends of the tubes, which extend from one tubeplate to the other and provide an open passage from the firebox to the smokebox. Through these tubes the hot gases, produced by the combustion of the fuel, after making their way round the brick arch, pass to the smokebox, so that each tube is filled with heat and surrounded by water. In this way the tubes serve the double purpose of providing the passage for the draught and of increasing the boiler heating surface. The most effective parts of the heating surface, of course, are the walls and crown of the inner firebox, where the water is in immediate contact with the fire, but the heating surface of the tubes makes it possible to extract a good deal more of the heat from the hot firebox gases before the latter pass finally out of the chimney.

When the locomotive is standing, the only draught available for the fire is that produced by the blower, which, when put on by the driver, takes a small amount of steam from the boiler, and passes it through steam jets, arranged round the blast-pipe, direct into the chimney. On starting, the driver shuts off the blower, and from then on the draught is induced by the action of the exhaust steam. This is led from the cylinders into a conically-shaped blast-pipe; the blast-pipe, erected vertically, narrows towards the top, through which the steam is ejected with considerable force. Precisely plumb with the blast-pipe is the chimney, extending downwards into the smokebox by what is known, from its shape, as a "petticoat." From the lower edge of the petticoat to the top of the chimney, whatever may be external shape of the chimney casing, inside there is a gradual outward taper, which is designed precisely to "fit" the inverted cone of steam issuing from the blast-pipe, in order that the maximum suction effect may be obtained.

The smaller the orifice through which the steam emerges, at the top of the blast-pipe, so much the fiercer is the draught. In earlier days, there were many ingenious ways in which drivers doctored the blast-pipes of their engines, in order to sharpen the blast, and so to make the boilers steam more rapidly. The opening paragraphs of

Chapter 1, however, have described the wastefulness and inefficiency inseparable from the spark-throwing induced by an unduly fierce blast. With a view to varying the diameter of the blast-pipe nozzle to meet different running conditions, the late Great Western Railway has made considerable use of a "jumper-top" type of blast-pipe. This is provided with a loose cap, which lifts under the influence of hard steaming, and so exposes additional blast openings, relieving the pressure in this way.

To the French engineer André Chapelon we owe in large measure the importance attached to-day to the streamlining, in every way possible, of the flow of the steam from the boiler through the main steam-pipe, superheater, valves, cylinders and blast-pipe to final exhaust through the chimney. One of Chapelon's methods for facilitating steam-flow has been to double the blast-pipe, and above it to crown the smokebox of his engines with a large double chimney in an elongated casing. This method helps to reduce back-pressure in the cylinders; at the same time it greatly increases the surface area of the "cones" of exhaust steam from blast-pipe to chimney, thus increasing the induced draught in the smokebox to an extent which more than compensates for the lower pressure at which, with present-day short cut-off working, the exhaust is being thrown away.

Double chimneys now have appeared on certain of the larger British locomotive classes, such as the Pacifics and the rebuilt 4-6-0 "Royal Scots" of the late L.M.S.R., and on some of the L.N.E.R. Pacifics also. It is significant that *Mallard*, the L.N.E.R. Pacific which in 1938 attained the world's record speed with steam of 126 m.p.h., has Chapelon's "Kylchap" exhaust arrangements; these include not only double blast-pipe and chimney, but the further refinement of three pairs of petticoats, of diminishing diameter, extending right down to the orifices of the twin blast-pipes.

A variant of the same idea is that devised by the French engineer, Lemaître, which is a series of blast orifices arranged in a ring and exhausting through a chimney of very large diameter. This type of exhaust is used on the locomotives of the Southern Region, where large-diameter chimneys may be seen on the "Merchant Navy" and "West Country" 4-6-2s, the "Lord Nelson" 4-6-0s, the "Q1" 0-6-0s, and many of the "Schools" 4-4-0s.

Another external feature of many modern engines has an immediate connection with the low pressure at which the exhaust steam of modern engines leaves their chimneys. With the very short chimneys that are the inevitable outcome of large-diameter boilers, short cut-off working at high speed tends to make the exhaust drift along the top of the boiler and obscure the front windows of the driver's cab, and with it his

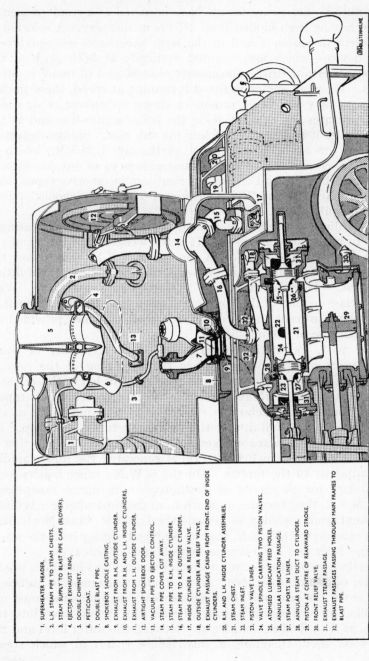

1. SUPERHEATER HEADER.
2. L.H. STEAM PIPE TO STEAM CHESTS.
3. STEAM SUPPLY TO BLAST PIPE CAPS (BLOWER).
4. EJECTOR EXHAUST RING.
5. DOUBLE CHIMNEY.
6. PETTICOAT.
7. DOUBLE BLAST PIPE.
8. SMOKEBOX SADDLE CASTING.
9. EXHAUST FROM R.H. OUTSIDE CYLINDER.
10. EXHAUST FROM R.H. AND L.H. INSIDE CYLINDERS.
11. EXHAUST FROM L.H. OUTSIDE CYLINDER.
12. AIRTIGHT SMOKEBOX DOOR.
13. VACUUM PIPE TO EJECTOR CONTROL.
14. STEAM PIPE COVER CUT AWAY.
15. STEAM PIPE TO R.H. INSIDE CYLINDER.
16. STEAM PIPE TO R.H. OUTSIDE CYLINDER.
17. INSIDE CYLINDER AIR RELIEF VALVE.
18. OUTSIDE CYLINDER AIR RELIEF VALVE.
19. EXHAUST PASSAGE CASING FROM FRONT END OF INSIDE CYLINDERS.
20. R.H. AND L.H. INSIDE CYLINDER ASSEMBLIES.
21. STEAM CHEST.
22. STEAM INLET.
23. PISTON VALVE LINER.
24. VALVE SPINDLE CARRYING TWO PISTON VALVES.
25. ATOMISED LUBRICANT FEED HOLES.
26. ANNULAR LUBRICATION PASSAGE.
27. STEAM PORTS IN LINER.
28. ANNULAR STEAM DUCT TO CYLINDER.
29. PISTON AT CENTRE OF REARWARD STROKE.
30. FRONT RELIEF VALVE.
31. EXHAUST STEAM PASSAGE.
32. EXHAUST PASSAGES PASSING THROUGH MAIN FRAMES TO BLAST PIPE.

Fig. 6. SMOKEBOX OF LONDON MIDLAND REGION PACIFIC LOCOMOTIVE, SHOWING CYLINDER, PISTON-VALVE AND VALVE-CHEST, AND DOUBLE BLAST-PIPE

look-out ahead. Serious accidents have occurred as a result of signals at danger having been hidden from drivers in this way. A solution of this problem has been found in the large sheet-steel wing-plates—a German device—which are mounted vertically at both sides of the smokebox of certain British locomotive classes, and of many in other countries. When an engine so fitted is running at speed, these smoke-deflectors, as they are called, produce a strong up-current of air which both concentrates the exhaust along the boiler centre-line and at the same time lifts it sufficiently to clear the cab roof. Smoke deflectors are used on the 4-6-0 "Royal Scots" of the late L.M.S.R., which in their original condition had the shortest chimneys of any locomotive class in Great Britain, and on various Southern locomotive types, such as the "Lord Nelson" and "King Arthur" 4-6-0s, the "Schools" 4-4-0s, and the "Mogul" 2-6-0s.

In streamlined and semi-streamlined locomotives, the boiler casing is designed to have the same effect. It is the wedge-shaped front of the Class "A4" streamline Pacifics of the late L.N.E.R. that serves the double purpose of cutting cleanly through the atmosphere and of lifting the exhaust. The "air-smoothed" "Merchant Navy" and "West Country" class engines of the Southern Region have an arrangement of deflector plates in front and on either side of the chimney provided for the same purpose of exhaust-lifting.

In the past, locomotive boiler barrels were generally of equal diameter from end to end, but since the beginning of the present century there has been a considerable development, led in this country by the Great Western Railway, in the type of barrel which tapers outwards from the smokebox to the firebox. The underside of the barrel is usually horizontal, and the maximum taper is on top. Its purpose is mainly to increase the space available for the collection of steam in the area in which the steam is generated the most rapidly, that is, adjacent to the firebox. On the G.W.R., taper boilers have been standard for all classes of locomotives with minor exceptions; on the L.M.S.R. they became standard from the time when Sir William Stanier went from Swindon to become the L.M.S.R. Chief Mechanical Engineer; and on the L.N.E.R. the late Sir Nigel Gresley built the whole of his large 4-6-2 and 2-6-2 engines with boilers of this type.

The collection of dry steam, to which reference has just been made, is a matter of great importance. In the boiler there must be sufficient water to cover the crown of the inner firebox; but the boiler must not be overfilled, or water will be carried with the steam down into the cylinders, as described in Chapter 4. Between the water level and the outer firebox shell, therefore, a small space is left in which steam collects ready for use.   In the majority of locomotives this space is supplemented by a "dome"; this is a small chamber mounted on or near the centre of the barrel, and covered by a curved sheet-metal casing that is the most conspicuous mounting on the boiler between chimney and cab.   Inside the dome is the mouth of the main steam-pipe from boiler to cylinders, which is entered through the regulator; the latter is opened and closed by means of the regulator handle in the driver's cab.

Not all railways used domed locomotives, however.   In earlier years the brothers Stirling, when in charge of locomotive design on the Great Northern, South Eastern, Glasgow & South Western and Hull & Barnsley Railways, built domeless locomotives in which steam was collected in a longitudinal perforated pipe located along the top of the boiler barrel.   Their argument in dispensing with a dome was that there was no necessity to weaken the boiler barrel by cutting in it the large opening to which the dome is riveted.   The characteristic appearance of these engines will be remembered, especially the famous Stirling 8 ft. single-drivers of the Great Northern Railway, with their unbroken line along the top of the boiler from the chimney back to the safety-valves.

The Great Western Railway continued to build domeless locomotives. In the standard Western Region boilers, the barrel is parallel as far as the centre, on which the safety-valves stand, and from there tapers sharply outwards to the firebox, the top of which is at an even higher level.   The latter is highest at its front corner, from which it slopes downwards on top to the cab.   It is in the high front corner that the steam is collected, also by means of a perforated pipe, but in this case arranged transversely.   The first Stanier engines on the L.M.S.R. had similar arrangements for steam collection, but the boilers of his later engines, though otherwise resembling those on the G.W.R., were provided with steam-domes set well back towards the firebox, and safety-valves in the usual position above the firebox.

An important development of the present century, bearing on the more efficient use of fuel, is the superheating of the steam before use. As we have seen in Chapter 4, the major proportion of the work of the steam in the cylinders is done by expansion, and all expansion is accompanied by a fall in temperature.   If steam is used at or near the saturation point, therefore, the fall in temperature may result in condensation, which will involve a loss of efficiency.   On the other hand, if the temperature of the steam can be raised before use by superheating, its volume is increased, and the range of expansion can be maintained in larger cylinders, or increased, without condensation. In this way the overall thermal efficiency is increased proportionately.

A superheater is now standard equipment for all locomotives except those (chiefly small shunting engines) which are not designed for continuous steaming.

To accommodate the superheater, a number of the boiler tubes are displaced by a smaller number of flue tubes of considerably larger diameter. Each of these flues houses a superheater "element," which is a nest of small steam tubes arranged in one continuous passage to and from a header which is located in the firebox. The main steam-pipe from the regulator is carried into the header, and according to the number of superheater elements, so the steam is divided up into small streams, each of which passes rapidly to and fro in the looped tube of its element, encased in the hot gases passing through the flues until it has been heated, in exceptional cases, to a maximum of 750° Fahrenheit and normally to about 650°. Returning finally to the header, the superheated steam then passes down to the valve-chests and cylinders.

When steam is shut off, if the necessary precautions were not taken, there would be a risk of burning out the superheater elements, emptied of their steam but still in contact with fierce heat, especially at the firebox end. Arrangements are made, therefore, to cool the elements when necessary. One familiar method is the snifting valve, usually located on the smokebox, singly or in a pair, just behind the chimney. Theoretically, when the regulator is open, the pressure of the steam keeps these valves closed; and when steam is shut off, they should open automatically and admit air to the superheater header, and through that to the superheater tubes. The effectiveness of snifting-valve action, however, is mainly at low speeds.

The safety-valves of a locomotive normally are mounted above the firebox, except on those of the Western Region, where, as already mentioned, they are found in the centre of the barrel in the position used by most railways for the dome. The late G.W.R. also remained faithful to the spring-loaded valve of the older Ramsbottom type, hidden under a shapely brass cover, whereas all other railways have standardised the "pop" type of valve, so named from the startling suddenness with which it opens and closes.

Pop valves are designed to open precisely at the maximum pressure at which the boiler is rated, and to release the surplus steam rapidly, whereas with spring-loaded valves, by the time the steam has forced the valve fully open the pressure may be in excess of that for which the valve is nominally set, or, alternatively, the valve must be so set that the first leakage of steam past it is at slightly less than the working pressure of the boiler. Safety-valve controls are locked in casings in such a way that they cannot be tampered with—a reminder of the fact that in earlier days not a few boiler explosions resulted from the fact that drivers had improperly overweighted or screwed up their safety-valves in an attempt to get more work out of their engines than that for which they were designed.

Steam pressures have been rising rapidly during recent years. At the beginning of the century 160 to 180 lb. per sq. in. was the common figure for new locomotive classes, with an occasional 200 lb.; with the advent of superheating, and the larger cylinders that it made possible, there was a tendency to drop the pressure, thus keeping the tractive effort unchanged. The advantage of so doing was some slight reduction in the cost of boiler maintenance; for every increase in working pressure entails, not only a stronger and heavier boiler structure, but heavier upkeep also.

Now, however, with the help of special alloy steels which increase the tensile strength of the boiler shell without adding to its weight, and with the attraction of short cut-off working and the increased range of expansion that it makes possible, pressure levels are no longer kept down as in earlier days. From about 1906, the Great Western Railway standardised 225 lb. per sq. in. for the boilers of its principal 4-6-0 classes, at a time when 180 lb. or less was the general standard elsewhere in the country; in 1926 there came the advance to 250 lb. in the G.W.R. "Kings" and the L.M.S.R. "Royal Scots," followed by the same pressure in the L.M.S.R. "Pacifics" of 1932 and the L.N.E.R. streamlined "Pacifics" of 1935; and, lastly, the Southern Railway moved up to 280 lb. with the Bulleid "Merchant Navy" and "West Country" 4-6-2 engines, and the Great Western followed suit with its "County" class 4-6-os. But 280 lb. is by no means the limit. In the United States many locomotives work at a steam pressure of 300 lb. per sq. in., and Chapter 2 has mentioned experiments with pressures up to 1,000 lb. per sq. in.

Reverting to boiler mountings, one often seen on modern locomotives, especially those of the late L.M.S.R. and G.W.R., is the casing of the "top-feed" apparatus. In the past it had been the invariable custom to deliver feed-water through clack-valves (valves which permit water to pass in one direction only) fixed on the side of the barrel, level with the centre-line, at a point adjacent to the smokebox. The introduction of this cold stream into the hot boiler has several disadvantages, chiefly connected with expansion and contraction, and these have been accentuated with the modern advance in boiler pressures and temperatures. The purpose of top-feed is to introduce the water, in the form of spray, through the dry steam which has collected above the water level in the boiler, and this change has proved of benefit to boiler maintenance. On Western Region engines the feed-pipes enter both sides of the safety-valve casing; on those of the late L.M.S.R. they are usually carried into a hooded casing ahead of the dome, under which the top-feed apparatus is located. Opinion is not unanimous, however, as to the reduction in boiler maintenance costs brought about by the use of top-feed.

On a certain number of locomotives the feed-water is heated, on its way from the tender tank to the boiler, by feed-water heaters, but the practice is much commoner on the mainland of Europe and in the United States than here. A French form of feed-water heater, the "A.C.F.I.," mounted along the top of the boiler behind the chimney, has been widely installed in that country, and was also used in Great Britain for a time on a number of L.N.E.R. 4-6-0 locomotives of the *ex*-Great Eastern Class "B12." In the United States and Canada such heaters are often carried transversely on the smokebox ahead of the chimney, where they form a very prominent feature of any head-on view. The source of heat for feed-water heating is usually exhaust steam tapped from the smokebox for this purpose.

The problem of introducing feed-water into the boiler against the pressure of the steam is solved by the use of either feed-pumps or injectors. In the earliest days, the mechanical feed-pump was the only means available, with the result that at any time a standing locomotive might be required to run up and down a length of line solely to fill the boiler. Then came the invention by Henri Giffard in 1858 of the injector, now in worldwide use. The action of the injector is based on the principle that a jet of steam issuing under pressure from a nozzle has a velocity considerably greater than that of a jet of water issuing under the same pressure from the boiler. If the jet of steam is allowed to unite and to flow with a stream of cold water, part of the steam condenses, and the velocity of the stream is thus increased to a higher figure than that at which a stream of water could leave the boiler under the same pressure. Although the pressure of the jet of steam used in the injector is the same as that of the boiler, therefore, the stream of feed-water with which it unites is accelerated sufficiently to enable it to overcome the counter-pressure of the water in the boiler, and against that pressure to force its entry through the clack-valve.

Later forms of the injector have been devised to use, in part, exhaust steam instead of live steam alone, and thereby to effect economies. There are limits to the temperature of the water that can be handled by an injector, and locomotives in which the feed-water is passed through a feed-water heater must normally be provided with a steam-driven pump for introducing the feed into the boiler. In all these matters a nice balance must be maintained between the various economies that are sought. Hot feed-water requires less heat than cold to turn it into steam; but if live steam is required in consequence for working a feed-pump, there is a certain loss of energy, though admittedly very small, to set against what has been gained.

One further boiler-mounting needing to be mentioned is seen on the majority of American locomotives, though not on British. On many American boiler barrels three domes are visible; the centre one is the steam dome, and it is flanked by two dome-shaped sandboxes. This position is favoured because the warmth of the boiler tends to keep the sand dry; in Great Britain sand-boxes usually are located under the running-plate. On some lines sand is fed by gravity only under the driving wheels, when necessary to prevent slipping; but the more usual method is steam sanding, whereby a jet of steam blows the sand from the sand-pipe right under the wheels. The particular value of the last method is in cross-winds, when the wind may blow gravity-fed sand off the rails before the coupled wheels reach it.

In concluding this chapter, we need to give some brief consideration to the fuel. As explained in Chapter 1, the abundance, cheapness and good quality of steam coal in the past to some extent have hampered the technical development of the British steam locomotive. Locomotives of simple design and relatively light weight could be relied on, with the help of long cut-offs and heavy coal consumption, to give a power output disproportionate to their size; and probably the policy was not altogether uneconomic. But conditions now have totally changed. Coal is more scarce and considerably more expensive, while its quality has declined. Much of the time lost by locomotives during the war years has been due to the poor coal in use, clinkering badly or dropping through the firebars in dust.

Once again, therefore, oil has come into the picture as a fuel which must be considered seriously. The choice of fuel is a matter of simple economics. In a country like the United States, oil-firing is an attraction in a state like California, where there is abundant indigenous oil, but coal must be brought from long distances through the mountains. As a result, oil-fired locomotives are in use extensively on the Southern Pacific, Santa Fe and other railways serving the Pacific coast.

In Great Britain, at the beginning of the present century, the Great Eastern Railway had about 60 express locomotives fitted to burn oil-fuel instead of coal. This arose because it was desired to find some use for an oily residue from the manufacture at Stratford of oil-gas for carriage lighting; James Holden, then Locomotive Superintendent of the G.E.R., therefore devised his oil-burning apparatus, which proved so successful that the company began to buy oil-fuel to supplement the oil-gas residue.   But this was in a day of rapidly-rising oil prices, and in a short time the price of oil rose to the point at which oil-firing became more expensive than firing with coal.   The oil-burners were therefore removed from the fireboxes of the engines concerned, which reverted to coal-burning.

Since then, there has been little attempt in Great Britain to use oil-fuel in locomotives except during coal disputes, when coal has been scarce.   Now, however, the time has come when the margin of cost between coal and oil-firing is contracting rapidly.   After the Second World War, the G.W.R. was the first railway to fit 20 of its 2-8-0 locomotives with oil-burning apparatus, in 1946; and later in that year the decision was reached to convert over 1,200 British locomotives, divided between the four main-line railways, to oil-firing.   The types of engine chosen were largely those with heavy coal consumptions, and it was estimated that the change-over would save a million tons of coal annually.   But the cost of fitting the locomotives and of installing the fuelling facilities has been so high that the change-over has now been suspended after less than 100 engines have been equipped for oil-firing.   The latter now have been re-converted to burn coal.

The inner firebox of an oil-fired engine is provided with a floor of firebrick, pierced with a number of apertures for draught purposes, and firebrick also is built up the firebox sides to a certain height, of maximum thickness under the firehole door, towards which the maximum heat is directed.   As the oil flows in a ribbon through the burner, it is atomised by a steam spray and carried into the centre of the firebox, where it ignites immediately.   The firehole door is closed and sealed, but a small peephole in it enables the fireman to watch the progress of combustion; efficient combustion also is evident if the exhaust from the chimney is not unduly darkened by brown or black smoke.   A tank is provided on the tender for the storage of the oil, heated as much as necessary by a steam coil in order to keep the oil fluid enough to run from the tender to the firebox.

One interesting class of oil-fired locomotive has been built in the United States in which the entire locomotive is reversed; the driver's cab comes first, then the boiler, with the chimney at the rear, and finally the tender.   The engines are articulated monsters of the 4-8-8-2 type, used on the Californian main lines of the Southern Pacific Lines, with their many tunnels.   As the oil can be piped to the firebox, there is no objection to having the firebox at the end of the engine remote from the tender.   The engine-crew thus have the great advantage of being at the front end of these enormous locomotives, with a magnificent look-out ahead, and well away from the fumes thrown out of the engine chimney.

On an oil-fired locomotive, needless to say, the fireman's work is greatly reduced as compared with coal-firing. All the toilsome shovelling of coal is brought to an end, and is replaced by supervision of the valves by which the flow of oil from the tender to the burner, and the intensity of the steam jets, are controlled. In this way the work resembles that of the fireman of one of the large American coal-fired locomotives, on which manual firing would be beyond human capacity, and has been replaced by mechanical firing. The coal, broken suitably small, is passed from the tender into the firebox by a steam-driven worm and screw gear, and the rate of coal consumption, according to the demands made by gradients, load and speed, is controlled by varying the speed of rotation of the screw. The Americans regard 50 sq. ft. of firegrate as the largest area that should be fired manually.

As yet, apart from inconclusive experiments with pulverised fuel, one British locomotive only has been fitted with a mechanical stoker. This is "Merchant Navy" Pacific No. 35005 of the Southern Region, which has been doing excellent work on hard assignments such as the "Devon Belle." Moreover, it has been fired with "slack" coal, of a quality which would have given poor results with ordinary manual firing. With the bigger engines, therefore, it is possible that mechanical firing may help to provide some solution of the present coal problem.

6

DESIGN—THE LOCOMOTIVE'S SUPPLIES

A N essential part of locomotive design is the method adopted for carrying the necessary supplies of fuel and water. Broadly speaking, the larger the locomotive, and the harder the work that it is called upon to perform, so much the heavier is its consumption for every mile that it travels. A second important consideration is the way in which these supplies are to be replenished.

Drawing a locomotive carefully up to a water-column and taking water takes time; running an engine to a coal-stage or coaling tower for coal is an even more lengthy operation. Moreover, the engine must be able to reach the place where the water-column or coal-stage are located before replenishment of supplies can take place. A locomotive should therefore be able to carry sufficient coal for a whole day's duties; to attempt to carry enough water would be a less economical proceeding, but as described later, the problem of water for main-line locomotives has been largely solved by the provision of water-troughs, from which the engine is able to refill its tank while running. The locomotive designer, therefore, has to strike a reasonable balance between allowing excessively for fuel and water supplies, which would mean the haulage of unnecessary weight, and, on the other hand, cutting fuel and water accommodation too severely, in which event too frequent calls for replenishment would waste the engine's time.

We have here the explanation of the two main divisions—tender and tank—into which locomotives fall. The tank engine is a self-contained unit, carrying its supplies on its own main frames—the coal in a bunker behind the cab, and the water usually in two large flat side-tanks on both sides of the boiler. A certain number of the smaller tanks used in shunting carry their water in a tank above the boiler, either in the shape of a saddle, curved to fit the barrel ("saddle tanks"), or curved on the underside and flat on top, as in Great Western practice, in which event, from the characteristic shape of the water containers, they become "pannier tanks." As a tank on the top of the boiler raises the engine's centre of gravity, it is not favoured on any locomotive required to run at speed; but this is of less concern to a shunting engine, which has relatively little trip working to do, and the advantage of the saddle or pannier tank is the ease with which the tank itself can be dismantled and removed when it is necessary to undertake boiler repairs.

18. An L.M.S.R. "Royal Scot" 4-6-0, *The Ranger*, as originally built, save for the addition of smoke-deflectors. The engine is climbing the 1 in 75 to Shap Summit with a down Perth express. (*Canon E. Treacy.*)

19. A rebuilt "Royal Scot" of the London Midland Region, *Welsh Guardsman*, with taper boiler, double chimney and high-sided tender, leaving Carlisle for Glasgow St. Enoch. (*Canon E. Treacy.*)

MODERNISATION OF EARLIER LOCOMOTIVE DESIGNS

20. The boiler unit with the girder frame or "cradle" that transmits its weight.
21. An immense 4-8-2-2-8-4 Garratt locomotive for the South African Railways, Class "GEA." Though weighing 185 tons in working order, and with a tractive effort of 63,030 lb., this 3 ft. 6 in. gauge locomotive has no axle-load exceeding 15 tons, and may run over 60 lb. per yard rails. (*Courtesy, Beyer Peacock & Co., Ltd.*)

22. A Garratt 2-6-6-2 locomotive, London Midland Region, leaving Toton sidings with a heavy coal train. Note the rotating coal hopper in place of the usual fixed coal space. (*Courtesy, British Railways.*)

23. An articulated 2-8-8-2 of the Great Northern Railway, U.S.A., heels to the curve. The pivotal action of the leading chassis is apparent. (*Rail Photo Service, Boston, Mass., W. J. Pontin.*)

BRITISH AND AMERICAN ARTICULATION

24. Walschaerts valve-motion, as seen on a Southern Region 4-cylinder 4-6-0 of the "Lord Nelson" class. (*Frank F. Moss.*)

25. One of the latest London Midland Region Class "5" 2-cylinder 4-6-0s, No. 44740, fitted with Caprotti poppet-valve motion. (*P. Ransome-Wallis.*)

PISTON-VALVE AND POPPET-VALVE LOCOMOTIVES

26. Pulling out of Liverpool with the 5.25 p.m. express to Euston—turbine-driven Pacific No. 6202, London Midland Region. (*Canon E. Treacy.*)

27. In action on the "Broadway Limited," Chicago-New York—turbine-driven 6-8-6 No. 6200 of the Pennsylvania Railroad. (*Rail Photo Service, Boston, Mass, Rev. Ira H. Eigsti.*)

BRITISH AND AMERICAN TURBINE LOCOMOTIVES

28. The traditional—a London Midland Region Class "4" 0-6-0 hauling a freight train near Bell Busk, Yorkshire. (*Canon E. Treacy*.)

29. The ultra-modern—an "austerity" 0-6-0 of the "Q1" class, Southern Region, built in war-time conditions. (*Courtesy, British Railways*.)

DEVELOPMENT OF LOCOMOTIVE LINE

30. Fitted temporarily for oil-firing since the war—Southern Region 4-4-0 No. 437 at South-ampton. The top of the oil-tank is seen above the tender. (*Frank F. Moss.*)

31. Cab-in-front oil-fired 4-8-8-2 locomotive of the Southern Pacific Lines, hauling the West Coast Limited through Glendale, Cal. The barrel-shaped tender is seen between engine and train. (*Rail Photo Service, Boston, Mass., G. M. Best.*)

OIL-FIRING IN BRITAIN AND AMERICA

32. 0-6-0 inside cylinder pannier shunting tank, Western Region. (H. J. Ashman.)

34. Standard 2-6-4 outside cylinder main line passenger tank, London Midland Region. (Canon E. Treacy.)

33. 0-6-2 inside cylinder suburban passenger tank, Eastern Region. (W. J. Reynolds.)

35. 4-6-4 outside cylinder express passenger tank, late London, Brighton and South Coast Railway. (F. E. Mackay.)

BRITISH SIX-COUPLED TANK TYPES

Originally intended for shunting and suburban passenger service only, in later years tank locomotives have found much more extended use. The one-time London, Brighton & South Coast Railway, later a part of the Southern, developed the use of main-line tank engines, first of the 4-4-2 and later of the 4-6-2 and 4-6-4 types, on its express services from London to Brighton, Worthing and Eastbourne, where runs of between 51 and 66 miles were well within average tank and bunker capacity. From then on, tank engines, many of which are fitted with water-scoops, so that they may replenish their tanks from water-troughs, have found a steadily increasing range of usefulness.

On the late L.M.S.R., for example, numerous 2-6-4 tanks have been used in passenger service, and in certain cases on runs up to 100 miles in length. The G.W.R. has worked a considerable volume of coal traffic in and around the Welsh valleys with tank locomotives of the 2-8-0 type, and has rebuilt a number of them with the 2-8-2 wheel arrangement, so increasing the coal bunker capacity to 6 tons and the water capacity to 2,500 gallons. On the L.N.E.R. specially powerful 4-8-0 and 0-8-4 tank engines have been built for use in the gravity marshalling yards, where heavy freight trains have to be pushed over the yard "humps" as part of the work of sorting and classifying the wagons.

In suburban work the earlier 0-4-4 and 2-4-2 tanks have now been replaced mainly by 0-6-2, 2-6-2 and 2-6-4 tanks, which in general are able to carry larger fuel and water supplies and are of more powerful types. Shunting on all railways is entrusted in large measure to small 0-6-0 tanks (pannier tanks on the Western Region), though here again the desirability of providing more adequate power and more ample supplies resulted in the introduction of 0-8-0 shunting tanks on the late London & North Eastern and Southern Railways.

The larger tank locomotives can carry from 2,500 to 3,000 gallons of water, and in one or two instances, such as the L.N.E.R. 2-6-4 freight tanks of Great Central design, up to 3,000 gallons. Coal bunker capacity is $3\frac{1}{2}$ to 4 tons. The smaller tank types are content with 1,200 to 1,500 gallons of water, and 2 to 3 tons of coal.

Main-line locomotives accommodate their supplies in a separate vehicle, or tender, and for reasons already given, tenders have been growing steadily in size and capacity. The growth has been more in height than in length, because longer tenders, added to more lengthy modern locomotives, would outgrow the capacity of many of the 60 ft., 65 ft., and 70 ft. locomotive turntables now in use. To increase their storage space, therefore, many modern standard tenders, such as those of the late L.M.S.R., have had their side-sheets raised until the tenders

F

are as high as the engine cabs, and must have their sides curved inwards at the top in order that they may not foul the overline bridges.

Generally speaking, British tenders are carried on six wheels. In earlier days, the London & South Western Railway made a practice of mounting the tenders of its express engines on two four-wheel bogies, so that they might have ample water capacity for such long non-stop runs as Waterloo-Bournemouth (108 miles), Salisbury-Exeter (88 miles), and Waterloo-Salisbury (83¾ miles); the L.S.W.R. never laid down any water-troughs, and storage space for 5,000 gallons was regarded as essential. The largest six-wheel tenders in the country are those attached to the Pacifics of the late L.M.S.R.; these have a capacity for 10 tons of coal and 4,000 gallons of water, and weigh 54¾ tons each in full running trim. Restriction to six wheels in this case is, as just stated, to keep within bounds the overall length of these engines and tenders, and so to avoid the necessity for wholesale replacement of existing 70 ft. turntables by tables of larger diameter. The coal spaces of these tenders are fitted with rams, worked by steam cylinders, which push the coal gradually forward towards the fireman, and so lessen his work.

With his L.N.E.R. Pacific locomotives, however, the late Sir Nigel Gresley preferred to use a 5,000-gallon tank capacity, as the water-troughs on the main lines of the late L.N.E.R. are more widely spaced than those on the L.M.S.R.; the official coal capacity is 8 tons, but it is possible to accommodate an additional ton without much difficulty. Such capacities make an eight-wheel tender essential. The heaviest tenders in Great Britain are those which the L.N.E.R. built for the non-stop running between London and Edinburgh, in which part of the space along one side of the tender is occupied by a covered passage-way from end to end, to permit of an exchange of engine-crews between engine and train. A tender of this type, fully loaded, weighs 62½ tons, or as much as two corridor coaches. Typical six-wheeled tenders attached to the medium-sized locomotives accommodate 3,500 to 4,000 gallons of water, and 4 to 6 tons of coal, and weigh loaded between 40 and 48 tons.

Modern American tenders leave such capacities as these completely in the shade, for they are proportioned to the size and power of the engines to which they are attached. From the earliest days the tenders of locomotives in the United States were carried on two four-wheel bogies. To-day, the principal American locomotive classes are provided at least with twelve-wheel tenders, on two six-wheel bogies; the fourteen-wheel tender is coming increasingly into favour, mounted on a leading four-wheel bogie, followed by five fixed axles; and the

Pennsylvania and Atchison, Topeka & Santa Fe Railroads go even further, for their latest and most powerful classes use tenders carried on two eight-wheel bogies, or sixteen wheels in all.

By comparison with British standards, the capacities of the biggest American tenders are colossal. In the United States there is just as keen anxiety as in Britain to keep the locomotive in continuous running for the maximum possible duration of time, and some of these through runs are of amazing length. For example, the Santa Fe R.R., just mentioned, with its latest 4-8-4 locomotives, has six workings with locomotive unchanged over the 1,772 miles between Kansas City and Los Angeles (1,787 miles if the Clovis route is used), and two over the 1,235 miles between La Junta and Los Angeles. There are changes of engine-crews at the various "divisional points," 200 miles or so apart, and at certain stages time is allowed in which to "service" the engines; also the oil supply (for these engines are oil-fired) must be replenished at least once *en route*. On other American and Canadian lines, through locomotive runs up to 1,000 miles are becoming common.

This helps to explain the vast coal and water capacities now necessary on tenders on the other side of the Atlantic. The latest New York Central fourteen-wheel tenders, attached to the "Niagara" class 4-8-4 express engines, for example, are arranged to carry a maximum of 46 "short" tons (41 British tons of 2,240 lb. each) of coal, and 18,000 gallons of water; they weigh no less than $187\frac{1}{2}$ tons in full running trim, or considerably more than the biggest British Pacific *with* its tender. Other American tenders carry up to 25,000 gallons of water, and numerous United States locomotives are now hauling tenders not far short of 200 tons in weight when fully charged, reaching a maximum of 203 tons with the latest Santa Fe sixteen-wheelers.

We now must devote some attention to the taking of water from track-troughs by locomotives travelling at speed—a practice confined to Great Britain and the United States. It was in 1859 that John Ramsbottom, at that time Locomotive Superintendent of the London & North Western Railway, laid down the first water-troughs in history, near Aber, on the Holyhead main line. In this way he made possible the long non-stop runs which are a feature of modern operating practice. More important was the fact that sufficient water-trough installations would make it unnecessary for locomotives on main-line runs to waste time in taking water at stations or to stop specially for this purpose; given suitable track conditions, also, troughs made possible the supply of water to locomotives at places where it was cheapest, most abundant, and of best quality.

The modern track-trough is of steel construction, and is rather over a quarter-of-a-mile in length. Each trough is about 18 in. wide and 6 in. deep, and is supplied at a number of points along its length from a capacious lineside storage tank fitted with a very sensitive ball-valve control. Rapid refilling of a trough on a busy main line, after the passage of one train, is essential if the engine of the next is to get a supply. The tower of a water-softening plant is frequently seen in association with the trough installation.

Under the tender or bunker of the locomotive there is a hinged scoop, in shape not unlike a shovel of large dimensions. Normally this is carried well clear of the track, but it can be lowered to the point at which the front cutting edge is well below the water level in the trough. The scoop is lowered by the fireman just before the train reaches the trough; it is a slight gradient in the track itself that actually dips the scoop into the water. The speed at which the train is travelling provides the force that lifts the water, cut out of the trough by the sharp edge of the scoop, up an inclined delivery pipe through a mushroom head into the tender tank.

The force with which the water is hurled into the tank is tremendous. This the passenger can appreciate to the full if he is travelling in one of the leading compartments of an express, and the tender tank has filled to capacity before the end of the trough is reached. Unless the scoop is raised in time, the water then comes pouring over the top of the tender, and drenches the first coach or two of the train. It is not easy to lift the scoop out of the trough against the pressure of the water, and this is why the engine-crew usually wait until the end of the trough is reached, where a slight up-grade in the track (corresponding to the down-grade at the point of entry) lifts the edge of the scoop clear of all obstructions; it can then be returned easily to its out-of-action position.

According to the height of the mushroom head of the delivery pipe above the trough, there is a minimum speed below which it is not possible to lift water into the tank—usually between 25 and 30 m.p.h. There is also a critical speed at which the maximum amount can be taken; in earlier days this was about 40 m.p.h., and the practice of certain railways in reducing speed to take water was thus explained; but improvements in the design of scoops have now increased the critical speed considerably. If water is taken at high speed, the excessive pressure tends to scatter the water at the point of the scoop, which is obvious from the cloud of spray seen in so many photographs of engines taking water.

In recent years, after some elaborate experiments in which the action of a scoop in an experimental tender was watched through thick plate-glass windows, the L.M.S.R. locomotive authorities redesigned their water-scoops, and fitted them with an appliance ahead of the scoop which canalises the water, and directs the flow towards the mouth of the scoop, so greatly reducing the splash. In this way water is economised, and the track benefits also by the reduction in the amount of waste water that pours constantly over it. In from 15 to 20 seconds of running the length of a track-trough, it is possible to pick up from 2,000 to 3,000 gallons of water.

In the United States, the rapid consumption of water in locomotive boilers, and the immense capacities of tender tanks, have made it necessary to scale up in a proportionate degree the taking of water from track-troughs, or "track-pans," as the Americans call them. Recently the New York Central System conducted a series of experiments, like those of the L.M.S.R. in this country, in which a cinema photographer had the hazardous task of standing on the top of the tender with his camera to record what happened at full speed. The aim of the experiments was to redesign the scooping apparatus to take full supplies of water at 75 m.p.h. and more.

As a result of this investigation, the scoops have been modified in such a way that over 7,000 gallons of water have been lifted in one single draught at 75 m.p.h. on a trough 2,000 ft. long, and with an effective scooping length of 1,700 ft. Although the scattering of water has been much reduced, even so there was an unavoidable wastage of 1,520 gallons while 7,113 gallons were being lifted into the tender tank. The scoop was remodelled to allow the cutting edge to go into the water at a very flat angle, and the delivery passage up into the tender was enlarged to have a uniform cross-sectional area of 100 sq. in. from the bottom to the top.

It has been necessary also on the New York Central tenders to provide the tender tank on top with fourteen vent pipes at different points along its length, in order to allow the air so violently displaced to escape as the water rushes in. These vents conduct away any surplus water, after the tank has filled to capacity, and drop it harmlessly at the track side, so preventing it from pouring up through the tank manhole and over the train. How necessary such vents are, from the safety point of view, may be judged from the fact that during the experiments previously referred to, windows of trains travelling in the opposite direction were broken by the terrific rush of water over the top of the experimental tender when picking up at high speed was in progress.

Replenishing coal supplies by the same method is hardly possible. On most of the leading American main lines, however, where engines are engaged on lengthy through runs, in order to avoid detaching them from their trains for re-coaling, at certain points coaling plants have been built spanning all the running lines. Drivers stop their trains with their tenders immediately below the stage, and refilling is carried out in a few minutes. Time is allowed in the train schedules for this purpose. Such a provision has never been required in Great Britain, as with our smaller locomotives tender capacities are ample for the performance of the longest continuous runs without replenishment.

7

BUILDING—FROM MAIN FRAMES TO
FINISHED LOCOMOTIVE

THE life of a new locomotive, or, in particular, the first engine of a new class, begins, in effect, in the Chief Mechanical Engineer's drawing office. There may be several reasons why a new design has become necessary. An accelerated train service may be planned, for which no suitable engines are available; or an existing class may be obsolescent and may need early replacement. In most cases the demand is for additional power; occasionally, however, as with the light L.M.S.R. 2-6-0 tender and 2-6-2 tank designs which appeared in 1947, up-to-date locomotives of very modest dimensions are needed on branch lines over which severe weight restrictions operate, to replace worn-out locomotives of early types.

After the Chief Mechanical Engineer has obtained authority to build the proposed locomotives, the latter's Chief Draughtsman works out the design in some detail, and prepares a dimensioned diagram, with estimated weights, for submission to the Chief Civil Engineer, who must approve the design from the point of view of clearances and track and bridge stresses. More detailed plans are then prepared, and when these have been passed by the Chief Mechanical Engineer, work begins on the drawings, running perhaps into several hundreds if the locomotive is of an entirely new type, from which all the parts will be made.

From the drawings it is now necessary to prepare the orders for all the materials that will be needed in the construction. Much of this material, such as steel plate for frames, boilers, cab and tender side-sheets, and so on, must be ordered from outside firms, as well as a great deal of the detail work, including, perhaps, cast steel cylinder and valve-chest blocks, brake-gear, safety-valves, and other specialised parts. For many of the smaller details, orders will be placed on various departments of the railway company's own shops in which the engines are to be built. A timed programme of construction is drawn up, showing the dates at which all the various materials ordered must be ready for use.

In the actual building of a locomotive, the first stage is the preparation of the main frames. These are cut from steel plate, from 1 in. to $1\frac{1}{8}$ in. in thickness, and have the openings slotted in them which are to receive the axle-boxes, with the exception, of course, of those for the bogie. In the erection, the frame-plates are set up on edge, at the correct distance apart, and with the cylinder-block or base of the smokebox between them at the leading end, the motion-plate in the centre, and additional lateral bracings as may be required, a framework of great strength and solidity is built up. The frames support the boiler, and transmit its weight and that of the chassis to the wheels. Externally, the frame-plates are easily recognisable, slanting upwards as two narrow plates from the buffer-beam towards the base of the smokebox, and then continuing past the driving wheels towards the rear end of the engine. In a locomotive such as a 4-4-2, 2-6-2 or 4-6-2, the frame-plates usually are riveted or welded to a subsidiary frame, in the form of a cradle, which supports the lower part of the firebox.

In other countries, the United States and Canada in particular, from the earliest days plate frames were abandoned in favour of bar frames. The original bar frames, as their name implies, consisted of assemblages of steel bars, but in most modern American locomotives the entire framing is cast in steel, and often includes also the cylinders and valve-chests in one single casting of great size and complexity.

It is of the utmost importance that the locomotive shall be built perfectly "square," or endless trouble may arise later through working parts being out of alignment. No trouble must be spared, therefore, in ensuring minute accuracy in the work of erection. With solid frame castings of the American type, the risk of frames being out of square does not arise, except that every precaution must be taken to prevent the castings from warping while they are cooling; but with plate frames the greatest care is necessary to see that they are erected precisely square with one another. In the erecting shop the main frame-plates stand on grooves in the heads of screw jacks, which can be adjusted until the frames are in exactly the right position relatively to one another.

The cast cylinder blocks are then brought into the erecting shop from the machine shop, where cylinders and valve-chests have been bored out to very precise dimensions. Here again, in setting the cylinders, minute accuracy is needed to ensure, both that the centre-lines of the cylinders are in perfect parallelism with the frames, and also dead in line with the driving axle. Long steel straight-edges and fine wires play their part in the making of these adjustments. It may be added that the many holes that have been bored in the frame-plates and the motion parts, through which will pass the bolts for the attachment of one to the other, are for the most part drilled to less than the finished size, so that any slight inaccuracy in the relation of one to the other may be corrected in the final broaching or reamering out to the finished size. The bolts needed for the more important attachments, also, are turned to the sizes required, so that they may be a dead fit. The same applies to those of the rivets which will be closed "cold."

After the cylinders have been fixed, many other attachments must be made to the frames, and then comes the erection of the motion, including pistons, piston-rods, crossheads, piston-valves and valve-rods, and so on. Meantime other erectors are at work on the axleboxes, which again must be set perfectly square with one another, or there will be constant overheating trouble as soon as the engine gets into service. Locomotive axleboxes are normally of cast steel, with bearings of gunmetal; the "brasses," through which the weight of boiler and chassis is transmitted to the axles, have recesses into which "white metal" is run—an anti-friction alloy consisting mainly of tin or lead, but containing also about 10 per cent. each of copper and antimony. While British railways until now have adhered resolutely to ordinary journal-type bearings in their locomotives, in the United States to-day increasing use is being made of roller bearings of the Timken and other types, which both are reducing the internal resistance of the locomotives to motion, and also are cutting maintenance costs appreciably.

It should be added, however, that London Transport has fitted roller-bearings on an extensive scale to its tube and other electric stock. At last the London Midland Region, also, has initiated a large-scale experiment by fitting roller bearings to two of its latest Pacifics and a number of Class "5" 4-6-0 engines.

While erection is proceeding, the wheels and axles are being prepared in the wheel shop. Each wheel has a cast-steel centre; that is to say, the boss, spokes and rim are cast, but not the tyre. The "seats" at each end of the axle, which are to receive the wheels, are turned to a diameter fractionally larger than that of the holes in the bosses of the wheels, to ensure a tight grip; each wheel is then forced on to its axle in a hydraulic press. The pressure required varies from 60 tons with a bogie or tender wheel to as much as 90 to 120 tons with a driving wheel. To make assurance doubly sure with driving and coupled wheels, keyways are cut into both wheels and axle, and into these steel keys are tightly driven.

Reference is needed here to the "B.F.B." type of cast-steel wheel centre used on the "Merchant Navy" and "West Country" Pacifics of the Southern Region, very similar to the "Boxpok" wheel centres that are so popular in the United States. This type was decided on after experiments in the laboratory at Ashford Works had revealed the flexing of the wheel rim of a spoked wheel that takes place in ordinary running conditions.   In the "B.F.B." wheel centre there is a much more even distribution of stresses, and as compared with spoked wheels the weight has been reduced by 10 per cent., which is of importance in that the wheels form part of the unsprung weight of the locomotive.

Wheel-tyres are rolled in one piece out of a solid steel bloom.   They are supplied by outside manufacturers, and on receipt at the locomotive works they are turned on the inside to a diameter very slightly less than that of the rim of the wheel centre.   Each tyre is then heated, usually by a ring of gas-jets, so that it expands.   In its expanded condition it is dropped on to its wheel centre; a lip on the outer edge of the tyre, arranged to bear against the rim of the wheel centre, ensures that the flange of the tyre is exactly in line with the inside of the wheel.   As the tyre cools, it shrinks, and so binds itself firmly to the wheel centre.   Additional security is provided by set-screws passed through the rim into the tyre, or by retaining rings, heated and driven into position round the junction between rim and tyre on the inside of the wheel.

Next, each pair of wheels and axles is mounted in a wheel lathe, where the tyres are turned to the exact profile that they require when new.   From time to time, when in service, they will require re-turning, as a result of the abrasive wear to which they are subject.   Finally, for reasons described in Chapter 4, each pair of driving or coupled wheels, with its axle, must go to the balancing machine, to be spun round at speed for the precise adjustment of rotating balance.

While the wheels and axles are in course of preparation, work on the boiler has been proceeding in the boiler shop.   A special type of steel is required for boiler work, usually of open-hearth acid quality, as the drastic treatment that it is to receive in flanging, punching and other ways, would cause inferior steel to crack.   The demands made by increased steam pressures, which otherwise might add considerably to weight because of the greater thickness of steel required to withstand increased internal strain, are being met by the use of alloy steels of a higher tensile quality.

The barrel of a boiler is formed by passing the steel plate, cut exactly to size, through plate-bending rolls, which in their action somewhat resemble a mangle.   With barrels up to 12 ft. long, two plates are used normally, and three plates with longer barrels, though barrels up to 11 ft. 6 in. long have been made from a single plate.   After the plates have been rolled to a circle, and the edges have been brought together, "butt strips" of steel plate are applied above and below the joint, and riveted up, so that each "ring" of the barrel has one longitudinal riveted joint.   Considerable strain may be put on the joint later, when the engine is in steam, if the plates of the barrel have not been finished to an absolutely true circle. The riveting is done expeditiously in hydraulic riveting machines. In the latest Pacific locomotives of the Southern Region, the joints of the barrel have been made by welding instead of riveting, as well as the circular joints between ring and ring, and a good deal of the work on the firebox assembly has been done by welding also. In the United States to-day experimental locomotive boilers are in use which are of welded construction throughout.

Building up the firebox is a more complicated operation. One of the most difficult jobs is that of forming the "throat plate," which connects the barrel to the firebox; a hydraulic press is used for this purpose, as well as for the other flanging and forming operations needed in building up the inner and outer fireboxes. The assembly of the firebox includes the screwing into position of hundreds of staybolts, which, as explained in Chapter 5, hold the inner and outer fireboxes at the correct distance from one another, against the internal pressure. All the joints in the boiler (other than welded joints) must now be caulked, to ensure that they are completely steam-tight; the tubes and flues are expanded into position in the smokebox and firebox tube-plates. The boiler is then ready for testing.

A hydraulic test is made first, to a pressure from 25 to 50 per cent. above that at which the boiler will be rated, and after that a steam test to about 10 per cent. above the designed working pressure. After the application of a coat of anti-corrosive paint, to preserve the plates from rust, the boiler is taken to the erecting shop.

The work on the frames of the locomotive, and that part of the motion which lies between them, must be practically complete before the boiler is lowered into position, as it is much more difficult to obtain access to the former once the boiler is in place. As the erecting shop overhead crane lowers the boiler, the latter must come to rest with the horizontal expansion angle-irons or carrying brackets on either side of the firebox resting squarely on the rear end of the main frames. Brackets attached to the frames fit over the expansion angle-irons, so preventing the back end of the boiler from lifting, when the engine is running, though allowing limited freedom for horizontal sliding movement; this is essential in order to allow for the effects of expansion and contraction. Wedges or flat springs are interposed between the expansion angle-irons and the frames, to assist in the distribution of weight. At the front end, the barrel is secured firmly to the smokebox. It is customary to bring the boiler to the locomotive with all the mountings—dome, safety-valves, and so on—already attached.

Provided that the work on the axle-boxes is finished, the chassis and boiler are now lifted bodily for the insertion of the driving and coupled axles, which with their wheels are waiting in readiness. If it is a bogie engine, the front end is supported on jacks while the motion is connected up, and the delicate operation of valve-setting is in progress; the efficient performance of the locomotive will depend in large measure on the care and accuracy with which valve-setting is carried out.

Other work is proceeding simultaneously. The boiler is "clothed" with magnesia blocks, asbestos, or other non-conducting material, to prevent the wasteful radiation of heat. The clothing is secured by a light framework of steel angles and strips, and the whole is then covered by the thin lagging of sheet-steel plate which forms the outer boiler casing. Inside the smokebox the blast-pipe is erected; it must be exactly central with the chimney, or the steaming of the locomotive will be adversely affected. A thousand and one other details require attention before the lengthy job of erection is completed.

In the year 1891 the then Great Eastern Railway performed the almost incredible feat, at their Stratford Works, of erecting a loco-motive complete in 9 hours, 47 minutes. The engine was of the 0-6-0 wheel arrangement—a goods engine of a type of which a number already were in service—and 44 men and boys took part. Another gang built the tender in a separate shop in the same time. The locomotive was put in steam immediately, and worked for several years before requiring her first general overhaul. Erection normally is a far less speedy operation than that, though with modern mass production methods, it has been greatly accelerated.

In days gone by, locomotive painting was a more elaborate job than it has now become, and was carried out in a separate paint shop. To-day the painting is carried out in the erecting shop, so that on leaving the erecting shop, the locomotive is ready for service. One or two formalities still remain, however.

When the boiler has been filled and the fire lit, careful inspection of the engine takes place, as the pressure rises, to see that there are no faulty joints at which leaks are developing. After one or two move-ments up and down the works yard, the locomotive is then ready for a "trial trip." This is made for about 20 miles along the main line from the works and back, to run the bearings in. During this journey, apprentices see to it that all the motion parts are kept thoroughly well lubricated; big-ends and axleboxes in particular should run perfectly cool. Close attention is paid also during the trial trip to the working of the motion, the brakes, the springs, the injectors, the sanding gear, and other details. At the end of the run the locomotive is taken to a weighbridge of special design, on which a fitter, specially appointed for the purpose, adjusts the springs in such a way that the correct proportion of the engine's weight is being carried by each axle; this is a matter of considerable importance to the bearings and smooth running of the engine generally.

If the trial trip has been satisfactory, the new locomotive is then run to the engine shed to which it is to be attached. During the running-in period, for two or three weeks, it will be used on light duties; if an express engine, it will work on stopping trains for some time before taking up its duties on high-speed expresses. When at last it appears at the head of one of the country's famous trains, if this is an express engine of an entirely new design, from eighteen months to two years may have elapsed since the idea of the new class first took shape in the Chief Mechanical Engineer's Department.

Among the details of equipment, the brakes and brake rigging play an important part; and before we leave the description of locomotive design and building, some reference to the systems in use is necessary. Continuous brakes—that is, brakes operable from the footplate on the train as well as on the locomotive—are divided into two main groups, vacuum brakes and compressed-air brakes. Some locomotives intended solely for freight service are fitted with steam brakes only. It is customary also to provide hand-brakes, for use when engines stand at the engine-shed, or in emergency; tank locomotives have these on the engine itself, and tender locomotives on the tender.

The principle of the vacuum automatic brake is that of a cylinder of large diameter, from which the air has been exhausted to form a partial vacuum, and in which there is a freely-moving piston; admission of air at atmospheric pressure into the cylinder, on the underside of the piston, forces the piston into the vacuum, and by suitable connections, called the brake rigging, the piston-rod exerts a pull by which the brake-blocks are pulled into contact with the tyres of the wheels. The vacuum train-pipe is continuous from the locomotive throughout the train, by means of flexible hose-pipes between the tender and the first coach, and from coach to coach.

In order to create the vacuum, the engine is fitted with two ejectors, a large and a small. Normally, the small ejector is continuously at work, and as it uses from 4 to 6 lb. of steam a minute, the drain on the boiler supply is by no means negligible. The large ejector is used to re-create the vacuum rapidly after the brakes have been applied. On many Great Western Railway locomotives, the small ejector is replaced by a vacuum pump which is worked off one of the engine crossheads, and which makes a characteristic clicking noise when the engine is running.

Vacuum cylinders usually range in size from 15 to 24 inches, though cylinders up to 30 inches diameter are used in some cases. The easy movement but perfect tightness of the piston is ensured by the use of a "rolling ring" of rubber between the piston and the cylinder wall. When the driver moves his brake-valve to destroy the vacuum, pressure rises throughout the train-pipe, and passes to the underside of the pistons, but is prevented from passing to the upper side by a non-return ball-valve. On the large ejector being opened, however, air is exhausted from both side of the pistons, and the pistons drop by their own weight to the bottom of the cylinders, so taking off the brake pressure.

Air-brakes require the provision on the locomotives of donkey-pumps for air-compression purposes, which often can be heard at work when the engines are stationary. The pump delivers compressed air to a reservoir on the engine; through the driver's brake-valve this is fed into the train-pipe, and past triple valves into auxiliary storage cylinders which are provided on each vehicle. The brake-operating cylinders in air-brake systems are smaller than those required with the the vacuum brake; they are made to act by a reduction of the pressure in the train pipe. This reduction, by means of the triple-valve, allows some of the compressed air in the auxiliary reservoirs to pass into the brake cylinders, so forcing the pistons outwards and applying the brakes.

To lift the brakes off the wheels, the driver restores the pressure in the train pipe from the supply in the main engine reservoir. By this action, the passage between the auxiliary reservoirs and the brake cylinders is closed by the triple valve, and a port is opened from the cylinder to the atmosphere, through which the compressed air escapes. A spring in the cylinder then pushes the piston back and so releases the brakes. The type of compressed air brake mainly in use is the Westinghouse.

In Great Britain generally the automatic vacuum brake is standard, except on electrified lines, where air-brakes are preferred, because the retarding action of air-brakes in general is more rapid than those of the vacuum type. The increase in British train speeds from 1932 onwards, and especially after the introduction of the streamline trains, resulted in the development of special vacuum brake-valves with more rapid action than previously. In other parts of the world, however, with the constant increase in train speeds there is a definite trend towards air-brakes even on railways which hitherto have used vacuum brakes. Throughout North America air-brakes are used universally on both passenger and freight stock; and on the streamline trains their efficiency of action is increased by the fitting of "clasp" brakes, with blocks acting on both sides of each pair of wheels.

8

SERVICE—THE LOCOMOTIVE UNDER TEST

THE present-day locomotive engineer is not satisfied merely to know that the locomotives of his design are capable of pulling certain loads at the prescribed scheduled speeds. It is also necessary to ascertain if the work of the engines is being performed with reasonable efficiency. A rough-and-ready guide is obtained from the consumption of coal and water proportionately to the work done, but as this consumption may vary considerably with the competence—or the reverse—with which the engine is handled by its crew, more accurate methods of measurement are necessary. Special tests of performance are customary, therefore, usually with the first engines of a new class. These are of two kinds—those conducted with mobile equipment, while the engine is actually at work on the road; and those carried out in stationary locomotive testing-plants, in unvarying test conditions, as described later in this chapter.

A simple form of testing, known as "indicating," is designed to show with what measure of efficiency the valve-motion is performing its functions. The indicator is a small steam cylinder, which is connected by a pipe of very small diameter directly to the interior of one of the locomotive cylinders, near one end. The indicating cylinder, by a suitable connection with the crosshead, is made to rotate forward and then backward with each return stroke of the piston-rod of the cylinder concerned.

When an indicator diagram is to be taken, the operator clips a sheet of paper round the outside of the indicating cylinder, and then opens a cock, which allows steam to pass from the engine cylinder into that of the indicator. The piston of the latter, to which there is attached a recording pencil moving over the rotating sheet of paper, rises to its maximum height with the admission of steam to the locomotive cylinder, falls gradually with the expansion, and then returns at its lowest level as the steam is exhausted, completing a diagram which in shape resembles a boot. This diagram gives an exact picture of what is going on inside the locomotive cylinder, and particularly of the expansion on the forward stroke and the compression on the backward stroke of the piston. From the indicator diagrams it is a simple matter to calculate the work done in the cylinder under all conditions of running, in terms of "indicated horsepower," or "i.h.p." for short.

The indicator is mounted on the running-plate of the locomotive, alongside the smokebox and above the cylinder which is being indicated. For the protection of the operator, a shelter of timber or sheet steel is erected round the smokebox of the engine, and gives external evidence that tests of this description are being carried on. A second type of test housed in these shelters is that of sampling and analysing the gases in the smokebox, to verify whether combustion of the fuel in the firebox has been thorough, or whether an undue proportion of the heat energy in the fuel is being thrown to waste out of the chimney. The latest indicating shelters are elaborate structures, in appearance like an additional cab at the front end of the engine; but even in the best conditions the combination of draughts with the heat from the smokebox, as well as the vibration of the engine, makes the job a not altogether enviable one for the indicating staff.

More comprehensive tests are conducted with the help of dynamometer cars, of which there are four in Great Britain, owned respectively by the late L.M.S., L.N.E. and G.W. Railways. Of these a modern example is one of the two L.M.S.R. cars, built at Horwich by the late Lancashire & Yorkshire Railway in 1912, and rebuilt at Derby Works, L.M.S.R., in 1929. The principal purpose of a dynamometer car is to measure the pull exerted by the locomotive on its train, from which can be calculated the drawbar horsepower (d.b.-h.p.); the difference between drawbar and indicated horsepower at any given moment gives the horsepower absorbed by the locomotive in moving itself. The dynamometer car, therefore, is coupled between the locomotive and the train; the drawbar of the coupling at the forward end of the car, pulling against a system of springs, actuates a pen which inscribes on a moving paper roll a continuous graph of the drawbar pull throughout the test journey.

The *ex*-L.M.S.R. car just referred to is a 50 ft. vehicle weighing 33 tons; a little over half its length is occupied by the instrument room, and the remainder of the car comprises a compartment with a table, a small kitchen, a store-room and a lavatory. At the centre of the car underframe a strong cross girder is built in, and acts as the anchorage for the drawbar-spring system. In front of this are the plate springs used for recording the drawbar pull, and behind is a second system of springs by which push also can be recorded. If all the springs are in use, a pull of 18 tons on the drawbar gives a total spring deflection of 6 inches, and the same deflection of the push springs is given with a thrust of 14 tons. By uncoupling a certain number of the spring plates, however, the full spring deflection can be attained in stages with loads down to as little as 2 tons.

The maximum drawbar pull is at the moment of starting, and with a heavy train may be over 15 tons; at speed a pull of about 2 tons is sufficient to keep a 400-ton train in motion at 60 m.p.h. on the level. In working the 604-ton test train up the Clyde valley to Beattock Summit from the north side, as described in Chapter 12, the L.M.S.R. Pacific *Duchess of Abercorn* exerted a continuous pull of from 5 to 7 tons (the latter up the final 2½ miles at 1 in 99, where d.b.-h.p. rose to 2,282 and i.h.p. to 3,333) in maintaining a speed of between 61 and 68 m.p.h., but this, of course, was an exceptional feat in Great Britain.

Immediately above the frame cross-girder, to which the springs are anchored, is the recording table. Over this there moves a paper roll 20 inches wide, driven by a flangeless wheel of 33·6 inches diameter which bears on one of the rails of the track. This diameter has been chosen to give exactly 600 revolutions to the mile. In order to reduce wear to a minimum, the driving wheel, which can be lifted off the rail by a screw inside the car, is kept in contact only while a test is in progress. The speed of the recording paper can be varied between 6 inches and 20 feet to the mile, as required, but the 6-inch rate is that normally used. A system of levers transfers the movement of the push and pull springs from the spring buckles to pens which describe continuous lines on the moving paper roll.

On the table there is mounted an electric clock, which by a series of contacts and a pen marks 2-second intervals along the length of the chart. The clock also provides the time element for an automatic speed recorder of which the distance element is driven off the mileage wheel. In addition, the latter drives the disc of a machine known as an integrator; in conjunction with the pull of the drawbar, the integrator calculates out the units of work done and transfers them through a pen to a serrated line on the recording roll, of which each peak represents so many units, usually 450 h.p.-minutes. Another pen shows the work done in accelerating and decelerating the train, as recorded by a pendulum ergometer.

It is of value for indicator tests to be in progress on the locomotive during each test run with the dynamometer car, so that the recordings may be associated with the exact locomotive conditions that produced them. Other recorders note the boiler pressure, steam-chest pressure, cut-off percentage, and regulator opening as each indicator diagram is taken (or, if the engine is not being indicated, at agreed locations), and communicate the figures to the operators in the car by telephone and loudspeaker, at the same time marking the roll, by an electrically-worked pen, with the location of each such observation. Seven pens in all are at work during the test, respectively recording drawbar pull, integrator calculation of work done, ergometer record, speed, distance, time, and location. The last-mentioned is used to note stations, and points at which details of locomotive working or indicating are given, as just mentioned.

The rate of water consumption by the locomotive is given by means of a U-tube gauge which shows the level of the water in the tender tank. On the Western Region dynamometer car the analysis of smokebox gases is carried out by automatic apparatus in the car, instead of in the indicator shelter, and the gases are piped through from the smokebox into the car for this purpose. From such comprehensive tests as those made possible by the use of a dynamometer car, a mine of information is obtained concerning the performance of the loco-motive under test, and particularly as to whether the efficiency is being obtained that might be expected from the design. Moreover, modifica-tions in design have been made frequently as a result of the experience so gained.

Tests carried out on the road with a dynamometer car are subject to a great many variable factors which are outside the locomotive itself, but may affect the results obtained. Gradients and train-weights vary; weather conditions, such as wind and rain, may affect train resistance and adhesion; even track that is not in the best of order may have an adverse influence on the power output of the locomotive. To obtain more constant test conditions, in 1936 the L.M.S.R. management authorised the building of a complete new mobile testing plant.

The testing unit comprises a special tender, a new dynamometer car, and three braking units. Each of the latter, like a bogie coach in appearance, is in effect an electric locomotive of 1,500 h.p. in which the function of the motors is reversed; that is to say, as the test train is being pulled by the locomotive, the braking unit or units absorb tractive power by generating current, which in its turn is absorbed by resistance grids, dissipating their heat to the atmosphere. One or more braking units are marshalled in each test train, between the locomotive and the dynamometer car, and by very sensitive master controls in the dynamometer car the units are used to provide a variable resistance which ensure that the train runs at a constant speed, irrespective of gradients, curves, or any other kind of external resistance with which the locomotive has to contend.

Three of these braking units are in service, geared for maximum speeds up to 50, 90, and 120 m.p.h. respectively, and the mobile unit chosen is in accordance with the type of locomotive under test. If necessary, however, two or three of the units may be used in conjunction, providing a total resistance up to 4,500 h.p. against the drawbar pull of the locomotive. The tender is of a special pattern in which the water, up to a capacity of 3,500 gallons, is metered as it is used, and the coal, to a total of 3 tons, similarly is measured during use. A reserve supply of 3 tons is carried in a bunker of normal type, for use at times other than those of the actual testing. A further part of the equipment is a cup anemometer and vane carried on a light structure projecting from the front of the locomotive under test; by electrical means these record on the dynamometer chart the speed and direction of the wind. This is by far the most complete mobile locomotive testing plant yet used in Great Britain.

In addition to the foregoing method of locomotive testing, however, it is desirable to conduct bench tests, such as those undergone by stationary steam engines, turbines, internal combustion sets, and so on, in absolutely unvarying conditions. These are practicable only in completely-equipped locomotive testing-stations, of which at present there are five in existence, one at Swindon Works of the late G.W.R., brought into use in 1905; one at Altoona Works of the Pennsylvania Railroad, U.S.A., opened in 1904, and another at Purdue University, U.S.A.; a fourth at Grünewald, near Berlin, Germany, built in 1931; and a fifth at Vitry-sur-Seine, near Paris, France, completed in 1933. Little has been heard of the Purdue plant for some time, and like that at Swindon, probably it is no longer fully adequate to cope with modern developments of locomotive power. So far as Great Britain is concerned, the late Sir Nigel Gresley was a strong advocate of the establishment in Great Britain of an up-to-date locomotive testing station, and in 1939 an agreement was reached between the L.M.S. and L.N.E. Companies to build one jointly on a site selected at Rugby. The Second World War held up the supply of the necessary machinery, but the work was completed in 1948, and this modern testing-plant is fully equal in capacity to those in France, Germany and the United States.

The principle of testing is this. The locomotive is run into the testing station, and the wheels are mounted on rollers, the spacing of which can be adjusted until each pair of rollers is precisely in line with the pair of wheels that it carries. A single millimetre out of centre may affect the results obtained by 1 per cent., and by more in proportion if the error of centre is increased. By its ordinary drawbar the locomotive is then connected to a dynamometer, just as though it were attached to a dynamometer car at the head of a test train.

When the regulator of the locomotive is opened, and the driving wheels revolve, they rotate the rollers, while the engine pulls against the dynamometer spring. The effect of the weight of the train, running up adverse gradients, and so on, is obtained by braking the rollers more or less heavily. For a satisfactory test, it is necessary to run the locomotive for at least a couple of hours continuously, keeping the speed constant throughout and measuring the speed and tractive power with the utmost accuracy. The brakes of the plant are self-regulating, and by hydraulic connection are made to work in exact unison. One of the greatest problems is so to design a dynamometer that it will record a pull of many tons without the point at which the pull is applied moving a fraction of a millimetre in the direction of the pull.

The Vitry testing plant in France has eight rollers, and so can take locomotives with up to eight pairs of wheels, six of which may be driving axles, for there are six pairs of rollers fitted with hydraulic brakes. At present the maximum length of locomotive which can be tested is 78 ft. 9 in., but there is room available for extension to 105 ft., if desirable at any future date. Axle-loads up to a maximum of 29½ tons can be accommodated. The dynamometer can record a drawbar pull up to no less than 44 tons, and the maximum power that can be absorbed by each individual brake is 1,900 h.p. The plant is designed to test locomotives up to a speed equivalent to 100 m.p.h. on the track.

There are material differences between the dynamometer results obtained in a testing-plant of this description and those obtained in road tests. In the former case there is no air resistance to be overcome by engine and tender, and there is no resistance caused by rolling and by journal resistance of the tender wheels and the idle engine wheels. There is no air cooling effect, through running at speed, to cause loss of heat from the boiler and cylinders; on the other hand, the vibration of the locomotive caused by running over rail-joints and other irregularities, which helps ash in the firebox to drop more readily through the firebars, and steam to come away more easily from the heating surfaces of the boiler, is almost entirely absent. But on the test plant it is possible to make test comparisons between one type of locomotive and another with absolute exactitude, because the test conditions cannot vary. For this reason these costly plants fully justify themselves, and have had no small influence on modern steam locomotive design.

From time to time locomotive tests of a special character are made. In 1941 the London Midland & Scottish Railway conducted an investigation into locomotive balancing, the purpose of which is described in Chapter 4. In that chapter it is pointed out that whereas the heavy rotating parts of a locomotive must be counterbalanced, opinion was divided among locomotive engineers as to the extent to which counterbalancing of the reciprocating parts should be applied. In any two-cylinder engine, some reciprocating balance is necessary, as without it considerable, and possibly dangerous, oscillations might be set up at speed. But the greater the proportion of this reciprocating balance, so much the greater is the objectionable "hammer-blow" effect produced on the rails with each revolution of the driving wheels, increasing with the speed.

In these tests a short section of line was selected on which the rails were coated thickly with grease. Engines were then run on to the greased track, and steam was applied, as a result of which the driving wheels slipped violently and continuously, until equivalent speeds of 100 m.p.h. or more had been reached, though actually the locomotive as a whole was moving very slowly. By the aid of motion-picture cameras and special devices for the measurement of stresses, some extraordinary records were obtained. Three L.M.S.R. Class "5" 4-6-0s, with 6 ft. driving wheels, were tested. The first had two-thirds of the reciprocating weights balanced; the second one-half; the third one-third.

When the first had been "revved up" to 103 m.p.h., the hammer-blow for the whole engine had risen to all but 30 tons, and the driving wheels were bouncing up and down on the rail to a total height of nearly 2½ inches. With 50 per cent. reciprocating balance the bounce had been reduced to less than ½-inch, and with 30 per cent. reciprocating balance only there was no lifting of the driving wheels at 99 m.p.h. But in the last case there was excessive oscillation of the engine, though there had been no abnormal oscillation with the engine in which the extent of hammer-blow was so startling. It may be added that the rails over the test length were badly damaged by this battering, and had to be removed; moreover, it was thought that an explanation had been found in these tests of some mysterious damage that rails had been found to have suffered in the track at various locations previously, until then unexplained.

Locomotives of all four main-line railways were tested, and as a result it was shown that the two-cylinder types were considerably the worst offenders. Four-cylinder engines, which in effect are self-balancing, with their four cranks dividing up the circle into equal parts, gave the best results, and three-cylinder engines on the whole were good, though not up to the four-cylinder standard. One exception, however, was the "Merchant Navy" Pacific class of the then Southern Railway, a three-cylinder design in which reciprocating balance has been omitted entirely. As a result there is no hammer-blow, and the omission did not result in any unsteadiness at high speed of the locomotives concerned.

In the United States, where, apart from articulated types, the steam locomotives are almost exclusively of two-cylinder designs, the size and power of most of the modern classes, coupled with rising speeds, has made it necessary to devote close attention to balancing. In the New York Central "Hudson" type locomotives of the "J3" class, which have developed a maximum i.h.p. of 4,725 at 75 m.p.h., and a maximum d.b.-h.p. of 3,880 at 65 m.p.h., balancing and the lightening of the motion parts have been so perfected that in tests conducted in 1938 the driving wheels of one of these engines were slipped to an equivalent rate of no less than 164 m.p.h. before they began to lift from the rails. It was found also that no damage had been sustained by the locomotive as a result of it having been worked at this phenomenal speed.

At various times since the beginning of the century British railway companies have exchanged locomotives for the purpose of comparative trials, and as mentioned in Chapters 1 and 2, certain of these events have had a profound effect on subsequent British locomotive history. Other exchanges have been made from time to time, but without any measurable effect on the subsequent locomotive practice of the railways concerned, though the appearance of the "strangers," in some cases far from their native haunts, has been a matter of considerable interest both to railwaymen and to the public.

From the time of the grouping, of course, engines of the various constituent companies of each group have been used freely over what, before the grouping, would have been "foreign" metals, and in not a few cases have proved more suitable for the duties concerned than those which they replaced. The L.M.S.R., in particular, carried out a systematic programme of testing whereby the less efficient classes all over their system were weeded out, in the interests of standardisation, and the fittest only have survived.

One of the first-fruits of nationalisation has been the most extensive series of locomotive exchange trials ever conducted in Great Britain. It involved 14 classes of locomotive—express passenger, mixed traffic, and heavy freight—and took place over 12 selected main routes in all parts of the country, for three months in the summer of 1948. The work of the principal classes of all four pre-nationalisation railways, with the help of dynamometer cars, thus was closely compared, with a view to settling the most efficient standards for future use.

9

SERVICE—THE LOCOMOTIVE AT THE SHED

EVERY locomotive is attached to a shed, at which it receives the servicing and general attention needed to keep it in efficient working order. All timetable trains and all other working movements on the railways must be provided with motive power; and these workings are divided up systematically between the various locomotive depots to which such power is assigned.

The size of engine-sheds varies with the number of motive power units which each is required to house, and ranges from small sub-sheds with one or two engines to large depots to which several hundred locomotives may be attached. For locomotive maintenance purposes, the railways are divided up into districts; generally the main shed, the largest and most important in the district, is under the control of a resident District Locomotive Superintendent, or similar officer, who also is in charge of all the smaller sub-sheds in the district, each under the immediate supervision of a shed foreman.

It is now customary to indicate on locomotives to which particular shed each engine is assigned. On the late L.M.S.R. this indication has been given hitherto on a small oval cast-iron plate affixed to the lower part of the smokebox door. Each L.M.S.R. locomotive district has had a reference number, shown on the upper part of the shed-plate, with a letter below which denotes the actual shed. To take a familiar example, the Western Division London District, based on Willesden, is No. 1; Willesden shed itself is "1A," and Camden, housing the express and mixed traffic engines for passenger trains from Euston and fast freights from Camden, is "1B." Other well-known sheds are Crewe North ("5A"), Crewe South ("5B"), Liverpool Edge Hill ("8A"), Carlisle Kingmoor ("12A"), Carlisle Upperby ("12B"), Kentish Town ("14B"), Leeds ("20A"), Birmingham Saltley ("21A"), Bristol ("22A"), Manchester Newton Heath ("26A") and Glasgow Polmadie ("27A").

On the L.N.E.R. locomotives the name of the shed has been painted in full on the left-hand side of the buffer-beam, below the engine number. The G.W.R. has had a code of two to four letters, painted on the side framing of the engine, below the running-plate at the extreme front end, immediately behind the buffer-beam. In the London Division, Old Oak Common shed, at which just over 200 engines are stabled, is "PDN" (for Paddington), Bristol St. Philips Marsh is "SPM," Plymouth Laira is "LA," Wolverhampton is "SRD" (for

Stafford Road), Newton Abbot is "NA," and so on. To those who occupy themselves in recording the numbers of locomotives and tracing their movements, these shed indications can prove a study of great interest. The S.R. alone has given no shed indication on its locomotives. The L.M.S.R. method is to be the future national standard.

The general day-to-day maintenance principle is that each locomotive shall spend some hours out of the twenty-four at the shed. But modern traffic conditions have made it impossible for many locomotives to return daily to their home sheds. As non-stop runs began to grow in length, and then as the through workings of locomotives were extended (until ultimately the L.M.S.R. had numerous daily through locomotive runs over the $401\frac{1}{2}$ miles between Euston and Glasgow), it became necessary for engines on such duties to receive their shed attention alternately at their home sheds and the sheds at the opposite end of their runs. Since then, in order to obtain the maximum possible use of locomotives while they are in steam, many engines, especially those in the "general purpose" (mixed traffic) or freight categories, have been worked to circuitous diagrams that may keep them away from their own sheds for days or even a week or more at a time.

While these developments may have been advantageous in keeping engines continuously at work, their effect on locomotive maintenance in general has been anything but good. In earlier days any shed with a tradition behind it took a pride in keeping its stud of locomotives in first-class condition. The same applied to engine-crews; each engine had its own driver and fireman (the old London, Brighton & South Coast Railway even painted drivers' names in the cabs of their locomotives), who often developed a real affection for their charge, and this was obvious in the care with which they treated it.

But in these days, even in the best conditions engines may be double-manned or treble-manned during the twenty-four hours, and sometimes pass through many different hands in the course of a week. Thus the personal interest has been lost. Similarly a shed which sends out an engine clean and in good running order, and receives it back after some days in a dirty and uncared-for state, is hardly encouraged, to say the least. At some sheds efforts have been made since the war to improve these conditions, and so far as the larger and more important classes of locomotive are concerned, express engines in particular, to keep the working of one engine to not more than two crews, but the general tendency is in the opposite direction.

In wartime, also, the tremendous demands made on locomotive power, and the shortage of staff and materials, made it exceedingly difficult to carry out normal maintenance, and British locomotive stock has suffered severely in consequence. At many sheds external cleaning has gone by default, and the filthy and neglected appearance of a large number of the engines is the unhappy result. Fortunately, the Great Western and Southern Railways did not abandon entirely their smart locomotive liveries, and even in war conditions managed to keep their express engines reasonably clean. Since then there has been a marked improvement in locomotive cleanliness at many sheds, and national colour-schemes have been evolved which provide a brilliant blue livery for the principal express engines, apple-green for the intermediate express passenger classes, and black, smartly lined out in colours, for other types.

So we may look forward to some resumption of the brightness which in the past made a British locomotive so good an advertisement for its owners. In recent years this advertising value has been realised to the full in the United States, where much has been done in "cleaning up" the external lines of locomotives, and in providing striking stream-line and semi-streamline casings, with brilliant schemes of colour, in order to catch the eye. Moreover, an attractively-finished and well-maintained locomotive is likely to be the subject of more care and attention by those who handle it than one which is not.

Engine sheds are of two types. The type of shed which is the cheaper to build, and occupies less space, houses its engines on parallel tracks, with a number of engines standing in line on each track. The disposing of engines in a shed of this type must be the subject of careful planning, so that each engine may be available for duty at the right time without the necessity for moving a number of others before it can be released.

The older type of depot, known from its shape as a "round shed" or "roundhouse," is a circular building with all its tracks radiating from a central turntable. Not more than two or three locomotives stand on each track, and it is a simple matter to move the turntable round to the track on which the required engine is standing, to run the engine on to the table, and to turn it to the exit road from the shed. The turntable thus is the key to the working of a round shed, and against this method of construction is the fact that any turntable failure can have serious consequences. A large shed of this type, such as the Western Region Old Oak Common depot, may comprise more than one roundhouse, and cover a considerable area of ground. In modern shed construction there is some tendency to return to the latter type, using reinforced concrete for the building.

In the United States, where turntables may have diameters from 110 to 130 ft., in order to accommodate the extremely lengthy locomotives of that country, it is the custom for the turntable to be in the open air, and for a series of covered "stalls," each long enough to accommodate one locomotive, and, of course, roofed in, to radiate from the table   The American roundhouse extends as far round the turntable circle as the number of stalls requires. Adjacent to any large American shed is the "back shop" in which a certain amount of machining and other operations connected with locomotive maintenance can be dealt with.

All the operation of a large locomotive shed has to be organised with the utmost care and attention, in order that servicing and general maintenance may be carried out with a minimum of detention for each engine; for locomotives are earning money only when they are at work on the road. On arrival at the shed from a turn of duty, the engine has its water tank filled up, and then moves to the coal stage. Except at the smaller sheds, where the expense of mechanical coaling plants would not be justifiable, manual coaling methods with hand baskets, or shovelling, have long since been done away with. The mechanical plants aim at doing in a few minutes a task which, with manual coaling of perhaps 6 to 9 tons to a single tender, previously needed over half-an-hour.

The first mechanical coaling plant in Great Britain was one built by the then London & North Western Railway at Crewe North Shed in 1910. In more recent years such plants have been brought into use at all the principal British locomotive sheds, where these towering structures dominate the whole of the locomotive yard. Though the actual designs differ the general principles are usually the same.

Above the engine coal road a capacious bunker is built, either in steel or in reinforced concrete. Coal is fed into this bunker from above, a common method being to lift the coal wagons up to the top of the bunker, by hydraulic, or, more usually, electric hoist, and then to invert them bodily, so that their contents shoot into the bunker. Another method is to tipple or empty the wagons into storage bins below the rail level, from which the coal is carried by skip-hoist up to the top of the main bunker and dropped in. The coal must be handled as carefully as possible, in order to reduce breakage to a minimum, and, indeed, to avoid both breakage and the coal-dust nuisance altogether if possible.

The engines then pass along the coal road, and under the bunker, one by one; when each engine is in position, the appropriate amount of coal is dropped through a chute on to the tender. As the coal falls, it is measured, so that an accurate record may be kept of the consumption of each locomotive. At some of the modern plants, the engine-crew themselves manipulate the plant, by means of a key corresponding to the tender capacity of their engine, and the coal measurement is done by an automatic appliance known as a "cubimeter."

The largest coaling plants have capacities up to 500 tons, and wagons may be lifted as high as 100 ft. above ground level in order to discharge their contents into the bunkers. In the United States and Canada, continuous locomotive runs are so lengthy and coal consumptions are so heavy that, despite enormous tender capacities, re-coaling is often necessary during the course of a run. For this purpose, as mentioned in Chapter 6, at certain selected points, large coaling plants are erected spanning all tracks of a main line, and locomotives stop under these plants, in the middle of ordinary passenger runs if necessary, in order to replenish their tenders.

The next operation is to empty the smokebox of its accumulation of fine ash, and to clean or to rake out the fire. As explained later in this chapter, a good deal is being done in modern locomotives to reduce the smokebox ash by means of self-cleaning smokeboxes, and similarly to facilitate fire-cleaning by means of drop grates. Apart from these locomotive improvements, the work is facilitated at many sheds by means of compressed-air plants for removing smokebox ash, and ash disposal plants for firebox ash.

What is actually done to the fire depends on whether the engine is needed in service again after a few hours, or is coming in for boiler washing or examination. In the former case the fire is merely cleaned, by the raking out of the clinker; in the latter it is dropped altogether. At the same time accumulated deposits of soot, which interfere with the steaming of the boiler, must be removed from the tubes. For this purpose a powerful jet is used, assisted by the use of a wire brush at the firebox end, where there are the thickest accumulations, and a longer rod with a swab at the tip of it for the more remote parts of the tubes. Compressed air is now preferred to steam for supplying the jet, and at some sheds a battery of air-compressors is installed for this purpose.

Various modifications have been made in locomotive design, in recent years in particular, in order to reduce the time taken to clean the fire and the smokebox at the end of a day's run. These include the rocking grates introduced by the L.M.S. and Southern Railways, which make it possible to prevent the accumulation of clinker by breaking it up as it forms, and so facilitate fire-cleaning. Assistance is provided also by the "drop grate" fitted to certain L.N.E.R. and S.R. locomotive classes, as described in Chapter 5, for dropping the fire.

A further improvement is the fitting of trap doors on the underside of the ashpan, opened by a handle at the side of the locomotive, to enable the fire to be dropped directly into an ashpit between the tracks, instead of raked out laboriously through the damper doors, as previously. The Bulleid Pacifics of the late Southern Railway have ashpans divided into three parts, each with its own self-cleaning hopper. It is easier, of course, to fit an ashpan of the self-emptying type to a locomotive which has its firebox in rear of the coupled wheels—as, for example, a 4-6-2, 2-6-2, or 4-4-2—than it is to locomotives of the 4-4-0, 4-6-0, 2-8-0, or similar types.

By the means outlined in the last paragraph, the time required for cleaning or dropping engine fires at the shed has been reduced to five or ten minutes, so greatly reducing congestion at the ashpits of busy sheds, and also justifying the cost of installing mechanical ash-handling plants. With a large locomotive not so fitted, that has come in from a long run after burning indifferent or dirty coal, the same job may take up to an hour or even two hours.

Another important development is the self-cleaning smokebox devised by the late L.M.S.R. and now becoming standard in the London Midland Region; it is indicated by the letters "S.C." painted on the smokebox door. In the course of ordinary running, fine ash is drawn from the fire through the tubes, and deposited in the smokebox, from which, in an engine not fitted with self-cleaning arrangements, it has to be shovelled out. In earlier days, when this deposit of ash was greatly increased by the fierce blast resulting from long cut-offs, it was no unusual happening for the lower part of the smokebox door to become red-hot because of this accumulation of incandescent ash behind it, especially if the door was not fitting tightly and was allowing air to be drawn in. If the ash piled up, also, it blocked the mouths of the lower rows of tubes, reducing the effective heating surface and the steaming capacity of the boiler.

In the self-cleaning smokebox, a baffle-plate is fixed horizontally across the width of the smokebox just below the level of the top of the blast-pipe. The effect of the baffle is to deflect the hot gases round the base of the blast-pipe, and then up through a coarse screen behind the smokebox door to the chimney. This causes a scouring action at the bottom of the smokebox which prevents ash from accumulating, carrying most of it up through the chimney instead. Experience has proved that there is no interference with draught caused in this way, and the scouring action is effective enough for the smokebox to be left for as long as a fortnight before any cleaning out of ash becomes necessary. Tube-cleaning also can be postponed until the engine is washed out, which is an advantage, as the baffle-plates have to be removed before the tubes can be reached for this purpose. Considerable economies in time and labour at locomotive running sheds are thus being made possible by rocking and drop grates and by self-cleaning smokeboxes.

Even though the fire may have been dropped, sufficient steam remains in the boiler for the engine to be moved under its own power by the stabling crew from the ashpit into the shed. According to when it is next required for service, it is allotted a place in which it will be accessible at the right time (the stabling of engines in the shed has a great deal to do with efficient shed working), standing over one of the deep inspection pits. Here a thorough examination takes place; it includes the motion, springs, and all the various controls and appliances by which the engine is worked; wheels are tested with a hammer for faulty tyres, and so on. On some railways fitter-examiners are detailed for this work, but on others it is the responsibility of the drivers only to make these examinations, and to book details of any repairs that may be required.

Defects needing attention are entered in the "repair book" or on the "repair card," together with any irregularities that drivers may notice in the course of running. Minor troubles receive immediate attention; more serious repairs may involve withdrawing the engine from traffic until they have been attended to. It is only in the event of serious trouble or damage which cannot be rectified at the larger running sheds that the locomotive is remitted to the main locomotive works for repairs. Otherwise the visits of each locomotive to the main works are confined to those for "general overhaul," which takes place periodically after the locomotive has run a predetermined number of miles, varying according to the type of engine. General overhaul includes stripping completely, and, if necessary, reboilering.

At the running sheds there are periodic inspections which take longer than the daily examinations. Water-gauge cocks, for example, are examined and tested every fifteen days. Once in three months the safety-valves are tested, to ensure that they are blowing off correctly at the rated pressure of the boiler. Every four months an inspector of the running department conducts a boiler inspection of a very thorough description. Cylinders and piston-valves are opened up for inspection after the engine has run 25,000 miles. The results of all these examinations are entered up on the "history sheet" or "examination book" of each locomotive, in which a continuous record is kept.

While soot accumulates on the inside of the boiler-tubes, scale— another poor conductor of heat—deposits itself on the outside, as well as over the outer surface of the inner firebox. Much has been done in recent years to reduce scale formation by the treatment of boiler water to reduce its hardness; softening plants are now in use at many of the larger sheds, and also at the water-troughs. As a precaution against the "priming" referred to in Chapter 4, that is, foaming due to the alkaline content of the soft water, many locomotives to-day are fitted with "continuous blow down"; this is a jet which makes it possible to to blow a small amount of water continuously out of the boiler, carrying with it the alkaline sludge, all the time the regulator is open. The use of this appliance, together with that of soft water, has helped to increase from the previous average of a week to a full month the periods between the regular washing out of modern locomotive boilers. It may be added that continuous blow-down is less favourably regarded by permanent-way maintenance engineers, because of the adverse effect that it may have on the track, particularly the ballast.

When boiler washing out is to take place, the remaining steam is blown out of the boiler; the sludge cocks, if the boiler is fitted with them, are opened to release any sludge, and closed again; and the engine must then be left about six hours to cool off. Boiler washers next take charge. Through a plug in the top of the firebox the boiler is filled from the shed hydrants, and a mudhole door in the base of the firebox is opened to remove the water and sludge that are released during the cleaning. The hose is then moved to a plug in the front tubeplate, so that water may circulate through the length of the barrel. Long rods of about $\frac{3}{8}$-in. diameter are inserted through the plug-holes, and scraped vigorously over all surfaces that can be reached, to loosen the scale and sediment, which passes away with the water stream through the mudhole door. In some sheds hot water, at a pressure of about 40 lb. per sq. in., is used for boiler washing out.

Directly the washing out is finished, the boiler examiner gets to work. His task is by no means easy, for with the limited access afforded by the apertures in the boiler already referred to, he has to see as much of the boiler interior as he can, noting in particular where pitting, corrosion, or other damage to plates is taking place. He does his work with the help of a small barrel-shaped electric lamp mounted on a stout wire about 3 ft. long, and an adjustable mirror. Then he must enter both smokebox and firebox, examining the tube-ends in each, and in the firebox paying special attention to the tightness of stays, as well as the condition of plates, brick arch, firebars, and so on.

The last duty of the boiler examiner is to replace the fusible plug; this is provided, in the crown of the inner firebox, to give warning of danger, by melting and admitting a jet of steam into the firebox, in the event of the water level in the boiler having fallen sufficiently to uncover the firebox crown. In so serious a contingency as this, if the fire were not damped immediately, there would be risk of a boiler explosion. With the boiler examiner, the boiler-washers also should by now have finished their work, replacing plugs and mud-doors, and refilling the boiler ready for the engine to be re-steamed.

The boiler examiner adds his notes to those of the fitter and the driver in the repair book, and fitters and boilersmiths set to work to effect any minor repairs that may be needed before the engine is due for its next turn of duty. If it is necessary to retain the locomotive for more extensive attention, however, the running shed foreman must arrange for another suitable locomotive to replace the one under repair, until the work has been completed.

The next operation is that of cleaning. In earlier days paraffin or some other suitable solvent was used to remove the exterior coating of grime and dust, with the help of scrapers and cloths, from the motion and paint-work, and polishing with oily waste followed. At the larger sheds to-day, however, much of this work is done by high-pressure cleaning plants, which economise greatly in time and labour. According to the time and staff available, therefore, the engine is made as presentable as possible before it leaves the shed.

During the cleaning process, or soon after, the steam-raiser gets to work on the locomotive, for even though the boiler may have been filled with hot water, getting steam up to the requisite pressure may take from two to four hours. First, using the gauge-glass cocks, he notes the level of water in the boiler; having satisfied himself that the boiler is filled properly, he begins to spread coal on the firebars. Various kinds of firelighters are used, ranging from a kind of box formed of pieces of old creosoted sleepers nailed together with a piece of paraffined waste or an old oiler pad in the centre, to plain pieces of sleeper with no such preparation. With these and a shovelful or two of blazing coal from the shed furnace, the engine fire is got going. It is the business of the steam-raiser to see that the boiler pressure is sufficiently high, on the arrival of the engine-crew to take over, to ensure that they will have the full pressure when the engine is ready to leave the yard.

Some of the bigger sheds are so well equipped with plant that they relieve the main locomotive works of a considerable proportion of the heavy repairs; they are provided, for example, with drop pits, generally operated by electrical means, for the quick release of wheels and axles, and with large wheel lathes in which tyres can be turned. A great deal of labour and careful planning thus is needed in keeping the motive power of a railway in sound running order, and in seeing that suitable locomotives are in steam and duly manned in readiness for every duty.

THE FOOTPLATE OF A "DUCHESS" TYPE PACIFIC, LONDON MIDLAND REGION

(No. 6230, *Duchess of Buccleuch*)

Key to the photograph opposite

1. Main steam manifold (valve which can completely isolate footplate controls from the steam supply).
2. Regulator handle.
3. Drifting position of regulator handle, a stop which admits a minute volume of steam to help destroy the vacuum in the cylinders and steam chest when "drifting" —i.e. coasting.
4. Screw-reversing handle. The screw is geared into the tooth sector-plate, which can be locked by—
5. Reversing gear lock.
6. Boiler pressure gauge.
7. Isolating cock for (6) above.
8. Steam supply-valve hand wheel for live steam injector (*left*) and for exhaust steam injector (*right*). (*Note:* The water supply valves are on the tender).
9. Gauge-glass water-level indicators.
10. Handles, operating cocks to isolate gauge glasses. The vertical pull-rods from the handles to the isolating cocks are evident.
11. Gauge-glass "blow-through" or "try" cocks to test whether gauges are showing a true water level.
12. Driver's brake valve, which applies steam brakes on engine and tender concurrently with vacuum brake on the train.
13. Steam control to large vacuum ejector (hand-wheel), and to small vacuum ejector (wooden handle behind hand-wheel).
14. Vacuum gauge.
15. Isolating cock for vacuum ejectors.
16. Carriage warming steam pressure gauge.
17. Carriage warming steam-control hand wheel.
18.* Speed indicator.
19. Whistle stop valve.
20. Coal pusher steam-control hand wheel.
21. Blower valve.
22.* Sand gun (for cleaning tubes); (*a*) controls the steam supply, (*c*) the sand supply, and (*b*) controls the aim, so that the stream of sand can be directed to any desired part of the tube-plate.
23. Sliding fire doors, worked by handle and levers. The arrow points to a small catch-lock* intended to hold the doors slightly open (to admit a little air above the fire).
24. Wash-out plug. (Duplicated alongside, and in several other places on the footplate).
25. Coal-degging pipe—a flexible hose for watering the coal on the tender, in order to keep down dust.
26. Steam sanding control. This applies either forward sands, **or** aft sands, according to the position of the control handle.
27.* Continuous blow-down steam control.
28. Lubricator pipes for intermediate buffing gear.
29. Live steam injector overflow pipe; the injector itself is immediately behind.
29A. Exhaust steam injector overflow pipe; the injector itself is immediately behind.
30. Water feed inlets from tender supply.
31. Hose connection supplying steam to the tender steam brake.
32. Hose connection supplying steam to coal pusher on the tender.
33. Hose connection of vacuum brake trainpipe.
34. Sliding ventilator in cab roof, pulled over by a vertical handle, and locked by a clamp to the left of it.

* This equipment has since been removed or rendered inoperative.

**THE FOOTPLATE OF A "DUCHESS" PACIFIC, LONDON MIDLAND
REGION**

36. (The key on the opposite page is by courtesy of O. J. Morris and Ian Allan, Ltd.)
(*Courtesy, British Railways.*)

37. Facing tube-plate to receive superheater header casting. (*Courtesy, British Railways.*)

38. Smokebox of "King Arthur" 4-6-0, Southern Region, showing multiple-jet blast-pipe. (*Frank F. Moss.*)

39. Shell of outer firebox, showing heads of stay-bolts and detail of riveting to boiler barrel. (*Courtesy, British Railways.*)

40. Thermic syphon, as applied to firebox of Southern Region Pacific locomotives. (*Courtesy, British Railways.*)

SMOKEBOX AND FIREBOX DETAILS

41. General view of the shed, showing the engine roads and outdoor inspection pits, and, on the right, the ash disposal plant. (*Courtesy, British Railways.*)

42. Another view of the shed, with the coaling plant seen prominently in the left foreground. (*Courtesy, British Railways.*)

A MODERN ENGINE SHED—CARNFORTH, LONDON MIDLAND REGION

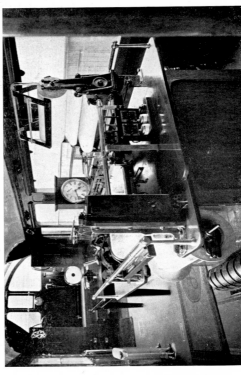

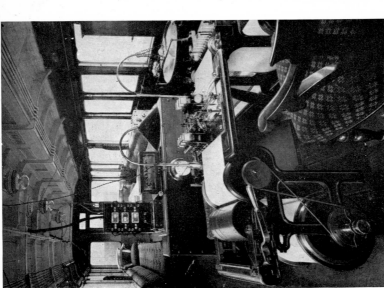

43 (left). Interior of the Western Region car. The main recording table is in the foreground with the recording pens in the centre. (Courtesy, British Railways.)
44 and 45 (right) Exterior and interior views of London Midland Region car No. 45050, the most modern of the British cars. (Courtesy, British Railways.)

DYNAMOMETER CARS AND THEIR EQUIPMENT

46. At the start of a dynamometer test. The Eastern Region car is at the head of the
1.10 p.m. express from King's Cross in the 1948 exchange trials, and the engine is London
Midland Region rebuilt "Royal Scot" *Queen's Westminster Rifleman.* (*F. R. Hebron.*)

47. The "stranger" at work. Hauling the 8.30 a.m. express from Plymouth to Paddington,
with the Western Region dynamometer car next the tender, is the London Midland Region
Pacific *City of Bradford.* (*M. W. Earley.*)

EXCHANGE OF LOCOMOTIVES FOR TEST PURPOSES

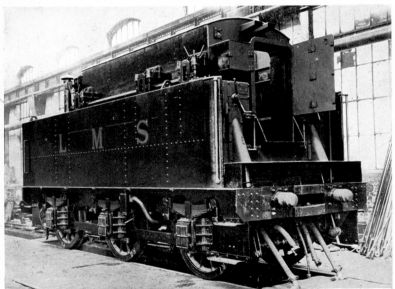

48. Speed and direction of the wind in front of the locomotive are measured and recorded electrically on the dynamometer roll by the cup anemometer and vane carried on the frame. (*Courtesy, British Railways.*)

49. Self-weighing tender, which makes it possible to keep an accurate watch on the locomotive's coal consumption during the test trip. (*Courtesy, British Railways.*)

LOCOMOTIVE EQUIPMENT FOR TEST JOURNEYS

50. Prepared for indicator tests—Western Region 4-cylinder 4-6-0 *Caldicot Castle* fitted with indicating shelter. (*Courtesy, British Railways.*)

51. On the locomotive testing-plant at Altoona, Pa., U.S.A.—a 4-8-2 locomotive of the Pennsylvania Railroad. (*Rail Photo Service, Boston, Mass.*)

INDOOR AND OUTDOOR LOCOMOTIVE TESTING

TAKING WATER AT SPEED

52. Eastern Region Pacific *Sansovino* shows a lively splash at Langley troughs as the tender tank overflows at the end of the trough.
(*F. R. Hebron.*)

~ 10 ~

SERVICE—THE LOCOMOTIVE ON THE ROAD

WE have now to follow the locomotive from the engine-shed on to its train, in order that we may see something of the methods by which it is handled on the road. On arrival at the shed, after checking in to the time clerk on duty, the driver and fireman pass to the notice-board. While the printed "weekly working notice" pamphlets, which are circulated to all drivers, give information as to all engineering work—such as track relaying, bridge reconstruction, and so on—that necessitates speed restrictions over the affected lengths, emergency notices have to be displayed from day to day. Pitfalls in mining areas may cause subsidences in the track; for drought or other reasons water may be unobtainable temporarily at certain stations; and it is vitally important that all abnormal conditions affecting the running shall be brought to the notice of the crews. An adjacent roster-board or some other means is used to notify to the driver and his mate which train they are to man, the service on which they will return, the number of the engine allotted to them, and the shed road on which it is standing.

The fireman now proceeds to the stores, in order to draw the day's equipment—his shovel, a bucket, spanners, lubricating oil, and so on. Lamps are required, unlighted by day and lighted by night, to indicate the class of train (or, on some lines, like those of the Southern Region, the route it is to follow); these may be on the engine already. Next, the crew have to conduct a thorough examination of their locomotive. While the driver is going the round of the motion, oiling crossheads, big-ends and side-rods, seeing that the oil-boxes of the mechanical or displacement lubricators are properly full and that all trimmings are adjusted, and trying the fit of nuts and cotters, to make sure that all is secure, the fireman is busy testing gauge-cocks, injectors, blower, dampers and sanding gear. The fireman must take care that the sand-boxes are full, and another task may be to trim the coal on the tender forward to the tender front. Although the engine has steam up, the fireman may need to put on the blower, to provide draught, if the pressure is not rising fast enough without this assistance, or to clear the smoke.

For these locomotive requirements, according to the size of the engine, a time of between 45 and 60 minutes is allowed as part of the working day between signing on and the schedule time of leaving the shed. One additional duty for the driver is to consult the repair book, to see if it will be necessary for him to pay special attention to the working or condition of any part of the engine during the course of the day's run.

The locomotive now leaves for the terminus or other station at which it is to be attached to its train. These engine movements are timetabled in such a way as to leave an ample margin of time before the actual departure. After backing on to the train, the fireman gets down to couple up, and to drop the lamps on to their appropriate lamp-irons at the head end, one over each buffer, for example, if it is an "express passenger" train. The head guard comes up to the engine to note in his "journal" the number of the engine and the driver's name, and at the same time to give the driver the weight of his train. A brake test is made by the guard, who must see that the brake has responded properly, at the far end of the train, before he gives the "right-away." At the larger stations, a locomotive inspector is on duty on the platform to keep in touch with crews and their engines, and to take appropriate action in any locomotive emergency.

As noted already in Chapter 8, the maximum drawbar pull required of the locomotive is on starting, to overcome the static friction in the journals of all wheels and axles throughout the train. The driver therefore puts his engine into full forward gear—65 to 75 per cent. cut-off—in readiness. On receiving the "right away" from the guard, it is the driver's duty to verify that the starting signal is duly "off" before he opens his regulator. The opening at first is partial, as even with the artificial increase of adhesion obtained by the use of sand, a full opening almost inevitably would cause the driving wheels to slip badly.

With the latest British Pacific types, as noted in Chapter 3, the increase in tractive effort, while the total adhesion weight on the three coupled axles has remained limited to between 60 and 67 tons, has so reduced the "factor of adhesion" (the ratio, in pounds per ton, of tractive effort to adhesion weight), that the utmost caution is needed by drivers in starting to avoid slipping, and they are not always successful. It is chiefly in starting that the auxiliary power offered by the American booster is so valuable, and it is curious that this useful contrivance, standard on many American locomotive classes, should never have got beyond the experimental stage in Great Britain.

The booster is a small two-cylinder engine, usually applied to a pair of small wheels in rear of the driving wheels, and so has a relatively high tractive effort, which gives useful auxiliary power in starting and on steep gradients. When a certain predetermined speed is reached, the booster is cut out of mesh, rather like the free-wheel of a bicycle, and offers no frictional resistance to motion at the higher speeds.

Directly the train is on the move, and often after no more than a few turns of the driving wheels, the driver begins to "notch up," or to reduce the cut-off percentage, and at the same time the regulator is opened wider. When full speed has been attained, the cut-off on a modern express engine should be back to between 15 and 25 per cent., and with a reasonably heavy train on a fast schedule, it should be possible to work with the regulator full open, so that there is no throttling of the steam on its admission through the regulator into the steam-pipe.

If the cut-off is brought much below 15 per cent., there is a risk of undue wear-and-tear of the valve-motion, and for this reason, where the running conditions are easy, the regulator may be kept partly open only, or working on the first port—a small auxiliary opening—in order to keep the train speed within bounds. Conversely, on the rising gradients it may be necessary to increase the cut-off, even with full regulator, in order to overcome the additional resistance caused by the pull of gravity.

In the adjustment of cut-off percentage and regulator opening, both to suit the constant changes of gradient and at the same time to make the most economical use of the steam, the driver's expert knowledge is called into play. It was, perhaps, on the G.W.R., where the design of locomotives with long-lap, long-travel valve-gear first became the standard practice of a British railway, that the greatest refinement in cut-off working developed. On a "King" or "Castle" class 4-6-0, Western Region, it is nothing unusual to see drivers making cut-off changes by no more than 1 or 2 per cent. at a time, with the help of the fine cut-off adjustment that the operation of their reversing gear makes possible. At the other end of the scale of competence there is the man who drives "on his regulator"—that is to say, immediately after starting the cut-off is fixed, and from then on variations in the supply of steam to the cylinders, to meet rising, level or falling track conditions, are made entirely by varying the regulator opening. In this connection, considerable assistance is given to drivers of modern locomotives by the provision of a steam-chest pressure gauge in addition to the gauge which shows the boiler pressure. It is not easy to deduce from the position of a regulator handle exactly how far the regulator has been opened, but an accurate indication of the actual pressure in the steam-chest leaves the matter in no doubt.

There is, of course, no precise standard of driving applicable to all engines. The methods required vary as between class and class, and even between engines of the same class, for it is rarely that two locomotives of one class behave in precisely the same way on the road. As argued in the opening chapter of this book, there might be more uniformity if British railways had developed better and more systematic methods of educating their enginemen. Some helpful information, however, is obtained from the locomotive inspectors, who spend most of their time riding with engine-crews, especially on new locomotives.

But with all this there is a good deal of reluctance to interfere with a driver's discretion, and as a result much of the driving practice which became traditional with engines of earlier types still persists. In consequence, a good many engines are not worked with the full efficiency that their design should make possible.

Firing a large modern locomotive is a task calling for considerable experience and skill. Methods vary considerably according to the shape of the firegrate, whether of the long and narrow type inevitable in the case of locomotives with driving wheels at the rear end of the chassis (such as the 4-6-0 type), or the wide square type, extending across the full width of the frames, found on 4-6-2, 4-4-2, and other classes with idle wheels under the cab. With the narrow firebox, the throwing of the coal by the fireman is largely in a straight forward direction, whereas with the wide firebox much of the fuel must be directed to the left or the right of the fire-door. The most effective type of fire is usually one made up in a saucer shape, from 6 to 8 inches deep over the middle of the grate, and from 2 to 3 inches higher along the two sides and under the door. This method allows the air needed for combustion to pass freely through the blazing mass.

Great Western locomotives in general have been designed to burn good quality South Wales coking steam coals, rather than the hard Yorkshire coals generally used by other Regions. Coking coals burn with a short flame, and need a thick fire to maintain the heat, so that on the Western Region the "haycock" fire is customary, higher in the centre than at the sides. A sharper blast also is needed for this type of fuel.

It is more easy for a fireman to come to grief through making up too thick a fire than from the fire being too thin. If the firebox is overfilled, the passage of air is obstructed, the firebox temperature falls, and imperfect combustion results in the production of carbon monoxide, which does no useful work in steam-raising and is thrown to waste out of the chimney. Another bad practice is to feed large lumps into the fire without breaking them up; this tends to leave parts of the firegrate bare, allowing the passage of cold air and also reducing the firebox temperature. The right method of firing is "little and often" rather than "much and seldom"; with coal of reasonably good quality, and a well-made fire, this gives such intense heat that the steaming capacity of the boiler is put to its maximum use, and the emission of smoke is reduced to a minimum. Bad coal or a thick fire causes the formation of clinker, which is very troublesome, though in modern locomotives with rocking grates there is a better chance than previously of breaking up clinker formation while the engine is running.

All through the journey, the fireman's glance is directed constantly towards the pressure gauge, to see if his work is keeping the boiler pressure as near to the rated figure as possible. Some of the hardest firing will be done in the early part of the journey, and before and on the rising gradients; over the easier stretches of line, the frequency of the firing will be reduced, and over the final length before the engine is to come off the train, firing will cease altogether, so that the fire may be dropped to the minimum that will suffice to get the train into the terminus on time, and to take the engine back to the shed. The use during the journey of fire-irons, such as the pricker, is avoided as far as possible, for they are awkward implements to wield within the confined space of the cab; this attention may be necessary at times, however, if the steam pressure is falling owing to clinker formation.

From time to time during the journey, also, the driver may lengthen the cut-off, to maintain the steam pressure, if he finds his fireman in difficulties with the fire. In addition to these duties, the fireman shares with the driver the responsibility of keeping a look-out for all signals, especially those which are visible from his side of the engine, but obscured from the driver's view by the boiler. It is always a pleasure to watch a competent engine-crew at work; between two experienced men who have been together for some time, the understanding is perfect, and the scientific management of the locomotive is being carried out to the best possible advantage.

It may be remarked here that the driver-to-be enters the railway service as an engine-cleaner. During his work of cleaning, which carries him over and under all parts of the locomotives, he gains his first knowledge as to the various parts and their working functions. After an examination of his knowledge, he becomes an "approved fireman," and starts work on the footplate. In normal times his progress would be gradual, from shunting engine up to express engine, but present shortage of labour has made it necessary to take many short cuts. During his work of firing, by watching his driver he acquires knowledge of the methods by which locomotives are handled, and is instructed as to the best methods of firing; also he is picking up by degrees the intimate acquaintance with the road that he will need as a driver.

Finally, after a further examination, he becomes a "passed fireman," that is to say, a fireman passed to act as a driver, and a similar ascent from shunting to express passenger engine takes place. Part of the examination of approved firemen and passed firemen, needless to say, is a test of eyesight, which must be up to a prescribed standard; more-over, colour blindness is a definite barrier to the footplate, as this would make it impossible for an engineman to distinguish between the colours of signal-arms or of signal lights at night.

At first the passed fireman may be required to drive at intervals only, such as busy summer week-ends, and then to revert to firing; similarly the approved firemen at first may alternate between firing and cleaning. Later on, they pass into the various "links" of engine-crews at each shed, which are responsible for certain sets of locomotive duties. By degrees they gravitate upwards to the "top link" or links at the shed, which comprise the most experienced drivers and firemen, entrusted with the chief and most lucrative express passenger train workings. It is a lengthy road from cleaning to express passenger driving, but in the interests of safe running and efficient working it is bound to be so.

At the end of the journey, the driver and fireman generally are relieved at the terminus by a "disposal crew," who take the engine back to the shed. If they have been making a long non-stop run, as, for example, on the London Midland Region from Euston to Carlisle, they board away for the night, and return on the following day. Other-wise they work the engine back to the shed themselves, hand it over to a stabling crew, return their tools and equipment to the stores, and book off duty.

The paths of passenger trains are laid down with precision, and in the case of express trains, the working timetables show not only starting and stopping times, but also the times at which the trains are expected to pass junctions and other important timing points intermediately. Frequent reference is made by the driver to his watch, to check the observance of time on the run, for he is required to account for lost time which cannot be explained by signal or permanent-way checks, overtime at stations, bad weather, or other causes outside the working of the engine.

No definite policy has been laid down in Great Britain as to whether drivers should be expected to make up time, so far as conditions permit, which has been lost by circumstances not under their own control. In the United States such recovery is certainly expected; in France, in normal times, a bonus is offered to engine-crews for the recovery of lost time. But the British idea of leaving all matters connected with locomotive working to the driver's discretion has had its effect in this matter also. It has been argued, moreover, that drivers may attempt time recovery by excessive speeds round curves, so that the practice may entail risk.

On the Continent and in the United States such risks are guarded against by fitting all locomotives intended for express passenger service (and many others as well) with self-recording speed indicators. Not only do these indicators give a visual indication to drivers of the speed at which they are running, but they also keep a continuous record of the speed on a moving tape, which is locked up in such a way as to be inaccessible to the crew. With such equipment, it is impossible for a driver to take his train round curves recklessly without the fact being recorded on the indicator tape.

The introduction of streamline trains into Great Britain in 1935 and 1937 made it imperative to equip the locomotives working these flyers with recording speed indicators of this type; from then on non-recording speed indicators have been fitted also to many British engines of other types. Before this was done, drivers had to rely entirely on their speed sense in reducing speed to conform with speed restrictions over curves or elsewhere; in consequence it was necessary for restrictions to be somewhat more severe than the conditions actually demanded, in order to allow for the probable under-estimation by drivers of the speeds at which they were travelling.

In addition to being deterred from reckless running by his self-recording speed indicator, in normal conditions a French driver is restrained from working his locomotive unduly hard, in the interests of time recovery, by the fact that he and his mate are offered a bonus for coal-saving. The balance between time-recovery and coal-saving bonuses thus encourages French engine-crews to apply the maximum of thought to the handling of their engines, in order to work them as efficiently as possible. Moreover, the systematic training of French drivers, including two years' service as fitters (as mentioned in Chapter 1) has made it possible for French designers to introduce into their locomotives many complications aimed at greater efficiency (of which compounding is one) in the full knowledge that the men will make the best possible use of them.

In Great Britain, as we have seen already, the tendency has been to put simplicity in locomotive design before all other considerations, in view of the varying competence of the men who will have to handle the engines. In this connection, one serious post-war error in Great Britain, arising out of labour shortage, has been the attempt to recruit footplate men for spring, summer and autumn only, when increased traffic requires larger staffs; in this way the more intelligent type of men have been deterred from taking up employment of this kind, owing to its lack of continuity, and maximum simplicity in locomotive handling is thus all the more necessary.   There is a good deal to be said, both for the complication, provided it is accompanied by suitable education and incentive for the men, and, on the other hand, for British simplicity; certainly the latter has been the subject of admiration, from time to time, by Continental visitors to this country.

Much has been done in recent years, under the compulsion of higher speeds and denser traffic, to improve the signal indications, particularly those of distant signals.   Many of these have been moved further out from the boxes that control them, in order to give drivers more space in which to pull up from high speeds if the signal indication is against them.   On the main lines, also, many distant signals have been changed from semaphores to electric colour-light signals, so that they may be visible from a greater distance away.   In addition, continuous colour-light signalling, either manually or electrically operated, and in many cases completely automatic (except at junctions or through station yards), is now in use.   These installations are particularly valuable in foggy or misty weather, as their penetrating beams can be seen from a considerably greater distance than the arms and lights of semaphore signals, whether by day or night.

In Great Britain, in foggy weather, the somewhat archaic method is still in use of warning drivers of adverse signals by the explosion of detonators clipped on the rail by fogmen.   Only on the late Great Western Railway, the Southend line of the late L.M.S.R., and the electrically-operated lines have any automatic train-stopping methods come into use.   On all Western Region main lines, ramps are laid down between the running rails of the track immediately ahead of every distant signal.   Under the cab of each locomotive there is an interceptor, which makes contact with the ramp as the locomotive passes over it.   If the distant signal is "off," the ramp is electrified, and the current causes a bell, mounted inside the cab, to ring.   If the signal is "on," however, the ramp is dead, and the interceptor then sounds a loud warning horn and makes a partial brake application.

The London Midland Region Southend line installation is of an inductive electric type, in which no actual contact is necessary between the locomotive pick-up and the track equipment, but audible warning and an automatic brake application follow the passing of any distant signal at caution.   Similar train control methods are largely in use in France and Germany, and on some of the principal United States main lines the principle if carried even further.   By means of continuous inductive electric currents, a colour-light panel mounted in the engine-cab, in line with the driver's eyes, shows continuous lighting—green **for** "clear," double yellow for "reduce speed," single yellow for a more severe reduction, and red for "stop."

Little has been said in this chapter concerning the working of freight trains. On the slower British freight trains, such as those carrying coal, in loose-coupled wagons without continuous brakes, starting a heavy train is possible only by the fact that, when stopping, the wagons close up to one another; on starting, therefore, the engine pulls the couplings out one by one along the length of the train, so that the load is imposed by degrees on the tender drawbar. Great care has to be taken in working these trains over summits or past the "dips" between two inclines, down and up, where the "snatch" on the couplings may easily pull some of the drawbars out altogether. The faster freight trains, however, have screw couplings and continuous brakes, and their working more resembles that of passenger trains.

In the United States, Canada, France, Germany and other countries, continuous brakes are in universal use on freight stock, and it is possible in these countries to expedite the working of freight accordingly. In America, with the powerful locomotives in use, over suitable routes trains of one hundred or more high-capacity bogie wagons, each carrying from 40 to 70 tons, are by no means uncommon; such a train may weigh up to 7,500 tons behind the engine tender (10,000 tons on some routes), and measure from four-fifths of a mile to more than a mile in length. Radio communication is coming into use increasingly, to enable locomotive drivers to communicate with train crews in the "cabooses" at the rear end of their trains, with receiving and transmitting stations at the lineside, and even with other trains, so greatly increasing the efficiency of train operation, particularly on single lines.

— 11 —

PERFORMANCE—L.M.S.R. PRE-GROUPING
LOCOMOTIVES

WHEN the Twentieth Century opened, speed enterprise among the constituent companies of what later became the London, Midland & Scottish Railway was confined, in the main, to the Midland Railway. The London & North Western and the Caledonian were rather under the shadow of the agreement with the East Coast companies which had been reached shortly after the "Race to Aberdeen" of 1895, that the time of the day trains between London and both Edinburgh and Glasgow should not be cut below a minimum of $8\frac{1}{4}$ hours. So the express services had settled down to a steady but unspectacular progress, in which weight rather than speed was the principal factor influencing locomotive performance.

Before continuing this chapter, it is worth while to recall some of the performances in the "Race to Aberdeen" just mentioned. Seven years earlier, competition between the West Coast (London & North Western & Caledonian) and East Coast (Great Northern, North Eastern and North British) Railways for the Anglo-Scottish traffic had flared up in a contest in speed between London and Edinburgh which continued, on and off, for most of the summer of 1888. But the speeds of the "Race to Edinburgh" pale by comparison with those of the "Race to Aberdeen." The latter was precipitated by the apparently trivial announcement that the night West Coast express from Euston to Aberdeen was to be quickened by 15 minutes. From the opening of the Forth Bridge in 1890, by tacit agreement, the East Coast, with the shorter route, had always been permitted a lead over their rivals, and this acceleration would whittle it down to a mere 5 minutes.

From July, 1895, onwards, acceleration after acceleration was advertised, by one group of railways as against the other, and not only so, but drivers were allowed, and even encouraged, to gain time handsomely. In seven weeks the best West Coast schedule was cut by $2\frac{1}{4}$ hours, and the East Coast by 1 hour, 55 minutes; and on the night of August 22nd-23rd, 1895, a run was made over West Coast metals from Euston to Aberdeen which even yet remains the fastest on record in Great Britain for the distance covered. The load of the train was whittled down to a mere 70 tons; a second train was run to make all the ordinary scheduled stops.

From Euston the Webb 2-2-2-0 compound *Adriatic* took the train over the 158·1 miles to Crewe in 147½ minutes; at Crewe, *Hardwicke*, one of the little 33-ton 2-4-0s of the Webb "Precedent" (colloquially "Jumbo") class, came on, and covered the 141 miles over Shap summit to Carlisle in the remarkable time of 126 minutes (67·2 m.p.h.); from Carlisle the Caledonian took charge, and completed the 150¾ miles over both Beattock and Gleneagles summits to Perth in 149½ minutes (a feat requiring the more expert driving and firing in that no water could be taken *en route*); while the final run was from Perth to Aberdeen, 89¼ miles, in 80½ minutes, at a brilliant start-to-stop average of 66·9 m.p.h. The Caledonian engines used were 4-4-0s of Dugald Drummond's design, with 6 ft. 6 in. driving wheels, 18 in. × 26 in. cylinders, and 150 lb. pressure, precursors of the famous McIntosh "Dunalastair" 4-4-0s, the first of which appeared in 1896.

As typical of the best British locomotive work at the end of last century on any of the constituent lines of the present L.M.S.R., I cannot do better than give details (Table 6) of a run behind one of the original "Dunalastairs," timed about 1896 by the late Charles Rous-Marten. The locomotive concerned had 6 ft.

TABLE 6

YEAR 1896

CALEDONIAN RLY. "DUNALASTAIR I" CLASS (4-4-0)

Engine: 4-4-0 of 721-735 series

Load, 170 tons

Distance		Times
miles		min. sec.
0·0	CARLISLE	0 00
13·0	Kirkpatrick	13 29
25·8	LOCKERBIE	25 50
39·7	BEATTOCK	37 41
49·7	Summit	52 48
63·2	Lamington	63 59
68·5	Thankerton	68 18
73·5	CARSTAIRS	72 01
84·0	Law Junction	82 50
94·3	COATBRIDGE	92 50
109·7	Larbert	107 59
117·8	}STIRLING .. .. .. {	115 28
0·0		0 00
4·9	Dunblane	7 41
7·6	Kinbuck	11 17
17·2	*CRIEFF JUNCTION	21 12
23·4	Dunning	26 27
33·0	PERTH	34 44

* Now Gleneagles

6 in. driving wheels, 18¼ in. × 26 in. cylinders, 160 lb. pressure, and a weight in working order of 47 tons, without tender. Yet, with 170 tons of train, the 10 miles at between 1 in 69 and 1 in 88 from Beattock to Summit were run at an average of 39·8 m.p.h.; from Carlisle start to Beattock, with nearly 12 miles at 1 in 200 against the engine and no pronounced descents, the average rate was 63·3 m.p.h.; and from Summit down to Carstairs the average was no less than 74·3 m.p.h.

With one of the later "140" class of 1904 (the "Dunalastair III" series) Rous-Marten recorded one startling feat. No. 140, after going hard at it up the Clyde valley with a 404-ton train, rushed the final 2½ miles at 1 in 99 to Beattock summit at a steadily-maintained 36 m.p.h., covering the 2·9 miles from Elvanfoot to Summit in 4 minutes

13 seconds. Not less than 1,445 i.h.p. was being developed by this 54½-ton locomotive—a miracle indeed.

On the Midland Railway the 7 ft. 9 in. Johnson single-drivers were doing fine work at the opening of the century, notwithstanding the difficult gradients of the Midland main lines. The late E. L. Ahrons set on record a run from Kettering to Nottingham, with an exceptionally heavy train of 325 tons, which 4-2-2 No. 125 had to tackle unaided owing to no pilot being available. The 5 miles from the dead start at Kettering, with 2½ miles up 1 in 160, took 11 minutes, leaving 48 minutes for the 46½ miles on to Nottingham, including the 8-mile climb from Harringworth viaduct to Oakham, partly at 1 in 167 and 143, and 3¾ miles up at 1 in 200 after the 30 m.p.h. slack over Melton Junction. Yet the single-wheeler lost only 1¼ minutes, and this was due to a slight permanent-way check at Widmerpool. Rous-Marten recorded runs with the same engines in which a load of 160 tons was taken from St. Pancras to Bedford, 49·8 miles, in 53½ minutes, and from there to Leicester, 49·3 miles, in 55½ minutes, the latter including such stiff tests as the 3 miles at 1 in 119 up to Sharnbrook summit. Another of the engines maintained an average of 80 m.p.h. for 13 consecutive miles downhill, and reached a maximum of 90.

London & North Western locomotive performance had few features of note until Francis William Webb retired in 1903, and was succeeded by George Whale. With the emergence of the 6 ft. 9 in. "Precursor" class 4-4-0 locomotives in 1904 and the 6 ft. 3 in. "Experiment" 4-6-0s in the following year, the Webb compound era came to an end. The introduction of restaurant cars and corridor stock was adding greatly to the weight of the trains, and there had been some substantial train service accelerations in 1902, so that the new motive power, simple and straightforward in design, proved an incalculable boon to the operating authorities. But it was not until the Schmidt superheater had made possible the design by Bowen Cooke of the superheated variants of these classes—the "George the Fifth" 4-4-0s in 1910 and the "Prince of Wales" 4-6-0s in 1911—that London & North Western locomotive performance reached its zenith. I had begun in 1908 the regular travelling that occupied the next 38 years of my life, and so made my first considerable use of L.N.W.R. express trains just at this most interesting time in the locomotive history of that company.

A year after *George the Fifth* had emerged from Crewe, I timed a run with an engine of this class which may have been equalled, but I should imagine has never been beaten by a 60-ton locomotive of such modest dimensions. The train was the 10·30 a.m. from Euston to Manchester and Liverpool, made up to 12 vehicles, three of them 12-wheel dining cars, and weighing in all 410 tons. It was a drizzling morning, and as in those days it was the exception rather than the rule to assist outgoing trains up Camden bank, *Wild Duck*, slipping violently on the 1 in 75, finally stalled. Here we stood for 5 minutes, before the services of a "pusher" could be obtained, and as a result passed Willesden Junction 11 minutes late.

From then on the running, set out in Table 7, was of sustained brilliance. Time recovery began at once; by Rugeley all the arrears had been recovered; and but for a check outside Crewe, we should have run in 2 minutes early. From Willesden to milepost 156, a distance of just over 150 miles was run at an average speed of 61·8 m.p.h. by an engine hauling 7½ times its own weight. Long uphill stretches at 1 in 330 were surmounted without the speed falling below 56 to 58 m.p.h.; and several falling grades at the same inclination produced maxima of 75 to 77½ m.p.h., particularly between Cheddington and Wolverton, where we averaged 74·5 m.p.h. for 16·3 miles. Over the run of 158·1 miles from Euston to Crewe the net time was 158 minutes, a superlative achievement. In subsequent correspondence with Mr. Bowen Cooke I ascertained that the coal consumption on this run had averaged no more than 33 lb. per mile; obviously the engine was in superb condition.

TABLE 7

YEAR 1911
L.N.W.R. "GEORGE THE FIFTH" CLASS (4-4-0)
Engine: No. 1595, *Wild Duck*
Load: 389 tons tare, 410 tons gross
Driver: Greenhalgh

Dist.		Sched.	Actual	Speeds
miles		min.	min. sec.	m.p.h.
0·0	EUSTON	0	0 00 stop†	—
1·3	*Milepost 1¼*	—	13 20	—
5·4	WILLESDEN JUNCTION	9	19 55	55½
11·4	Harrow	—	26 25	—
17·4	WATFORD JUNCTION	23	32 55	62½
24·5	Hemel Hempsted ..	—	40 04	—
31·7	TRING	40	47 40	56½
40·2	Leighton	—	54 50	76
46·7	BLETCHLEY	55	60 10	71½
52·4	Wolverton	—	64 50	77¼
59·9	Roade	68	71 40	58½
62·8	BLISWORTH	71	74 35	—
69·7	Weedon	—	80 50	66
75·3	Welton	—	86 15	58
82·6	RUGBY	91	93 30	*32
88·1	Brinklow	—	100 20	—
93·5	Bulkington ..	—	105 50	—
97·1	NUNEATON	107	109 00	75
102·3	Atherstone	—	113 25	—
106·5	Polesworth	—	116 55	75
110·0	TAMWORTH	119	119 50	68
116·3	LICHFIELD	—	125 20	58½
124·3	Rugeley	133	132 55	—
127·2	Colwich	—	135 35	—
133·6	STAFFORD	143	142 15	*40
138·9	Norton Bridge ..	149	148 40	—
143·4	Standon Bridge ..	—	153 40	55½
147·6	Whitmore.. ..	159	157 55	58½
153·3	Betley Road	—	163 20	77½
			sigs.	
158·1	CREWE	171	170 45	—

Net time: 158 min.
* Service slack † Stalled on Camden bank

North of Crewe the "George the Fifth" 4-4-0s showed equal competence. In modern days of Pacific haulage of the West Coast trains, it is strange to recall that 4-4-0 engines could and did haul 400-ton trains over Shap Summit without assistance. Table 8 gives details of one such run, on the then 2 p.m. from Euston (later the

"Midday Scot"), on which No. 1188, *Penmaenmawr*, would have completed the 90·1 miles from Preston to Carlisle in 103 minutes, or slightly less, but for a concluding check, and actually gained a little time on the gruelling climb from Carnforth to Shap Summit. On the last 2 miles of the 12½-mile ascent to Grayrigg, at 1 in 106, the lowest speed was 33 m.p.h., while the 4 miles at 1 in 75 to Shap Summit brought the speed down to 19 m.p.h.

For the period at which they were designed, the contemporary "Prince of Wales" class 4-6-0 engines were probably the speediest locomotives in the country with driving wheels as small in diameter as 6 ft. 3 in. Late in 1914 I had a run on what later became the up "Mancunian"—9·45 a.m. from Manchester to Euston—in which No. 2293, *Percy Bysshe Shelley*, with a train of 215 tons, covered the 176·9 miles from Wilmslow to London in a net time of 170 minutes. Though we left Wilmslow 4 minutes late, and had a stop of just over 2 minutes at Armitage, not to mention permanent-way slowings at Tamworth and Chalk Farm, we were into Euston 4 minutes early. There were sustained speeds of 71½ m.p.h. on the level, 75 m.p.h. on 1 in 505 down, and 77½ on 1 in 335 down. From Welton to Willesden we ran the 69·9 miles in 62 minutes 5 seconds, at an average speed of 67·6 m.p.h., and went up the long 1 in 333 to Tring at a minimum of 57½ m.p.h.

As an example of what the "Prince of Wales" 4-6-0s could do with heavy trains, the run shown in Table 9, with a 60-axle train of 465 tons, may be cited. In this case the 15-miles climb, 6 miles at 1 in 333, from Bletchley up to Tring, was completed in 16 minutes 28 seconds, with a minimum speed of 49 m.p.h., and down to Watford and past Harrow a maximum of 74 m.p.h. was reached. To cover the 69·9 miles from Welton to Willesden in 67 minutes 35 seconds, with this 465-ton load, *plus* 40-ton tender, was an outstanding effort for a locomotive of but

TABLE 8

YEAR 1914
L.N.W.R. "GEORGE THE FIFTH" CLASS (4-4-0)
Engine: No. 1188, *Penmaenmawr*
Load: 372 tons tare, 390 tons gross

Dist.				Sched.	Actual		Speeds
miles				min.	min.	sec.	m.p.h.
0·0	PRESTON	..	..	0	0	00	—
4·8	Barton	..	..	—	8	20	—
12·7	Scorton	..	..	—	16	40	61
21·0	LANCASTER	..	..	23	25	10	—
24·1	Hest Bank..	..	..	—	27	45	74
27·3	CARNFORTH	..	..	30	30	30	—
30·5	*Milepost 9½*	..	..	—	—		53
34·6	Milnthorpe	..	..	—	37	30	65
40·1	OXENHOLME	..	..	44	43	50	—
47·2	Grayrigg	..	..	—	55	05	33
53·2	TEBAY	..	..	62	61	40	62½
58·7	*Shap Summit*	..	..	72	72	15	19
60·7	Shap	..	..	—	75	15	†83½
72·2	PENRITH..	..	..	86	85	05	*50
79·3	Calthwaite	..	..	—	92	15	—
85·2	Wreay	..	..	—	97	30	74
					p.w.s.		
90·1	CARLISLE..	..	..	104	103	55	—

Net time: 103 min.

* Service slack   † At Clifton and Lowther

66 tons weight. The engine concerned was No. 160, *King of Serbia*, and the tare load exceeded by 34 tons the 400-ton maximum laid down for this class at that time.

Much was hoped of the four-cylinder "Claughton" 4-6-0 locomotives when Bowen Cooke introduced them to the L.N.W.R. in 1913, especially as it was expected that the design would profit from the lessons learned in the running of the G.W.R. 4-6-0 *Polar Star* over L.N.W.R. metals two years earlier. Unfortunately, however, when the new engines emerged, it was found that the working pressure was only 175 lb. as compared with the G.W.R. 225 lb.; that long-travel long-lap valves had not been provided, so that short cut-off working with full regulator would be impossible; and that, owing to weight limitations, the boiler was on the small side in relation to the cylinder volume. Consequently, as mentioned already in Chapter 1, the engines were uncertain in their work, and seldom did any better than the considerably lighter "George" 4-4-0s and "Prince" 4-6-0s. Officially, the 400-ton maximum tonnage rating of the latter was not increased to more than 420 tons for the "Claughtons."

Nevertheless, some exceptional runs were put up by the "Claughtons" when they were in first-class condition, fresh from the shops. Probably the most notable performance that I ever recorded with one of them was when the first of the series, No. 2222, *Sir Gilbert Claughton*, was less than a year old, and, I must confess it followed a preliminary conversation with the crew. With Driver John Ford, of Crewe, at the regulator, and a 44-axle train of 310 tons behind the tender, from the dead start at Oxenholme the engine attained 48 m.p.h. up 5 miles at 1 in 106-120-133, fell back to 46½ on the final 2 miles at 1 in 106 to Grayrigg, attained 75 on the 5½ miles "breathing space" from Grayrigg to Tebay (but little easier than level), and finally breasted Shap Summit, after climbing 1½ miles at 1 in 147 and 4 miles at 1 in 75, at a minimum of 38 m.p.h. The entire ascent of 18.6 miles from the

TABLE 9

YEAR 1915

L.N.W.R. "PRINCE OF WALES" CLASS (4-6-0)

Engine No. 160, *King of Serbia*

Load: 434 tons tare, 465 tons gross

Dist.					Times	Speeds
miles					min. sec.	m.p.h.
0·0	RUGBY ..	..	..	..	0 00	—
7·3	Welton ..	..	..	..	12 04	—
12·9	Weedon ..	..	..	..	17 11	71
19·8	BLISWORTH	..	..	..	23 29	—
22·7	Roade ..	..	..	..	26 30	57
30·2	Wolverton	..	..	..	33 15	72
35·9	BLETCHLEY	..	..	..	38 45	—
42·4	Leighton ..	..	..	..	45 29	—
46·5	Cheddington	..	..	..	49 55	—
50·9	TRING ..	..	..	..	55 13	49
58·1	Hemel Hempsted	..	..	..	62 20	—
65·2	WATFORD JUNCTION		..	..	68 27	74
71·2	Harrow ..	..	..	..	73 51	74
					sigs.	
77·2	WILLESDEN JUNCTION		..	..	79 39	—
82·6	EUSTON	..	..	..	88 08	—

Net time: 87 min.

Oxenholme start to the summit was thus completed in 23 minutes 11 seconds. I have never personally recorded a better time than this over the stretch of line concerned, from a start at Oxenholme, in ordinary passenger service.

In the same year, 1913, a brilliant test run was made with No. 1159, *Ralph Brocklebank*, when a 360-ton train was taken from Crewe to Carlisle, 141·0 miles, in 142½ minutes, or 140½ minutes net. The times set out in Table 10 were those recorded in the dynamometer car, to the nearest quarter-minute. It is evident by the rapid recovery from all slacks that the engine was being driven "all out," as equally from the minimum speed of 37 m.p.h. at Shap Summit. A misfortune was the severe signal check on Grayrigg bank, which brought the speed down from 47 to 17 m.p.h.; but for this, the climb of 31·4 miles from roughly sea level at Carnforth to the 915 ft. altitude of Shap would have been completed in about 33 minutes. All service slacks were most carefully observed, and the run reflected great credit on the handling of the engine by Driver Hardstaff of Crewe, who was responsible.

TABLE 10

YEAR 1913
L.N.W.R. "CLAUGHTON" CLASS (4-6-0)
Engine No. 1159, *Ralph Brocklebank*
Load: 343 tons tare, 360 tons gross
Driver: J. Hardstaff (Crewe)

Dist.				Times	Speeds
miles				min. sec.	m.p.h.
0·0	CREWE ..	..	..	0 00	
4·8	Minshull Vernon	..	..	7 00	65
11·8	Hartford ..	..	..	12 45	77¼
16·2	Weaver Junction..	..	..	16 15	*58
21·2	Moore ..	..	..	20 45	76
24·0	WARRINGTON	..	..	23 15	*55
31·0	Golborne	..	..	30 00	64/59
35·8	WIGAN ..	..	..	34 15	71¼
38·1	Boar's Head	..	..	36 30	55
41·6	Coppull ..	..	..	40 15	58½/55
44·2	Balshaw Lane	..	..	42 15	76
45·5	Euxton Junction ..	..	..	43 15	*58
48·6	Farington	..	..	46 15	70¼
50·9	PRESTON	..	..	49 15	*25
55·7	Barton ..	..	..	55 30	62¼
60·4	Garstang..	..	..	59 45	70¼
67·6	Galgate ..	..	..	66 00	68
71·9	LANCASTER	..	..	70 00	*51
75·0	Hest Bank	..	..	72 45	73
78·2	CARNFORTH ..	..	..	75 30	66
82·7	Burton ..	..	..	79 30	59
85·5	Milnthorpe	..	..	82 00	72
91·0	OXENHOLME ..	..	..	87 15	54
				sigs.	47/17
98·1	Grayrigg..	..	..	97 30	—
104·1	Tebay ..	..	..	103 45	70
109·6	Shap Summit	..	..	110 30	37
118·9	Clifton ..	..	..	120 15	·67
123·1	PENRITH	..	..	124 30	*50/70
141·0	CARLISLE	..	..	142 30	—

Net time: 140½ min.
* Service slack

Up to the formation of the London Midland & Scottish Railway in 1923, the neighbouring Midland Railway depended for the principal express duties on its compound 4-4-0 locomotives. After the grouping many more of these engines were built. Although actually there was need for considerably more powerful motive power units than these, on the basis of economical running the compounds had certainly justified themselves as compared with other contemporary classes in the L.M.S.R. group.

The paper entitled "A Modern Locomotive History," read by Mr.

E. S. Cox before the Institution of Locomotive Engineers in January, 1946, revealed that in comparative tests between Crewe, Preston and Carlisle, the compounds burned 0·087 lb. of coal per ton-mile as compared with 0·105 lb. by the "Prince of Wales" 4-6-0s and 0·112 lb. by the Caledonian "60" class 4-6-0s; per drawbar-h.p.-hr. the relative consumptions were 4·06 lb., 5·07 lb., and 5·19 lb. Over three years of observation, from 1928 to 1930, the average coal consumptions per train-mile of the three classes were 46·5, 51·1 and 66·3 lb., and of the L.N.W.R. "George the Fifth" 4-4-0s 56·4 lb., though these last figures do not take into account train loads or average speeds. Moreover, the Midland compounds were relatively light on repairs, their index cost of 136 comparing with the 149 of the "George the Fifth" and the 157 of the "Prince of Wales" classes.

For a time, therefore, the Midland compounds spread their activities over a large part of the L.M.S.R. system, and it has always been my opinion that much of their best work was done off the Midland lines on which the design originated, and particularly in Scotland. On the Western Division lines (previously L.N.W.R.) the drivers, accustomed for many years to the long cut-off and partially open regulator methods compelled by L.N.W.R. design and valve-setting, found it by no means easy to settle down to compound working, and to the niceties of handling the Deeley regulator, which when opened to the first port only admitted high-pressure steam direct to the low-pressure cylinders. Later on, however, and particularly on the 2-hour trains between Euston and Birmingham, there were performances which ranked with the foremost 4-4-0 locomotive work of the period.

One such, in 1929, appears in Table 11. Allowing for the Watford delay, the compound 4-4-0 ran to Coventry in a net time (91¾ minutes for the 94·0 miles) which equalled the schedule allowance of the much

TABLE II

YEAR 1929
MIDLAND COMPOUND CLASS (4-4-0)
Engine: No. 1053
Load: 259 tons tare, 275 tons gross

Dist.		Sched.	Times	Speeds
miles		min.	min. sec.	m.p.h.
0·0	EUSTON	0	0 00	—
5·4	WILLESDEN JUNCTION..	9	9 00	59
11·4	Harrow	—	15 00	62
			sigs.	35
17·4	WATFORD JUNCTION ..	22	21 35	25
			p.w.s.	
20·9	King's Langley	—	27 00	—
24·5	Hemel Hempsted	—	31 00	56
28·0	Berkhamsted	—	34 40	58½
31·7	TRING	37	38 30	61
36·1	Cheddington	—	42 20	75
40·2	Leighton	—	45 35	77½
46·7	BLETCHLEY	51	50 55	72
50·0	*Milepost 50*	—	53 45	69
52·4	Wolverton	—	55 40	75
59·9	Roade	63	62 40	57½
62·8	BLISWORTH	66	65 30	66
69·7	Weedon	—	71 25	72½
75·3	Welton	—	76 30	61½
82·6	RUGBY	85	83 20	*35
89·1	Brandon	—	90 00	70
90·0	*Milepost 90*	—	90 47	71
94·0	COVENTRY	97	95 05	—

Net time, 91¾ min.   * Service slack

more powerful three-cylinder 4-6-0s when the service was accelerated in 1935. Features of note were the acceleration up 1 in 335 from 25 m.p.h. at Watford to 58½ m.p.h. at Berkhamsted, where the speed was still inclined to rise; then followed the average of 72·3 m.p.h. for 20·7 miles from Tring to Wolverton, while for 43·6 miles, from Tring to Welton, a mean speed of 68·8 m.p.h. was kept up. On the level, betwen Rugby and Coventry, 71 m.p.h. was attained.

A better example could not have been found of the work of a Midland compound fully extended than that in Table 12. On the 106-minute booking from St. Pancras to Leicester that preceded the introduction in 1937 of the accelerated schedules, and to maintain which in earlier days these 4-4-0s were limited to a maximum tare load of 240 tons, No. 1086 had to tackle an eleven-coach train weighing 329 tons tare and 350 tons gross—a most formidable proposition over such gradients. Yet, by superb handling of his engine, Driver Coyne of Millhouses shed (Sheffield) just succeeded in keeping time. Naturally, there was a loss of time to Luton; the engine surmounted the long 1 in 176 climbs to Elstree tunnel and past St. Albans at minimum speeds of 45

TABLE 12

YEAR 1936
MIDLAND COMPOUND CLASS (4-4-0)
Engine No. 1086
Load: 329 tons tare, 350 tons gross
Driver Coyne (Millhouses)

Dist.		Sched.	Actual		Speeds
miles		min.	min.	sec.	m.p.h.
0·0	ST. PANCRAS	0	0	00	—
1·5	Kentish Town	4	4	17	—
6·9	HENDON	10	12	23	57½
12·4	Elstree	—	18	42	45
15·2	Radlett	—	21	34	67½
19·9	ST. ALBAN'S	25	26	09	47
24·6	Harpenden	—	31	36	—
30·2	LUTON	35	37	01	67
32·8	Leagrave	—	39	25	64
37·3	Harlington	—	43	18	—
41·8	Ampthill	—	46	46	80/75
49·8	BEDFORD	52	53	32	77
53·0	Oakley	—	56	44	60
56·6	Sharnbrook	—	60	24	—
59·8	Milepost 59¾	63	64	17	42
65·0	WELLINGBOROUGH	68	69	08	72/66
68·2	Finedon	—	72	29	—
72·0	KETTERING	75	75	49	59
78·5	Desborough North	—	83	33	45
82·9	MARKET HARBOROUGH	88	88	00	68/*53
86·3	East Langton	—	91	32	62
89·7	Kibworth North	—	95	10	47
95·4	Wigston Magna	—	100	30	70/*60
99·1	LEICESTER	106	106	10	—

* Service slack

and 47 m.p.h. respectively, and did not get above 67 on the short downhill stretches. But 80 m.p.h. was attained on the descent to Bedford, where the lost time had almost all been regained. Further fine feats were the minimum of 42 m.p.h. up the 3¼ miles at 1 in 119 to Sharnbrook summit, and of 45 up the 9-mile climb to Desborough, finishing at about 1 in 130. It will be noted that the 88·5 miles from Hendon to Wigston Magna were run in 88 minutes 7 seconds, a magnificent achievement for this 60-ton locomotive with such a load.

One final Midland compound performance requires mention, not so much from the standpoint of speed as that of endurance. Before the general acceleration that began in 1932, competition between the East and West Coast railways, by then the L.N.E.R. and L.M.S.R., had developed into a test as to which could table the longest runs without intermediate stop. By 1927 the L.M.S.R. was covering the 299 miles between Euston and Carlisle without a stop, and the L.N.E.R. had announced, accordingly, that from May 1st, 1928, the "Flying Scotsman" would make a daily non-stop journey over the 392¾ miles between King's Cross and Edinburgh. To this announcement the L.M.S.R., which could not follow suit without a daily division of its "Royal Scot" into independent Glasgow and Edinburgh portions, made a character-istic and rather diverting reply. Very secretly, arrangements were made on the preceding Friday, April 27th, to divide the "Royal Scot" in this way for one day only. A good deal of the L.N.E.R. thunder was stolen by this demonstration that both the 401·4-mile run from Euston to Glasgow and the 399·7-mile journey from Euston to Edinburgh—each of them longer than the L.N.E.R. 392·7 miles—could be made without any intermediate stop if the L.M.S.R. so desired.

While the eight-coach Glasgow section had the services of a "Royal Scot" 4-6-0 (No. 6113, *Cameronian*), the six-coach Edinburgh section was worked through by Midland compound 4-4-0 No. 1054, which was fitted for the occasion with a tender of more than the normal coal capacity. For the run the compound, with a gross load of about 190 tons, took 8 hours, 11 minutes and the average speed was thus 48·6 m.p.h. The journey was completed on a coal consumption of no more than 35 lb. per mile, and great credit attaches to Fireman A. Pink in that he was able to maintain a clean fire, for more than 8 hours of continuous steaming, on a grate with an area no larger than 28·4 sq. ft. The regulator was shared between Drivers G. T. Stones and D. Gibson. This was by far the longest non-stop run that has ever been made by a 4-4-0 locomotive in Great Britain.

Before leaving the pre-grouping designs of the L.M.S.R., I must mention a journey with a notable class of locomotive on the late Lancashire & Yorkshire Railway. Much of the passenger traffic of this company, over exceedingly steep grades and slack-infested routes, was entrusted to 2-4-2 tank engines, and probably the most onerous duty that fell to them was that of working the principal afternoon express train northwards from Salford to Colne. For 20 miles from the start, this line is almost continuously uphill; 4 miles from Salford, after slowing for Clifton Junction, there is a climb of 2 miles at 1 in 96; a mile short of Bury and 9 miles after starting, there begins a 1 in 119-140 rise which continues for most of the next 6 miles; and finally, from Stubbins Junction, there is the arduous ascent of 5 miles at 1 in 66-81 to Baxenden summit. In the 27·9 miles from Salford to Burnley the train must be lifted through a difference in level of roughly 750 ft.

The superheated version of the Aspinall 2-4-2 tank design has 20½ in. × 26 in. cylinders, 5 ft. 8 in. driving wheels, no more than 18·8 sq. ft. of firegrate, 180 lb. pressure, and a weight in working order of 66½ tons—modest dimensions indeed for working a load of ten bogie vehicles over such a road. Nevertheless, as may be seen in Table 13, Driver Turner and No. 1532 took their 255-ton load up the 1 in 96 incline to Ringley Road with no greater drop in speed than from 40 to 34 m.p.h.; a rate of 39 m.p.h. was continued steadily up the 1 in 128 past Ramsbottom; and mile after mile of the 1 in 66-81 was climbed at between 29½ and 28½ m.p.h.. On the short level stretches the engine got up to 55 and 57 m.p.h., so that eventually Driver Turner gained 4 minutes net on the 49-minute schedule.

Shortly afterwards I made a run on the footplate of the same engine, with an equal load, when Driver Shorrocks achieved times all but as good; the climb to Ringley Road was made on 40 to 45 per cent. cut-off, and from Ramsbottom to Baxenden on 50 to 55 per cent., in both cases with full regulator. We finished the last exacting effort with pressure no lower than 160 lb., and with between 2 and 3 inches of water still showing in the "glass." On such a run as this, the driver must be cautious about even so trivial a happening as running over the level crossing at Helmshore, where heavy road traffic makes the rails greasy, and may cause the engine to slip in the middle of the worst ascent. Another variety of slipping on this run that always intrigued me was the slipping of coaches at Accrington, round a platform curve so sharp that three men had to be stationed on the platform for the purpose of signalling triangularly to the driver that he really had lost the last two vehicles of his train!

TABLE 13

YEAR 1922
L. & Y.-R. 2-4-2 TANK CLASS
Engine No. 1532
† Load: 229 tons tare; 255 tons gross
Driver Turner (Agecroft)

Dist.		Sched.	Actual	Speeds
miles		min.	min. sec.	m.p.h.
0·0	SALFORD	0	0 00	—
1·7	Pendleton	—	4 10	45
3·9	Clifton Junction..	7	7 30	40*
6·4	Ringley Road ..	—	11 30	34
8·1	Radcliffe North Junction	—	13 40	55
			sigs.	40
9·9	BURY	17	15 55	45
12·5	Summerseat	—	19 30	41
13·9	Ramsbottom	23	21 40	39
			sigs.	33
14·6	Stubbins Junction ..	—	22 45	39
16·8	Helmshore	—	26 45	29
18·7	Haslingden	—	30 55	29½
20·0	Baxenden	—	33 30	28½
22·2	ACCRINGTON† ..	40	37 25	10*
23·9	Huncoat	—	40 25	—
25·3	Hapton	—	42 05	57
26·8	Rose Grove	46	43 45	45*
27·9	BURNLEY BARRACKS	49	45 55	—

Net time: 45 min.

* Service slack † Two coaches slipped at Accrington; load forward, 200 tons gross

12

PERFORMANCE—THE L.M.S.R. UNDER FOWLER
AND STANIER

IN 1927, after the formation of the L.M.S.R., the "Royal Scot" 4-6-0 design appeared. Dynamometer car tests between Euston and Carlisle showed that the new locomotives could maintain the 52 m.p.h. schedules of the period, with 440-ton trains, on a coal consumption of about 37 lb. per mile, or 3·25 lb. per drawbar-h.p.-hr. On a test run between Euston and Crewe, No. 6100, *Royal Scot*, worked a train of 509 tons in each direction at an average speed of 53·9 m.p.h., on 45·4 lb. of coal per mile, or 2·93 lb. per drawbar-h.p.-hr., whereas a "Claughton" 4-6-0 with 380 tons needed 46·6 lb. per mile, or 5·02 lb. per drawbar-h.p.-hr.; and on similar tests between Crewe and Carlisle, the coal consumed per 1,000 ton-miles was 76 lb. with the "Royal Scot" class, 87 lb. with Midland compound 4-4-0s, and 104 lb. with 4-6-0 "Claughtons." This time the lessons learned in a second exchange of locomotives with the G.W.R., when the latter's *Launceston Castle* came over to the L.M.S.R. for test runs between Euston and Carlisle in 1926, had been learned and applied, and the results were obvious in the economical running of the "Scots."

But it was a matter of years before they settled down to the quality of performance that they displayed in the years up to the Second World War. This was often brilliant, as in the run set out in Table 14. It was made on the 4·10 p.m. express from Manchester to Euston, in 1939, when that train had to cover the 36.5 miles from Stafford to Nuneaton in 38 minutes, start to stop, and to continue over the 97.1 miles to Euston in 92 minutes. Yet, in the capable hands of L. A. Earl, of Camden, a master of his craft, the "Royal Scot" with an 11-coach train of 375 tons bettered the schedule from Stafford by fully 8½ minutes. The most energetic stretch of running was over the 69·9 miles from Welton to Willesden, covered in 54 minutes 47 seconds, at an average of 76·8 m.p.h. throughout; out of this the most impressive stretch was the 15·0 miles from Bletchley up to Tring, which was actually completed in 12 minutes 4 seconds, at all but 75 m.p.h., and with a minimum speed of 68 m.p.h. up to the summit. On this run the schedule of the "Coronation Scot" streamliner, due in Euston 13 minutes later, was being improved on, though with a 4-6-0 locomotive as against a Pacific, and with 60 tons more of train. This run was timed by Mr. R. E. Charlewood.

Mention should be made here of one of the earliest essays of the L.M.S.R. in really high speed running, which took place on 19th and 20th September, 1933, and in which "Royal Scot" locomotives were concerned. Special trains conveying guests of the Humber-Hillman-Commer Company were being run between Euston and Coventry, and although no tighter times than 90 minutes down and 88 minutes up had been laid down for the 94-mile journey, drivers had been given a fairly free hand as to running ahead of schedule. As a result, engine No. 6129, *Comet*, with a light load of seven coaches weighing 212 tons gross, came up from Coventry to Euston in 79 minutes 1 second notwithstanding a dead stand for signals on Camden bank, and a couple of slight checks earlier in the run. Tremendous speeds were made—90 m.p.h. before Weedon, 80 minimum at Roade, 92 at Castlethorpe, a minimum of 82 through Cheddington before the first signal check, 90 at King's Langley, and 91½ at Wembley. From Welton to Willesden 69¾ miles were covered in 50 minutes 53 seconds or very little over 49 minutes net, at an average of just over 85 m.p.h. Marchant and Aldridge were the driver and fireman respectively.

TABLE 14

YEAR 1939
L.M.S.R. "ROYAL SCOT" CLASS (4-6-0)
Engine No. 6125, 3rd Carabinier
Load: 356 tons tare, 375 tons gross
Driver: L. A. Earl (Camden)

Dist.				Sched.	Actual		Speeds
miles				min.	min.	sec.	m.p.h.
0·0	STAFFORD	..	..	0	0	00	—
4·1	Milford			—	6	43	60
9·3	Rugeley	..		11	11	20	74
17·3	LICHFIELD			18	17	51	72/†82
23·6	TAMWORTH			24	22	35	75
31·3	Atherstone			—	29	11	64
					sigs.		
35·6	*Milepost 98*			—	33	10	—
36·5	}NUNEATON	..	{	38	35	10	—
0·0				0	0	00	—
3·6	Bulkington			—	6	35	54
5·1	*Milepost 92*			—	8	07	60
9·0	Brinklow	..		—	11	27	75
13·9	*Rugby No. 7*			—	15	30	*50
14·5	RUGBY	..		16	16	31	*41
21·8	Welton			—	24	33	‡60
27·4	Weedon ..			—	28	58	78½
34·3	BLISWORTH			34	34	23	75
37·2	Roade	..		37	36	50	68
44·7	Wolverton			—	42	23	§85
50·4	BLETCHLEY			48	46	52	75/76½
56·9	Leighton ..			—	51	55	75/78
61·0	Cheddington			—	55	06	73
65·4	TRING	..		62	58	56	68
69·1	Berkhamsted			—	62	02	77
79·7	WATFORD			74	69	51	‖83½
83·8	Hatch End			—	73	13	—
89·0	Wembley ..			—	77	17	82
91·7	WILLESDEN JUNCTION			84	79	20	77½
96·1	*Milepost 1* ..			—	84	19	—
97·1	EUSTON ..	..	..	92	86	47	—

* Service slack   † At Hademore troughs
‡ On entering Kilsby tunnel
§ At Castlethorpe   ‖ At King's Langley

Even more meritorious, in view of a much heavier load of 335 tons (eleven coaches) was the feat of Driver J. Jones and Fireman Charge in making a net time of 77 minutes; on this latter trip the 69¾ miles from Welton to Willesden occupied 51 minutes, 47 seconds—exactly three minutes less than Earl's time in the run just previously described, but with 40 tons less of train—which involved an average speed of 80·8 m.ph. for this distance. In the reverse direction, on these special trips of 1933, the best time with the 335-ton train also was made by

Earl; notwithstanding a loss of 2 minutes by signals after Tring, Rugby, 82½ miles, was passed in 76 minutes 3 seconds, and Coventry was reached in 87 minutes 8 seconds, or 85 minutes net. These runs were timed by Mr. R. E. Charlewood and Mr. D. S. M. Barrie.

The most spectacular performances in L.M.S.R. locomotive history have been made since the introduction of the Stanier Pacifics in 1933. Among these were the runs made by *Princess Elizabeth*, one of the original "Princess Royal" series, on November 16th-17th, 1936, on certain trials between Euston and Glasgow preparatory to the inauguration of the "Coronation Scot" in the following year. As has often been the case with test runs on the L.M.S.R., performances were planned and carried out which in scope were far outside anything that would be needed in normal running. Thus, although the streamline train, when it entered service, had a 6½-hour schedule in each direction, inclusive of a 2-minute stop at Carlisle, the test runs were arranged to be made in six hours flat each way, non-stop over the distance of 401·4 miles. Actually this schedule was

TABLE 15

YEAR 1936
L.M.S.R. "PRINCESS ROYAL" CLASS (4-6-2)
Engine No. 6201, *Princess Elizabeth*
Driver: T. J. Clarke; Fireman: C. Fleet (Crewe)

	Load, tons tare Load, tons gross		225 230		255 260
Dist.		Sched.	Actual	Sched.	Actual
miles		min.	min. sec.	min.	min. sec.
0·0	EUSTON ..	0	0 00	360	344 15
5·4	Willesden Junc. ..	8	7 24	352	335 45
			p.w.s.		p.w.s.
8·1	Wembley ..	—	10 38	—	332 38
17·4	WATFORD ..	18	18 55	342	325 38
31·7	Tring ..	30	29 55	331	315 30
46·7	BLETCHLEY ..	41	40 32	318	304 27
59·9	Roade ..	51	50 53	308	294 33
69·7	Weedon ..	—	58 19	—	287 08
82·6	RUGBY* ..	70	68 33	289	276 05
97·1	Nuneaton ..	82	81 08	277	264 33
106·5	Polesworth ..	—	88 22	—	257 00
110·0	Tamworth ..	95	92 53	264	252 58
124·3	Rugeley ..	106	103 36	253	242 25
133·6	STAFFORD* ..	114	111 52	245	233 46
147·6	Whitmore ..	127	123 47	233	222 53
158·1	CREWE ..	136	132 52	223	213 17
174·3	*Weaver Junction* ..	149	146 00	209	200 37
182·1	WARRINGTON	156	153 30	202	193 34
193·9	WIGAN ..	168	164 55	190	182 42
209·0	PRESTON* ..	183	179 15	175	168 55
218·5	Garstang ..	191½	188 05	167	161 00
230·0	LANCASTER ..	200	196 35	158	152 07
236·3	Carnforth ..	205	201 28	153	147 12
249·1	Oxenholme ..	215	211 38	143	137 18
256·2	Grayrigg ..	—	218 04	—	131 22
262·2	Tebay ..	227	223 05	132	126 15
267·7	*Shap Summit* ..	233	228 12	127	121 50
281·2	Penrith ..	245	240 05	114	109 15
294·2	Wreay ..	—	250 00	—	99 12
299·1	CARLISLE* ..	260	255 24	97	93 20
307·7	Gretna ..	268	263 27	90	86 10
324·9	Lockerbie ..	282	277 40	77	72 49
338·8	Beattock ..	293	287 35	66	62 29
348·8	Beattock Summit..	306	297 06	57	54 20
			p.w.s.		
362·3	Lamington ..	—	309 25	—	43 17
372·6	CARSTAIRS* ..	328	319 30	33	34 30
377·6	*Craigenhill Summit*	—	324 44	—	30 16
383·1	Law Junction ..	338	329 38	22	24 30
			p.w.s.		p.w.s.
388·5	MOTHERWELL..	344	336 34	16	16 50
			p.w.s.		p.w.s.
394·8	Newton* ..	—	339 50	—	9 05
400·4	Eglinton Street ..	—	351 06	—	2 28
401·4	GLASGOW CTL.	360	353 38	0	0 00

* Speed reduced to 35 m.p.h. or less

p.w.s.—permanent-way speed restriction, 35 m.p.h. or less

improved on by 6½ minutes going north, with a seven-coach load of 230 tons; on the following day, with load increased to 260 tons by the addition of an eighth coach, and in wet and stormy weather with a strong side-wind, the schedule was cut by 15¾ minutes to 5 hours 44 minutes 15 seconds, with the result that the extraordinary average of 70 m.p.h. was maintained over the entire journey, Beattock and Shap summits included.

Table 15 gives the times of both these historic runs. As yet little had been done towards the improvement of curve alignments and the laying in of "two-level" junctions, with the result that slacks of varying severity were imposed at about fifty different locations in each direction, additional to the regular service slacks at Rugby, Crewe, Preston, Carlisle and elsewhere. The general limit of speed was 90 m.p.h., though this was slightly exceeded on the down journey with $95\frac{1}{2}$ m.p.h. beyond Cheddington, and $93\frac{1}{2}$ at Betley Road, south of Crewe.

Some amazing feats of climbing were performed. Long stretches at 1 in 335-326 to Tring and Roade were surmounted at 77 m.p.h. The 31·4 miles from Carnforth, roughly at sea level, to Shap Summit were run in 26 minutes 44 seconds, at an *average* of 70·1 m.p.h.; passing Milnthorpe at $85\frac{1}{2}$ m.p.h., *Princess Elizabeth* went right up the $12\frac{1}{2}$-mile bank to Grayrigg, finishing at 1 in 106, without speed falling below $66\frac{1}{2}$ m.p.h., and then attained $78\frac{1}{2}$ on the short falling stretch to Tebay; finally the 4 miles at 1 in 75 to Shap Summit reduced the speed to 57 m.p.h. The assault on Beattock was no less memorable, for the engine ran the 49·7 miles from passing Carlisle, a little above sea level, to the 1,014 ft. altitude of Beattock summit at a mean speed of 71·5 m.p.h. The two long stretches at 1 in 200 to Brackenhill summit were surmounted at from 70 to 75 m.p.h., and after 90 m.p.h. on the level beyond Lockerbie, the engine climbed a third 1 in 200, to Beattock station, at a minimum of 80 m.p.h. before tackling Beattock bank proper. The whole 10 miles, inclined at 1 in 69 to 1 in 88, were completed in 9 minutes 31 seconds, at more than a mile-a-minute average, and the summit was cleared at 57 m.p.h., an unprecedented feat.

In view of the bad weather conditions, the increased load, and the shorter overall time of the run, the following day's performance was even more startling. Among its high lights were the acceleration, partly up 1 in 100, from a 40 m.p.h. slack through Law Junction to $62\frac{1}{2}$ over Craigenhill summit; then a speed rising to 80 m.p.h. by Elvanfoot, up the gentle grades of the upper Clyde valley, with a minimum of $66\frac{1}{2}$ m.p.h. on the final $2\frac{1}{2}$ miles at 1 in 99 to Beattock summit. From Carlisle, passed very slowly, to the 914 ft. altitude of Shap, the average speed was 66·2 m.p.h., and included an acceleration up 1 in 131 (Carlisle to Wreay) from 20 to 65 m.p.h., and up 7 miles of 1 in 125 (from below Clifton nearly to Shap) from 55 to 64 m.p.h. Between Winsford and Coppenhall junction, near Crewe, a speed ranging from 90 to 95 m.p.h. was kept up on level track. Up the 1 in

370 from Rugby, passed slowly, to Kilsby tunnel, speed rose from 35 to 75 m.p.h., and Tring summit was breasted at 77½; maxima were reached of 91 m.p.h. at Lichfield, 90 at Castlethorpe and 91 at Kings Langley.

It is of interest to note that whereas the coal consumption of *Princess Elizabeth* going north was 46·8 lb. per mile, in the more difficult conditions of the record southbound run this figure was reduced to 44·8 lb. per mile; for this reduction, Fireman Fleet, who had a very tough assignment on these two days, deserved every credit. Notwithstanding the times made, the engine was far from being driven "full out." Going north, the ascent of Shap was made at from 25 to 32 per cent. cut-off, with full regulator, and that of Beattock required 30 to 37½ per cent.; in the reverse direction 20 to 28 per cent. was used from Lamington to Beattock summit and 30 to 35 per cent. from Clifton up to Shap. At the times of maximum effort on these climbs, the highest indicated horsepowers recorded in the dynamometer car were from 2,340 to 2,450.

The next performance event of note immediately preceded the introduction of the "Coronation Scot." A Press trip was arranged on June 29th, 1937, from Euston to Crewe and back, with the new streamline Pacific No. 6220, *Coronation*, and the new train, less one of the two kitchen cars, making a load of 270 tons behind the tender. On the down journey it had been arranged that Driver Clarke, of Crewe, should work to the schedule times of the "special" as far as Stafford, but after that he would be permitted to see what speed the engine could develop down the falling gradient from Whitmore towards Crewe. The power of the new locomotive was apparent in such sustained speeds as 82 m.p.h. up the 1 in 339 past Hatch End, and over 80 all the way from Watford up to Tring, but speed was not allowed to exceed 87½ m.p.h. at any point. So the express passed Watford, 17·4 miles from Euston, in 17 minutes 2 seconds; Tring, 31·7 miles, in 27 minutes 45 seconds; Bletchley, 46·7 miles, in 38 minutes 57 seconds; Rugby, 82·6 miles, in 66 minutes 28 seconds; and Stafford, 133·6 miles, in 109 minutes 56 seconds.

Until that date, the highest recorded speeds in Great Britain had been those reached on special occasions by the L.N.E.R. "Silver Jubilee" streamliner—112½ m.p.h. on September 27th, 1935, and 113 m.p.h. on August 27th, 1936—and there was little doubt that the L.M.S.R. authorities were bent on beating these figures. The only section of line with alignment and gradients suitable for the purpose was the descent northwards from Whitmore, which for some distance is down at 1 in 177. On the gentle rise between Standon Bridge and

Whitmore, therefore, the engine was opened out, so that Whitmore was passed at 85 m.p.h. The subsequent acceleration is set out in Table 16; this shows that in 8 miles the average speed over consecutive full miles rose from 87·4 to 112·5 m.p.h.; of this increase, from 95·7 to 107·8 m.p.h. was down the 1 in 177 for 3 miles, and from 107·8 to the peak of 114 m.p.h. was down 1 in 269, with the speed still inclined to rise.

But with Crewe no more than 2 miles away, immediate reduction of speed was imperative. The mile between posts 156 and 157 was covered at an average of 104·7 m.p.h., and though the brakes were now in action with the utmost vigour, only half-a-mile remained before the two sets of double cross-over roads that herald the approach to Crewe station. The first of these we struck at 57 m.p.h. It says much for the first-class condition of the permanent way that the curves were taken with no worse casualty than the breakage of one or two rail chairs. The actual time over the 158·1 miles from Euston to Crewe was 129 minutes 46 seconds, and a start-to-stop average of 73·1 m.p.h. had been maintained from London. Times and speeds on this run were recorded jointly by Mr. D. S. M. Barrie, Mr. S. P. W. Corbett, and myself.

TABLE 16

YEAR 1937
L.M.S.R. "PRINCESS CORONATION" CLASS (4-6-2)
Engine No. 6220, *Coronation*
Load: 263 tons tare, 270 tons gross
RECORD SPEED LENGTH ON TEST RUN

Mileposts	Passing Times	Differences	Speeds
Ex-Euston	min. sec.	sec.	m.p.h.
148	123 16·8	—	—
148¼	123 37·6	20·8	86·5
149	123 58·0	20·4	88·2
149½	124 7·8	19·8	90·9
150	124 27·0	19·2	93·6
150¼	124 46·0	19·0	94·5
151	125 4·6	18·6	96·8
151¼	125 22·8	18·2	98·9
152	125 40·4	17·6	102·3
152½	125 57·8	17·4	103·4
153	126 14·8	17·0	105·9
153¼	126 31·4	16·8	107·1
154	126 48·0	16·6	108·4
154¼	127 4·4	16·4	109·8
155	127 20·6	16·2	111·1
155¼	127 36·6	16·0	112·5
156	127 52·6	16·0	112·5
157	128 27·0	Steam off	

So far as records are available, the return journey that day (Table 17) was the fastest ever made on L.M.S.R. metals. Each of the two main stages—Crewe to Rugby, 75·5 miles, and Rugby to Euston, 82·6 miles—was completed in less than an hour, and the total time of precisely 119 minutes for the 158·1 miles gave a start-to-stop average speed of 79·7 m.p.h. For 150·3 miles from Betley Road to Kilburn, including severe slacks through Stafford and Rugby, the mean speed was 83·3 m.p.h.; for 72·3 miles from Welton, south of Rugby, to Kilburn it was as high as 89·0 m.p.h. High lights were the acceleration from 71½ to 74 m.p.h. up the 1 in 177 of Madeley bank; another from 40 through Rugby to 75 up the 1 in 370 to Kilsby tunnel; and the 10 minutes 13 seconds for the 15·0 miles from Bletchley up to Tring, an average of 88·1 m.p.h. with a minimum of 86½ m.p.h. on the long 1 in 333. Near Castlethorpe 100 m.p.h. was maintained for 1½ miles, and there were several maxima of well over 90 m.p.h., including 99 m.p.h. at King's Langley and 96 m.p.h. at Harrow. The schedule of the "Coronation Scot" was beaten by 25 minutes between Crewe and Euston alone on this memorable journey. One impression that remains in my mind is that of overtaking the up "Lancastrian," which had been diverted to the slow road to keep out of our way, with its windows a mass of excited spectators, for all the world like a travelling grandstand.

The maximum power output of one of the L.M.S.R. Pacifics was demonstrated a couple of years later, after the emergence from Crewe of the first non-streamlined "Duchess" with double blast-pipe and double chimney. Test runs were made in each direction between Crewe and Glasgow with No. 6234, *Duchess of Abercorn*, and a train of 20 coaches weighing 604 tons empty and 610 tons gross, which was worked over Shap and Beattock summits in both directions without assistance on timings roughly corresponding with those observed in winter by the "Royal Scot." It was shown in the running that these could be improved on substantially; going north, the engine gained 7½ minutes from Carnforth to Carlisle, and coming south there was a gain of no less than 9½ minutes from Glasgow to

TABLE 17

YEAR 1937
L.M.S.R. "PRINCESS CORONATION" CLASS (4-6-2)
Engine: No. 6220, *Coronation*
Load: 263 tons tare, 270 tons gross
Driver T. J. Clarke, Fireman J. Lewis (Crewe)

Dist.		Sched.	Actual	Speeds
miles		min.	min. sec.	m.p.h
0·0	CREWE ..	0	0 00	—
1·1	*Milepost 157*	—	2 23	—
4·8	Betley Road	—	6 06	71½
8·0	Madeley ..	—	8 44	74
10·5	Whitmore..	11	10 42	†80½
14·7	Standon Bridge	—	13 32	90
19·2	Norton Bridge	18	16 51	*74
21·2	Great Bridgeford	—	18 25	82
24·5	STAFFORD	23	20 58	—
25·0	*Stafford No. 1*	—	21 45	*30
28·6	Milford ..	—	25 13	75
30·9	Colwich ..	—	27 05	80/*71
33·8	Rugeley ..	31	29 18	90
37·1	Armitage ..	—	31 02	88
41·8	LICHFIELD	37	34 44	—
44·6	*Hademore ..*	—	36 36	92/89
48·1	TAMWORTH	42	38 55	90
51·6	Polesworth	—	41 27	*78
55·8	Atherstone	—	44 41	83/*71
61·0	NUNEATON	54	48 29	90
64·6	Bulkington	—	50 58	86
66·7	Shilton ..	—	52 29	93½
70·0	Brinklow ..	—	54 42	*85
74·9	*Rugby No. 7*	—	58 25	88½/*40
75·5	RUGBY ..	66	59 27	*40
77·8	Hillmorton..	—	61 51	67½
79·9	*Kilsby Tunnel North End ..*	—	63 35	75
82·8	Welton ..	—	65 46	86
88·4	Weedon ..	—	69 41	92/*79
95·3	BLISWORTH	82	74 24	92
98·2	Roade ..	84	76 22	88½
103·3	Castlethorpe	—	79 36	100
105·7	Wolverton	88½	81 08	*83
111·4	BLETCHLEY	93	85 10	89
117·9	Leighton ..	—	89 32	93/*85
122·0	Cheddington	—	92 21	89/87
126·4	TRING ..	107	95 23	86½
130·1	Berkhamsted	—	97 59	90/*85
133·6	Hemel Hempsted	—	100 16	93
137·2	King's Langley	—	102 30	99
140·7	WATFORD JUNCTION	117½	104 53	*84
144·8	Hatch End	—	107 45	85
146·7	Harrow ..	—	109 00	96
150·0	Wembley ..	—	111 05	95
152·7	WILLESDEN JUNCTION	127	112 50	*85
155·1	Kilburn ..	—	114 33	*79
157·1	*Milepost 1 ..*	—	116 57	—
158·1	EUSTON ..	135	119 00	—

* Service slack   † At top of Madeley bank

Carlisle and of 4 minutes from Carlisle to Carnforth. These sections included the lifting of the train over the principal summit points in both directions.

Skeleton details of the running are shown in Tables 18 and 19. On the northbound run (Table 18) relaying operations at Winsford caused a delay of $22\frac{1}{2}$ minutes, but from there onwards a clear road was obtained, apart from the signal check approaching Lancaster. An astonishing climb was made from Carnforth to Shap summit, on which an average speed of 56·5 m.p.h. was maintained, and 5 minutes 40 seconds of lost time was recovered. Cut-off was unchanged at 25 per cent., with full regulator, from Carnforth to Tebay, and was advanced to 35 per cent. for the final 4 miles at 1 in 75; the speeds here were 75 m.p.h. beyond Carnforth, 67 minimum before Burton ($2\frac{1}{2}$ miles up at 1 in 134), 74 before Milnthorpe, 41 up the final 1 in 106 to Grayrigg, 75 past Tebay, and exactly 30 minimum on the 1 in 75. The 132·3 miles from Winsford Junction to Carlisle were completed in 132 minutes, or 131 minutes net, from pass to stop.

TABLE 18

YEAR 1939
L.M.S.R. "DUCHESS" CLASS (4-6-2)
Engine No. 6234, *Duchess of Abercorn* §
Load: 604 tons tare, 610 tons gross
Driver to Carlisle: G. Garrett, Fireman S. Farrington (Crewe)
Driver from Carlisle: J. Marshall, Fireman D. Lynn (Polmadie)

Distance			Sched.	Actual
miles			min.	min. sec.
0·0	CREWE	..	0	0 00
2·7	*Coppenhall Junction*	..	5	5 45
				p.w.s.‡
8·7	Winsford Junction..	..	11	33 30
16·2	Weaver Junction ..	..	18	40 40†
24·0	WARRINGTON ..	..	25	47 35†
27·5	Winwick Junction ..	..	29	51 00
35·8	WIGAN	..	38	58 50
39·1	Standish Junction	..	42	63 20
45·5	Euxton Junction ..	..	49	69 50
50·9	PRESTON.. ..	..	55	75 45*
52·2	Oxheys	..	58	79 40
60·4	Garstang	..	66	88 00
				sigs.
71·9	LANCASTER ..	..	76	98 15†
78·2	CARNFORTH ..	..	81	104 05
91·0	OXENHOLME ..	..	95	115 30
104·1	Tebay	..	111	130 20
109·6	*Shap Summit* ..	..	120	137 25
123·1	PENRITH	..	133	149 00†
127·9	Plumpton	..	137	153 30
141·0	}CARLISLE.. ..	{	150	165 30
0·0		{	0	0 00
8·6	Gretna	..	11	10 40
25·8	LOCKERBIE ..	..	28	28 10
39·7	Beattock	{	41	pass
			43	39 40
49·7	*Beattock Summit* ..	..	61	56 10
66·9	Symington ..	{	pass	74 00
			76	78 25
73·5	CARSTAIRS ..	..	83	86 40*
84·0	Law Junction ..	..	94	97 20†
89·4	MOTHERWELL ..	..	100	103 20†
93·9	Uddingston ..	..	104	107 50*
95·7	Newton	..	108	110 25
98·3	*Rutherglen Junction*	..	112	113 25
102·3	GLASGOW CENTRAL ..		118	118 25

Net times: Crewe-Carlisle, 142 min.
Carlisle-Glasgow, 116 min.

* Severe service slack   † Moderate or slight service slack
‡ Stop and single line working   § With double blast-pipe and chimney

It was intended at first to stop at Beattock, but as this would have entailed rear-end assistance to re-start, the normal "Royal Scot" stop at Symington eventually was substituted, in order that the locomotive might tackle Beattock bank unaided. In order to conserve steam, therefore, cut-offs were not advanced beyond 20 to 25 per cent.

up the long 1 in 200 ascents past Gretna and Ecclefechan (7½ and 4½ miles respectively), on which the sustained speeds were 53 and 57 m.p.h.; speed rose to 80 m.p.h. north of Lockerbie, and up 4½ miles at 1 in 200 to Beattock station had fallen to 60 m.p.h. when the foot of the bank proper was reached. The 10 miles between Beattock station and the summit were covered in 16 minutes 30 seconds; here the cut-off was advanced finally to 40 per cent., and this enabled the locomotive with its 610-ton load to breast the summit at a shade under 30 m.p.h.

Two hours later the train started the return journey to Crewe, and the first stage, from Glasgow down to Carlisle (Table 19), with Driver N. McLean at the regulator, in certain respects was the most outstanding feat of locomotive performance in British railway history. With roughly twice the load of the "Coronation Scot," *Duchess of Abercorn* reached Carlisle in a time only 1½ minutes more than that allowed the streamliner, covering the 102·3 miles in 106½ minutes. An average speed of 46·7 m.p.h. was maintained from Motherwell up to Law Junction, where the flattest part of the climb is at 1 in 137 and most of it is 1 in 102, while

TABLE 19

YEAR 1939

L.M.S.R. "DUCHESS" CLASS (4-6-2)

Engine No. 6234, *Duchess of Abercorn* §

Load: 604 tons tare, 610 tons gross

Driver to Carlisle: N. McLean, Fireman A. Smith (Polmadie)

Driver from Carlisle: G. Garrett, Fireman S. Farrington (Crewe)

Distance				Sched.	Actual	
miles				min.	min.	sec.
0·0	GLASGOW	..	..	0	0	00
12·9	MOTHERWELL	..	..	19	19	45
18·3	Law Junction	..	..	29	26	40
28·8	CARSTAIRS	..	..	43	39	30*
35·4	Symington	..	..	51	48	15
39·1	Lamington	..	..	—	52	08
44·5	Abington	..	..	—	57	13
47·0	Crawford	..	..	—	59	36
49·7	Elvanfoot	..	..	—	62	03
52·6	*Beattock Summit*	..	..	69	64	40
62·6	Beattock	..	..	79	73	35
76·5	LOCKERBIE	..	..	91	84	25
93·7	Gretna	..	..	106	97	45
102·3	}CARLISLE..		{	116	106	30
0·0				0	0	00
4·9	Wreay	..	..	—	8	59
7·4	Southwaite	..	..	—	11	52
10·8	Calthwaite	..	..	—	15	11
13·1	Plumpton	..	..	19	17	45
17·9	PENRITH	..	..	24	21	50†
31·4	*Shap Summit*	..	..	43	40	15
36·9	Tebay	..	..	48	44	40
42·9	Grayrigg	..	..	—	50	23
50·0	OXENHOLME	..	..	60	56	30
62·8	CARNFORTH	..	..	71	67	00
69·1	LANCASTER	..	..	76	72	20
80·6	Garstang	..	..	87	84	00
90·1	PRESTON..	..	..	97	93	35*
99·4	Coppull	..	..	—	105	53
105·2	WIGAN	..	..	116	113	05†
117·0	WARRINGTON	..	..	128	126	10†
124·8	*Weaver Junction*	..	..	136	134	25†
141·0	CREWE	..	..	153	153	05

* Service slack, severe † Service slack, slight or moderate

§ With double blast-pipe and chimney

from Symington up to Beattock summit the average was no less than 63·4 m.p.h. Actually, on the 1 in 99 up to Law Junction a speed of 43 m.p.h. was being sustained steadily; and in the upper Clyde valley speeds were 50 m.p.h. past Symington, 65 at Lamington, 62 before Abington, 65 at Crawford, 63 before and 68 after Elvanfoot, and a minimum of 63 up the final 2 miles at 1 in 99 to Beattock summit. For the hardest of the work here, cut-offs of 30 to 35 per cent. were

TABLE 20

DETAILS OF WORKING ON TEST RUNS, CREWE TO GLASGOW AND BACK, ENGINE No. 6234, "DUCHESS OF ABERCORN" (4-6-2

| | Crewe to Glasgow | | | | | | Glasgow to Crewe | | | | | | |
| | Carnforth-Shap Summit | | | Gretna-Beattock Summit | | | Motherwell-Beattock Summit | | | | Carlisle-Shap Summit | | |
	Carnforth to Oxenholme	Oxenholme to Tebay	Tebay to Summit	Gretna to Lockerbie	Lockerbie to Beattock	Beattock to Summit	Motherwell to Law Junc.	Law Junc. to Carstairs	Carstairs to Symington	Symington to Summit	Carlisle to Plumpton	Plumpton to Penrith	Penrith to Summit
Length of ascent, miles	12·96	13·08	5·69	17·27	13·96	10·13	5·42	10·53	6·74	17·28	13·03	4·77	13·68
Average drawbar horsepower ..	1,870	1,668	1,830	1,598	1,609	1,724	1,923	†	1,520	1,860	1,822	2,000	1,560
Maximum drawbar horsepower ..	2,120	1,934	2,065	1,733	1,823	2,081	1,998	1,978	1,638	2,282	2,511	2,394	2,331
Maximum indicated horsepower*	3,209	2,806	2,963	2,236	2,556	2,761	2,583	2,567	2,138	3,333	3,248	3,241	3,021
Average speed of ascent, m.p.h.	68·0	53·0	47·9	59·3	72·5	36·8	46·7	49·4	46·1	63·4	43·9	71·4	44·4
Cut-off range, per cent. of stroke..	20-25	25	25-35	20-25	20-25	30-40	20-30	30-35	20-25	30-35	30-35	20-30	30-40
Boiler pressure, lb. per sq. in. ..	250	245	240	250	245	245	250	250	245	245	245	230	245

* Calculated   † Not taken, as section included some coasting

used, and the average drawbar-h.p. of 1,923 from Motherwell to Law Junction was the highest of the round journey (with one short exception); on the final climb to Beattock summit, drawbar-h.p. rose to a maximum of 2,282, and the maximum i.h.p. to 3,333, the most exceptional figure reached during the day.

A similar display was given by Driver Garrett southwards from Carlisle. Up the first 4½ miles at 1 in 131 to Wreay speed accelerated from the Carlisle start to 42 m.p.h., and this required 30 to 35 per cent. cut-off, and the development of a maximum drawbar-h.p. of 2,511 and i.h.p. of 3,348. Cut-off was eased slightly over the level stretch from Plumpton to beyond Penrith, and then advanced by degrees to 40 per cent. up the 7 miles at 1 in 125 to Shap. Speed rose to 73 m.p.h. on the level length before Penrith, but was reduced to 53 round the station curve; on the final 7 miles at 1 in 125 to Shap station the minimum was 38 m.p.h. The maximum drawbar-h.p. here was 2,331 and the maximum i.h.p. 3,021. Such interest attaches to the details of locomotive working up these exacting gradients that the figures are set out separately in Table 20.

By normal standards of working, the coal consumption was high—68·7 lb. per mile—but this must be regarded in the light of the work performed. In relation to power output the figure was 3·12 lb. per drawbar-h.p.-hr., which in all the circumstances was quite moderate. Water was being consumed at the rate of 53·1 gallons per mile; 24·2 gallons per drawbar-h.p-hr.; and 7·74 gallons per lb. of coal burned.

Coming now to the 4-6-0 designs, it is necessary to include some

TABLE 21

YEAR 1937
L.M.S.R. "JUBILEE" CLASS "5XP" (4-6-0)
Engine No. 5660, *Rooke*
Load: 302 tons tare, 305 tons gross
Driver W. North, Fireman H. George (Leeds)

Dist.				Sched.	Actual	Speeds
miles				min.	min. sec.	m.p.h.
0·0	LEEDS	..	..	0	0 00	—
1·7	Armley	..	..	—	4 03	39½
4·6	Newlay	..	..	—	7 24	60/58
7·6	Apperley Bridge		..	—	10 24	61
10·7	*Leeds Junction (Shipley)*	..	14	13 44	*22
13·8	Bingley	..	..	—	17 54	62½
17·0	KEIGHLEY	..	..	21	21 11	*52½
20·0	Steeton	..	..	—	24 04	67
23·1	Cononley	..	..	—	26 45	72
					p.w.s.	40
26·2	SKIPTON	..	..	30	30 22	—
					p.w.s.	18
29·9	Gargrave	..	..	—	35 09	58
34·7	*Milepost 229¾*	..	..	—	40 12	54
36·2	HELLIFIELD	..	..	42	41 49	60/*46
39·5	*Settle Junction*	..	..	45	45 00	*63
41·4	Settle	..	..	—	47 00	55/50
47·4	Horton	..	..	—	54 00	53½/51
52·2	Ribblehead	..	..	—	59 43	47½/49
53·4	*Blea Moor*	..	..	63	61 20	46
58·3	Dent	..	..	—	66 35	63
61·6	Garsdale	..	..	—	69 34	68
64·6	Ais Gill	..	..	75	72 34	55
71·5	Kirkby Stephen	..	..	—	78 51	71/66
79·7	Ormside	..	..	—	86 03	71
82·2	APPLEBY	..	..	90	88 15	63
88·3	New Biggin	..	..	—	93 11	79/75
97·5	LAZONBY	..	..	—	100 48	70/72
99·9	*Milepost 295*	..	..	—	—	64
103·0	Armathwaite	..	..	—	105 30	75
106·2	Cotehill	..	..	—	108 19	62/71
112·1	*Petteril Bridge*	..	..	115	113 58	*20
113·0	CARLISLE	..	..	117	117 00	—

Net time: 116 min.

* Service slacks

reference to the test journeys which were made with Class "5XP" 4-6-0 No. 5660, *Rooke*, over the Midland Division in October, 1937. The most notable runs were between Leeds and Carlisle, which involved the ascent in each direction to the 1,167 ft. altitude of Ais Gill. For the test a train of nine coaches had been made up, weighing in all 305 tons; the schedule of 117 minutes northbound and 125 minutes southbound was considerably faster than anything previously tabled over this course. Actually, it was kept in the northbound direction, and improved on by over 9 minutes in the southbound; full details of the times and speeds are given in Tables 21 and 22.

Going north (Table 21), principal interest centred in the climb of 13.9 miles over the open fells from Settle Junction to Blea Moor, almost entirely at 1 in 100. This was begun at no more than 63 m.p.h.; yet 8 miles of the climb had passed before the speed fell even to 60, and Blea Moor was breasted at 46 m.p.h., with an average of 51.1 m.p.h. for the entire ascent. Drawbar-h.p. averaged 1,129 and reached a maximum of 1,244, equal to 1,844 i.h.p., and this on a cut-off unchanged at 35 per cent. Had it not been that downhill speeds were

TABLE 22

YEAR 1937
L.M.S.R. "JUBILEE" CLASS "5XP" (4-6-0)
Engine No. 5660, *Rooke*
Load: 302 tons tare, 305 tons gross
Driver W. North, Fireman H. George (Leeds)

Dist.		Sched.	Actual	Speeds
miles		min.	min. sec.	m.p.h.
0·0	CARLISLE	0	0 00	—
0·9	*Petteril Bridge Junction* ..	3	2 21	*20
2·7	Scotby	—	5 10	46/57
6·8	Cotehill	—	9 51	56
8·4	Low House	—	11 31	55
10·0	Armathwaite ..	—	12 55	74
13·1	*Milepost 295* ..	—	15 32	69
15·5	LAZONBY	19	17 26	80½
19·8	Langwathby ..	—	20 59	67/72
24·7	New Biggin ..	—	25 10	69
27·9	Long Marton ..	—	27 48	75
30·8	APPLEBY	35	30 30	67
33·3	Ormside	—	32 21	77½
38·3	Crosby Garrett ..	—	37 10	58/62½
41·5	Kirkby Stephen ..	—	40 24	54
44·9	*Mallerstang* ..	—	44 18	48/53
48·4	Ais Gill	59	48 36	46½
51·4	Garsdale	—	51 33	64/62
54·7	Dent	—	54 41	67/64
59·6	*Blea Moor*	70	59 14	71
65·6	Horton	—	64 04	76½
73·5	*Settle Junction* ..	82	70 44	*60
76·8	HELLIFIELD ..	85	74 08	*48
78·3	*Milepost 229¾* ..	—	75 58	52
			p.w.s.	
83·1	Gargrave.. ..	—	80 30	71
			p.w.s.	20
86·8	SKIPTON	96	85 13	—
			p.w.s.	40
89·9	Cononley ..	—	89 20	—
93·0	Steeton	—	92 11	73½
96·0	KEIGHLEY ..	105	94 58	*44
99·2	Bingley	—	98 18	68
102·3	*Leeds Junction Shipley* ..	112	101 56	*24
105·4	Apperley Bridge ..	—	105 38	63/70
111·3	Armley	—	111 11	55
			sigs.	
113·0	LEEDS	125	115 38	—

Net time: 113 min.   * Service slack

more restrained than in normal practice, there might have been a gain on time to Carlisle; net time was about 115 minutes for the 113·0 miles.

On the following day the engine had already worked through from Glasgow when the run appearing in Table 22 commenced at Carlisle. Between Glasgow and Carlisle the most notable achievement had been the maintenance of an average of 57·8 m.p.h. up the climb of 16·9 miles

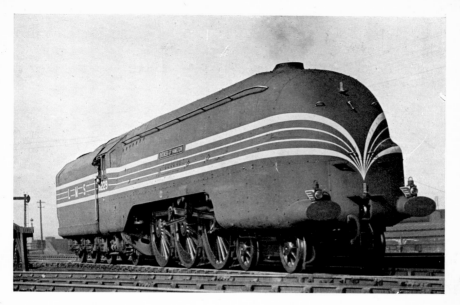

53. A fully streamlined 4-6-2 of "Princess Coronation" class, late L.M.S.R. The London Midland Region has since removed the streamlining from all these engines. (*Canon E. Treacy.*)

54. An "air-smoothed" 4-6-2 of the "Merchant Navy" class, Southern Region, showing the exhaust deflecting arrangement at the front of the smokebox. (*Courtesy, British Railways.*)

TYPICAL LOCOMOTIVE STREAMLINING

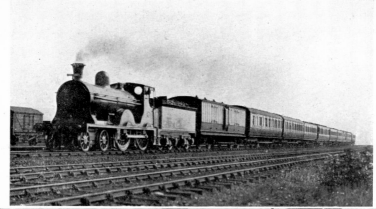

55. One of the noted McIntosh 4-4-0s of the late Caledonian Railway—No. 766 of the "Dunalastair II" series—leaving Carlisle with a Glasgow express. (*F. E. Mackay*.)

56. In their heyday—London & North Western "George the Fifth" 4-4-0, *Racehorse*, passing Kenton with an up Perth express. (*F. E. Mackay*.)

57. A 2-4-2 tank of the late Lancashire & Yorkshire Railway. The superheated version of this class figures in an express passenger run in Chapter 11. (*W. Hubert Foster*.)

THE "SMALL ENGINE" ERA

58. A "Precursor" 4-4-0 piloting a "Prince of Wales" 4-6-0 out of Euston on "The Corridor"—the one-time 2 p.m. to Glasgow. (*F. E. Mackay.*)

59. A 4-cylinder "Claughton" 4-6-0 piloting a 3-cylinder "Royal Scot" 4-6-0 on an up Liverpool express near Berkhamsted. (*M. W. Earley.*)

DEVELOPMENT OF NORTH WESTERN MOTIVE POWER

60. One of the original "Patriot" series, with parallel boiler, of which the first were converted from 4-cylinder "Claughton" 4-6-0s, leaving Preston. (*Canon E. Treacy.*)

61. One of the "Jubilees," a later design, with taper boiler. *Western Australia* is seen near Ais Gill summit, 1,167 ft. above sea level, with an Edinburgh-St. Pancras express. (*M. W. Earley.*)

MIDDLEWEIGHT EXPRESS ENGINES—CLASS "5XP," LONDON MIDLAND REGION

62. A "Princess Royal" Pacific, *Princess Arthur of Connaught*, of the original series of twelve engines. (*Canon E. Treacy*.)

63. One of the later "Duchess" series, *City of Sheffield*, with larger and higher-pitched boiler, handles the 15-coach "Royal Scot" express. (*Canon E. Treacy*.)

LONDON MIDLAND PACIFICS CLIMBING THE 1 IN 75 OF SHAP

64. Wheel-balancing machine, with a pair of driving wheels in course of balancing.
65. Riveting a boiler seam with the boiler riveting machine.   (*Courtesy, British Railways.*)

LOCOMOTIVE BUILDING AT CREWE WORKS

66. Lowering a 2-8-0 freight chassis and boiler on to the wheels. (*Courtesy, British Railways.*)

67. Applying the motion details to a "Duchess" class Pacific. (*Courtesy, British Railways.*)

LOCOMOTIVE BUILDING AT CREWE WORKS

68. One of the London Midland Region Class "2" 2-6-0s, specially designed for light branch work, at Manchester Victoria. (*H. C. Casserley.*)

69. The latest London Midland Region type, Class "4" 2-6-0, No. 3005, at Bletchley. These engines are fitted with every modern improvement for increasing steaming efficiency and reducing shed costs. (*H. C. Casserley.*)

IMPROVING LOCOMOTIVE PERFORMANCE

from Hurlford station, after leaving Kilmarnock, to Polquhap summit; this involved the maintenance of 60 m.p.h. up 1 in 180, and a fall only from 66 to 61 m.p.h. up the final 1 in 150, all on 36 per cent. cut-off and with a maximum drawbar-h.p. of 1,232.

From Carlisle (Table 22) the amazing feat was performed of lifting the train up the 48·4 miles to Ais Gill summit in 48 minutes 36 seconds, at an average of almost precisely a mile-a-minute. Though the regulator was kept wide open, and cut-offs ranged mostly from 35 to 40 per cent., the boiler found steam without difficulty, and pressure kept constant at round about the 225 lb. mark. Most exceptional features of this running were the 55 m.p.h. maintained up 2½ miles at 1 in 130 to Low House; no less than 80½ m.p.h. attained down 1½ miles at 1 in 220 past Lazonby; no lower speed than 67 up the gradual rise to Appleby; and the minima, on the 1 in 100 lengths, of 58 above Ormside (3 miles), 54 at Kirkby Stephen (2 miles) and 48 at Mallerstang (after another 2½ miles), with, finally, 46½ at Ais Gill (the last 3 miles). From Ormside up to Ais Gill drawbar-h.p. averaged 1,054 and reached a maximum of 1,113, while the maximum i.h.p. was 1,773.

TABLE 23

YEAR 1938
L.M.S.R. "JUBILEE" CLASS "5XP" (4-6-0)
Engine No. 5622, *Nyasaland*
Load: 225 tons tare, 235 tons gross

Dist.		Sched.	Actual	Speeds
miles		min.	min. sec.	m.p.h.
0·0	LEICESTER	0	0 00	
			p.w.s.	15
3·7	Wigston Magna ..	—	9 04	—
7·5	Great Glen	—	14 00	65
9·4	*Kibworth North* ..	—	15 38	63
12·8	East Langton	—	18 11	89
16·2	MARKET HARBOROUGH	19	21 00	*38
20·6	*Desborough North* ..	—	26 04	60
23·5	Glendon	—	28 23	86
27·1	KETTERING	31	30 51	93/*82
30·9	Finedon	—	33 33	89
			sigs.	5
34·1	WELLINGBOROUGH ..	37	40 30	
36·4	Irchester	—	43 25	57
39·3	*Milepost 59¾* ..	43	46 29	56
42·5	Sharnbrook	—	49 03	87
46·1	Oakley	—	51 33	93/82
49·3	BEDFORD	51	53 50	87
57·3	Ampthill	—	59 51	72
58·9	Flitwick	—	61 09	77
61·8	Harlington	—	63 30	73
66·3	Leagrave	—	67 14	71
68·9	LUTON	70	69 11	84
71·8	Chiltern Green ..	—	71 20	86
74·5	Harpenden	—	73 70	78
79·2	ST. ALBAN'S	79	76 54	86
83·9	Radlett	—	80 01	95
86·7	Elstree	—	82 00	76
92·2	HENDON	90	85 46	91
97·6	Kentish Town ..	96	90 34	—
			sigs.	
99·1	ST. PANCRAS	99	96 10	—

Net time: 84½ min.
* Service slack

The 73.5 m.p.h. speed maintained from Armathwaite up to Ormside, and the 55·8 m.p.h. up the gruelling 15·1 miles from Ormside to Ais Gill, deserve also to rank among the finest achievements in British locomotive annals.

As an example of the exceptional speed capacity of the "5XP" class 4-6-0 engines of the "Jubilee" series, I give in Table 23 details of what is probably the fastest run that has ever yet been made over Midland metals. The locomotive, No. 5622, *Nyasaland*, with a seven-coach

K

train of 235 tons, was working on the mile-a-minute schedule from Leicester to St. Pancras (99·1 miles in 99 minutes) introduced with the 1937 accelerations, and was delayed soon after starting by a bad permanent-way check near Wigston. Then followed the amazing display here reproduced, with maxima in succession of 89, 93, 93, 95, and 91 m.p.h., the almost incredible time of 15 minutes 21 seconds for the 19·6 miles from Bedford up to Luton, on which the lowest rates up long 1 in 200 banks were 72 and 71 m.p.h., and a sustained speed of 57-56 m.p.h. up 3 miles at 1 in 120 to Sharnbrook summit.

Over the 52·9 miles from Sharnbrook summit to Hendon, including the whole of 13¼-mile climb from Elstow to milepost 34, the average speed was 80·8 m.p.h.—a figure that I have never known equalled or even approached on any other run. The losses of time by checks were 4 minutes by the initial permanent-way slowing, 5 minutes by the prolonged signal check, to a walking pace, at Wellingborough, and 2¾ minutes approaching St. Pancras, leaving a net time of 84½ minutes for the run, and a net start-to-stop average of 70·4 m.p.h. The work of the engine on this trip would compare closely with that required of the L.N.E.R. "Silver Jubilee" streamliner with a precisely equal load, though the latter, of course, was over a considerably longer distance.

TABLE 24

YEAR 1938
L.M.S.R. "JUBILEE" CLASS "5XP" (4-6-0)
Engine No. 5636, *Uganda*
Load: 231 tons tare, 245 tons gross

Dist.			Sched.	Actual		Speeds
miles			min.	min.	sec.	m.p.h.
0·0	CARLISLE	.. ..	0	0	00	—
2·0	Kingmoor..	.. ..	—	3	41	54
4·1	Rockcliffe	.. ..	—	5	45	65
6·1	Floriston..	.. ..	—	7	32	79
8·6	Gretna ..	.. ..	10	9	31	69½
13·0	Kirkpatrick	.. ..	—	13	34	61
16·7	Kirtlebridge	.. ..	—	16	58	76
20·1	Ecclefechan	.. ..	—	19	51	68½
25·8	LOCKERBIE	.. ..	28	24	39	79
28·7	Nethercleugh	.. ..	—	26	53	76
31·8	Dinwoodie	.. ..	—	29	22	68½
34·5	Wamphray	.. ..	—	31	40	74½
36·9	Murthat ..	.. ..	—	33	40	70
39·7	BEATTOCK	.. ..	40	36	10	66
42·2	Auchencastle	.. ..	—	38	43	51
45·3	Greskine ..	.. ..	—	42	50	40
47·7	Harthope ..	.. ..	—	46	40	33½
49·7	Summit ..	.. ..	57	50	08	35½
52·6	Elvanfoot	.. ..	—	53	08	68½
57·8	Abington	.. ..	—	57	27	76
63·2	Lamington	.. ..	—	61	38	79
66·9	SYMINGTON	.. ..	73	64	35	70½/76
70·0	Leggatfoot	.. ..	—	67	11	70½/77½
73·2	Strawfrank Junction	..	80	70	33	*31
74·8	Carnwath	.. ..	—	73	06	43½
79·1	Auchengray	.. ..	—	77	38	62
82·2	Cobbinshaw	.. ..	93	80	49	54½
85·3	Harburn ..	.. ..	—	83	48	67
90·5	Midcalder	.. ..	102	88	52	*57
99·4	Merchiston	.. ..	113	99	40	eased
100·6	EDINBURGH	.. ..	116	104	15	—

* Service slack

required of the L.N.E.R. "Silver Jubilee" streamliner with a precisely equal load, though the latter, of course, was over a considerably longer distance.

A fourth run with one of these capable engines is worthy of a place in this gallery. It was made through the Scottish Lowlands with the down "Midday Scot," the Edinburgh portion of which before the war was detached at Carlisle, and run independently from there with a "5XP" 4-6-0 on a non-stop schedule of 116 minutes for the 100·6 miles from Carlisle to Princes Street. On this occasion the engine was No. 5636, *Uganda*, with a load of 245 tons, and the log of the run, timed by Mr. A. A. Torrance, appears in Table 24. The 79½-ton locomotive succeeded in keeping, as far as Symington, the schedule of the "Coronation Scot" streamliner, with its 108-ton engine and 310-ton train. This involved sustained minima of 61 and 68½ m.p.h. up the two lengthy 1 in 200 ascents before Lockerbie. The train was through Beattock in 36 minutes 10 seconds; then the 10 miles of Beattock bank proper were mounted in 13 minutes 58 seconds, with no lower speed than 33½ m.p.h. on the steepest pitch, which averages about 1 in 72. Another smart climb was up the 5 miles to Cobbinshaw, steepening from 1 in 220 to 1 in 97, on which speed fell from 62 to 54¼ m.p.h. By Midcalder, 90·5 miles in 88 minutes 52 seconds from the start, the engine had gained 13 minutes on schedule, and could have completed the run with ease in 100 minutes, but was then deliberately eased to avoid too early an arrival, so that the total time was 104¼ minutes.

In dealing with L.M.S.R. performance, also, a word is needed concerning the versatile Class "5" 4-6-0 locomotives of the standard Stanier design, which are probably the speediest British locomotives ever yet built with driving wheels of no more than 6 ft. diameter. Shortly after the first of these engines had been turned out, in 1934, a test run was made with No. 5020 from Euston to Crewe on which the engine had to tackle a load of no less than 468 tons tare and 495 tons gross, including the dynamometer car. Yet the engine managed to pass Willesden, 5·4 miles, in 9 minutes 52 seconds; Watford, 17·4 miles, in 22 minutes 35 seconds, and Tring, 31·7 miles, in 37 minutes 14 seconds, maintaining 54½ m.p.h.

TABLE 25

YEAR 1937
L.M.S.R. CLASS "5" (4-6-0)
Engine No. 5264
Load: 258 tons tare, 260 tons gross
Driver Beebe, Fireman Foulkes (Trafford Park)

Dist.		‡Sched.	Actual	Speeds
miles		min.	min. sec.	m.p.h.
0·0	LEICESTER..	0	0 00	—
3·2	*Wigston North Junction* ..	—	5 15	52/*30
7·5	Great Glen..	—	10 17	67
9·4	Kibworth North	—	11 58	65
12·8	East Langton	—	14 35	86½
16·2	MARKET HARBOROUGH ..	18	17 15	*43
20·6	Desborough North	—	22 33	56
23·5	Glendon	—	25 00	77½
27·1	KETTERING	29	28 05	*66
30·9	Finedon	—	31 05	79
34·1	WELLINGBOROUGH ..	35	33 40	*61
36·4	Irchester	—	32 52	69
			p.w.s.	23
39·3	*Milepost 59¾*	40½	39 44	30
42·5	Sharnbrook	—	42 50	86½
46·1	Oakley	—	45 38	†66
49·3	BEDFORD	48½	48 12	85
57·3	Ampthill	—	55 05	55
58·9	Flitwick	—	56 40	63
61·8	Harlington	—	59 35	60
65·1	*Milepost 34*	—	62 52	59
66·3	Leagrave	—	64 05	64
68·9	LUTON	68	66 17	74/67
71·8	Chiltern Green	—	68 50	73
74·5	Harpenden	—	71 10	65
79·2	ST. ALBAN'S	76½	75 30	—
83·9	Radlett	—	79 25	78
86·7	Elstree	—	81 36	70
92·2	HENDON	87	85 33	91
97·6	Kentish Town	93	89 53	—
99·1	ST. PANCRAS	96	92 36	—

Net time: 91 min.

* Service slack   † Speed reduction for water-troughs   ‡ Special test schedule

to the top of the 1 in 335. Then came 77 m.p.h. down the further slope, and times of 49 minutes 42 seconds to Bletchley, 46·7 miles; 61 minutes 43 seconds to Roade, 59·9 miles; 64 minutes 44 seconds to Blisworth, 62·8 miles; and 85 minutes, 56 seconds, or 85 minutes net, to Rugby, 82·6 miles. This fine effort, for a locomotive of such modest dimensions, was recorded by Mr. R. E. Charlewood.

A Class "5" run with lighter load, but much higher speeds, set out in Table 25 was made during the tests which preceded the introduction of the accelerated Midland schedules of 1937, and was timed by Mr. G. J. Aston and Mr. D. S. M. Barrie. From the log it will be seen that the engine ran freely at speeds up to 91 m.p.h.; indeed, I have timed one of these locomotives at 90 m.p.h. over a considerable distance down 1 in 200, with a maximum of 92 m.p.h., when hauling a load as heavy as 400 tons. With allowance for the smaller boiler, the attained speed of 56 m.p.h. at Desborough summit (up 4½ miles at 1 in 132) and the minimum of 50 m.p.h. up the long rise to milepost 34, fall little if at all below the "5XP" hillclimbing exploits just detailed. In this case the 52·9 miles from Sharnbrook summit to Hendon were run at an average of 68·9 m.p.h., which would have been nearer 70 m.p.h. but for the bad permanent-way slowing on Irchester bank. By a locomotive designed for mixed traffic service, of a type used as much on freight as on passenger trains, and of but moderate dimensions, this was a striking demonstration of the operating possibilities brought about by modern boiler and front-end design.

No chapter on London Midland Region locomotive performance would be complete without reference to the exceptional work, for a 4-6-0 design, now being displayed by the Fowler "Royal Scots" that have been rebuilt with the Stanier taper boiler, double blast-pipe and chimney, and other modern refinements. In the 1948 locomotive exchanges, "Royal Scots" were pitted against the considerably more powerful Pacific classes, and in the capable hands of Driver Brooker, of Camden shed, gave a remarkable account of themselves. Over the Eastern and Southern Region main lines, these 83-ton 4-6-0s were required to haul loads equal to those of their Pacific rivals, notwithstanding which the "Royal Scot" times and speeds over certain sections were the fastest in the trials.

One outstanding achievement of No. 46162, *Queen's Westminster Rifleman*, was east of Westbury, Western Region, after the engine had lost some time up from Plymouth by reason of bad weather. With a load of 480 tons, the 4-6-0 started out of Westbury with such terrific vigour as to climb the 6 miles at 1 in 222 to Patney with no greater fall in speed than from 67 to a steady 59 m.p.h., at which the drawbar horsepower, dynamometer car recorded, rose to 1,630. The summit at Savernake, 25·5 miles, was passed in 27 minutes 28 seconds from the start, and inclusive of a permanent-way slowing, Reading, 59·6 miles, was reached in 62 minutes 49 seconds, or in a net time of exactly one hour. But for the out-of-course Reading stop, due to the absence of the Reading slip-coach, the 95·6 miles from Westbury to Paddington might have been run in 96½ minutes net, whereas the schedule allowed 113 minutes.

On Southern Region metals, No. 46154, *The Hussar*, was responsible for by far the most outstanding performance in the exchange trials from Exeter to Waterloo. From Axminster, wiih 515 tons, Driver Brooker accelerated up the 11¼-mile climb from the start to 59 m.p.h. on the easier grades, and then maintained 58 m.p.h. up 1 in 200, so clearing milepost 133¼, 11·3 miles, in 15 minutes 56 seconds from the start. With a top speed of 87 m.p.h. below Crewkerne, this brought the train from Axminster over Hewish summit to Yeovil Junction, 21·9 miles, in 25 minutes 26 seconds, start-to-stop, though the time-table allowed 29 minutes. Equally forceful was the start from Salisbury, now with 520 tons behind the tender, when No. 46154 attained 48½ m.p.h. up the initial 1 in 169 gradient, did not fall below 47½ on the 1 in 140 past Porton, and accelerated further to 53 m.p.h. up the 1 in 245 to Amesbury Junction, so that the 4-6-0 passed Andover, 17·4 miles, in 20 minutes 17 seconds. On the hardest climbs of this run, drawbar horsepowers ranged from 1,493 to 1,782.

Over the 105·5 miles from Grantham to King's Cross, Eastern Region, *Queen's Westminster Rifleman* brought a 545-ton train in 114 minutes net, as compared with the 122 minutes allowed, with a notable time of 25 minutes 29 seconds for the 27·0 miles from Huntingdon to Hitchin, mostly on grades adverse to the engine. These feats are matched constantly by what the engines are doing in their own Region, especially between Leeds, Carlisle and Glasgow St. Enoch, where the rebuilt "Royal Scots" now are scorning to take assistance, even with trains exceeding 400 tons in weight, over the 1,167 ft. altitude of Ais Gill summit. Indeed, this may be claimed, with some justification, as the most capable and efficient 4-6-0 design, especially in relation to dimensions and weight, that Great Britain has yet produced.

13

PERFORMANCE—L.N.E.R. PRE-GROUPING LOCOMOTIVES

OF the companies which were brought by the grouping into the London & North Eastern system, it was the Great Northern which had established the highest standard of speed. "It is the straight-forward dash of the Great Northern, and the high standard of excellence maintained in all its services," wrote Foxwell and Farrer in their *Express Trains, English and Foreign*, of 1889, "which have won it the distinguished place it holds in public estimation. Especially in regard to speed it has long merited the gold medal—a fact to be borne in mind now that the recent efforts of the North Western have dazzled some observers. What the Great Northern would show us if it controlled the entire road to Scotland we can only conjecture; at present much of its own high-pressure energy has to be expended in stirring up the North Eastern and the North British to do their share towards the main result. Would any company except the Great Northern ever have contemplated and carried out an effective competition for traffic between London and *Manchester*, with such a roundabout route, and the extra disadvantage of having to work in harness?"

The last reference was to the fact that in 1884 the G.N.R. was actually running between King's Cross and Manchester in 4¼ hours, over a route 202½ miles long, and including the summit at Dunford, 966 ft. above sea level, in double harness with the then Manchester, Sheffield & Lincolnshire Railway, which worked the trains between Sheffield and Manchester. The G.N.R. 4¼ hours equalled the best L.N.W.R. time at that period, though over a route longer by nearly 20 miles and incomparably harder; and it was 5 minutes better than the fastest Midland schedule. But the blossoming in 1897 of the M.S. & L. into the Great Central Railway, and the opening of the latter's independent route to London for passenger traffic in 1899, altered matters considerably. Eventually the G.N.R. gave up the unequal contest. It is interesting to recall that in 1925 the L.N.E.R. made one last attempt to popularise the King's Cross-Manchester route, and this time with an all-Pullman train which brought the overall journey time down to 4 hours 7 minutes. By then, however, the best L.M.S.R. time was 3½ hours, and the public refused to be attracted by this short-lived experiment.

The previous chapter opened with a brief recital of the feats of speed achieved by the West Coast companies in the "Race to Aberdeen" of 1895, and we must now deal briefly with the East Coast reply. On the Great Northern the famous 8 ft. single-drivers of Patrick Stirling's design held sway; the North Eastern depended on William Worsdell's 4-4-0 locomotives, which in scale had reached the N.E.R. Class"M"; and the North British relied on 7 ft. 4-4-0s of the standard Holmes design. As Foxwell and Farrer indicated in the quotation I have given from their book, by 1895 the East Coast generalship was still poor, and the overall times of many of the runs they made were ruined by "waiting time" at the intermediate stops, particularly York and Edinburgh—a matter in which their West Coast rivals appeared to have few scruples.

On the penultimate night of the "Race," however—August 21st-22nd, 1895—the East Coast authorities resolved to "fight the devil with fire," and made their classic time of 8 hours 40 minutes from King's Cross to Aberdeen, 523½ miles in 520 minutes, all stops included. The load was no more than 105 tons, which a Stirling 8-footer ran over the 105·5 miles from King's Cross to Grantham in 101 minutes; another engine of the same type continued over the 82·7 miles to York in 76 minutes. From York North Eastern 4-4-0 No. 1620 worked the train forward over the 80·6 miles to Newcastle (*via* the High Level Bridge) in 78 minutes; while the sister engine, No. 1621, made the outstanding time of 114½ minutes over the 124·4 miles from Newcastle to Edinburgh. For the East Coast this was really the end of the "Race," as despite the spectacular West Coast demonstration on the following night, the former made no further record attempts.

But perhaps the most amazing feat of all, in view of the formidable difficulties of the section concerned, was that of a North British 4-4-0 in covering the 59·2 miles from Edinburgh to Dundee in precisely one hour; while the concluding 77 minutes for the 71·3 miles from Dundee to Aberdeen was also a fine time, in view of the severe gradients and the fact that a lengthy stretch of single line had to be negotiated. Between London and Edinburgh the 6 hours 19 minutes of this run remained a record between the English and Scottish capitals until from July, 1937, the "Coronation" streamliner began to make a daily run in both directions in 6 hours.

My regular travelling, which began in 1908, was just in time for me to see the last of the Great Northern Stirling 8-footers on main-line duty. Table 26 compares a couple of runs on the 5·30 p.m. Newcastle "diner" from King's Cross, on the first of which the motive power forward from Grantham was provided by an engine of this type, and on the second by one of the later Ivatt single-drivers of the "266" class, which had been introduced in 1898. The "eight-footer" (actually built in 1895, though to a design of 25 years earlier) handled the six-car train without difficulty. The start was relatively slow, but before Newark the veteran was doing 70½ m.p.h., and on the level before Bawtry sustained 65 m.p.h. on the level. It will be seen that the 38 miles from Barkston to Bawtry were run in 37 minutes. A considerably faster start was made by the Ivatt single, which with a maximum of 75 m.p.h. between Hougham and Claypole had attained "even time"—20·9 miles in 20 minutes 50 seconds from the start—by Carlton-on-Trent. Allowing for delays, No. 1008 made the run of 82·7 miles from Grantham to York, including Selby bridge slack, in 91 minutes net, and No. 266 in 89¾ minutes.

In 1898 there appeared from Doncaster the first of the 6 ft. 7½ in. large-boilered 4-4-0s of Ivatt's design, No. 1321. Seventeen years later, soon after the opening of the First World War, I had a run behind No. 41 of this class (the present L.N.E.R. Class "D2") which showed the surprising capacity of an engine of no more than 47½ tons weight when fully extended. The train concerned was the 2.20 p.m. afternoon Scotch express from King's Cross, which at that time frequently had 4-4-0 haulage from Grantham to York. In Table 27 this run is compared with that of No. 58, one of the superheated batch of this class (now L.N.E.R. "D1") built by Ivatt in 1911, and weighing 53½ tons apiece.

TABLE 26

YEAR 1909
G.N.R. "SINGLE" CLASSES (4-2-2)
Load: 188 tons tare, 200 tons gross

Engine No.			†1008	‡266
Dist.		Sched.	Actual	Actual
miles		min.	min. sec.	min. sec.
0·0	GRANTHAM	0	0 00	0 00
4·2	Barkston	—	8 05	6 35
9·9	Claypole	—	13 10	11 20
14·6	NEWARK	16	17 15	15 20
20·9	Carlton	—	23 15	20 50
26·4	Tuxford	—	29 20	26 20
33·1	RETFORD	36	36 · 25	33 50
38·4	Ranskill	—	41 40	39 15
42·2	Bawtry	. —	45 05	43 00
			sigs.	
50·5	DONCASTER	54	54 50	51 45
57·5	Moss	—	62 30	59 40
64·3	Templehirst	—	69 35	66 20
			p.w.s.	sigs.
68·9	SELBY*	78	74 35	74 25
75·6	Escrick	—	83 55	83 40
82·7	YORK	94	93 25	92 40
82·7	Net times (min.)	94	91	89¾

* Severe service slack
† Stirling 8 ft. 1½ in. type   ‡ Ivatt 7 ft. 6 in. type

Both locomotives handled their 425-ton load to time, at almost identical speeds. The smaller engine did extraordinarily well to reach 69 m.p.h. by Claypole; the minimum up Tuxford bank was 37 m.p.h., and by Retford we were again up to 64½ m.p.h., so gaining over a minute from Newark to Doncaster. On to York the little machine just held her own with a train which, tender included, was almost exactly ten times her own weight. My best run with superheated 4-4-0 No. 58, which often worked this train about the time referred to, was one on which, with a load of 410 tons, we passed Doncaster in exactly 55 minutes, with speeds of 72½ m.p.h. beyond Hougham, 66 sustained across the Trent valley as far as Carlton, and then minima of 41½ at Markham and 42½ at Piper's Wood summits, but this run was badly delayed beyond Doncaster. On the run tabulated the speeds of No. 58 approximated closely to those of No. 41.

As is evident by the performance of the North Eastern Railway "M" class 4-4-0 engines in the "Race to Aberdeen" already mentioned, the speed appetite of that company had been whetted, and resulted, in July, 1902, in the institution of what for almost exactly 21 years remained the fastest scheduled run in the British Empire—from Darlington to York, 44·1 miles, in 43 minutes, at 61·5 m.p.h. start to stop. The advent in 1899 of the Wilson Worsdell 6 ft. 10 in. 4-4-0 engines of the handsome "R" class—among the first in Great Britain to be fitted with piston-valves— had made such a timing relatively easy. The train concerned (12·20 p.m. from Newcastle to York, with through Midland coaches for Bristol) was usually a light one of five or six coaches, and the section of line

TABLE 27

YEAR 1915
G.N.R. 4-4-0 CLASSES
Load: 402 tons tare, 425 tons gross

Engine No.			41	†58
Dist.		Sched.	Actual	Actual
miles		min.	min. sec.	min. sec.
0·0	GRANTHAM	0	0 00	0 00
6·0	Hougham ..	—	9 40	9 50
14·6	NEWARK	17	17 25	17 35
20·9	Carlton ..	—	23 20	23 35
26·4	Tuxford ..	—	30 10	30 15
33·1	RETFORD	39	38 30	38 25
42·2	Bawtry ..	—	47 45	47 50
50·5	DONCASTER ..	58	57 15	57 10
54·7	Shaftholme Junction ..	63	62 15	62 00
60·5	Balne	—	68 50	68 05
68·9	SELBY*	79	78 35	77 55
75·6	Escrick ..	—	87 25	87 15
82·7	YORK	97	96 50	96 20

* Severe service slack
† Superheated, 51-65 series

concerned is one of the straightest and most level in the country. The fastest run that I have ever known with an "R" was made on this express, and is set out in Table 28; it was timed by Mr. R. J. Purves. Three miles after the Darlington start the train was travelling at 60 m.p.h.; up the 1 in 391 from Croft Spa to Eryholme there was an acceleration to 69 m.p.h. From then on, speed remained between 70 and 78 m.p.h. until steam was shut off for the long curve into York. Between mileposts 37 and 2, the average speed for 35 miles was 72·8 m.p.h., with this 165-ton load; over the 21 miles from Otterington to Beningbrough it was as high as 75 m.p.h.

On the Great Eastern Railway, from 1900 onwards, when the class was first introduced, James Holden's "Claud Hamilton" 4-4-0 loco-motives were performing prodigies of work in relation to their size and the extreme difficulties of the slack-infested main lines of the Eastern Counties. As with all Great Eastern designs, strict weight limits were imposed on the designer by the permanent way authorities, but within these limits Holden turned out sturdy machines which, provided that too close a watch was not kept on fuel consumption, would do the hardest of work without complaint. My own personal interest in the old Great Eastern is that my railway career began on it, in 1903, and continued with it until the G.E.R. was swallowed up in the L.N.E.R. at the beginning of 1923. Moreover, the first journey that I ever made on a locomotive footplate was in 1908 with the summer "Norfolk Coast Express," one of the most arduous assignments in British locomotive history.

TABLE 28

YEAR 1911
N.E.R. "R" CLASS (4-4-0)
Engine: No. 1672
Load: 152 tons tare, 165 tons gross
Driver Watson (Gateshead)

Dist.				Sched.	Actual		Speeds
miles				min.	min.	sec.	m.p.h.
0·0	DARLINGTON	..	..	0	0	00	—
2·6	Croft Spa ..	..	..	—	3	54	66
5·2	Eryholme ..	..	..	—	6	14	69
6·9	Cowton	..	..	—	7	40	—
10·4	Danby Wiske	..	..	—	10	33	73
14·1	NORTHALLERTON	..	..	14	13	46	70½
17·5	Otterington	..	..	—	16	36	73½
21·9	THIRSK ..	..	..	21½	20	04	78
26·1	Sessay	..	..	—	23	33	—
28·0	Pilmoor	..	..	—	25	09	72
30·7	Raskelf	..	..	—	27	23	73½
32·9	Alne	..	..	32	29	09	76½
34·4	Tollerton ..	..	..	—	30	20	75
38·6	Beningbrough	..	..	—	33	45	74
42·5	Poppleton Junction	..	..	40	37	00	†72½
44·1	YORK ..	..	..	43	39	34	—

† Before shutting off steam

It was in the previous year that a corridor restaurant car train of new stock was introduced for this service. The 12 vehicles had a tare weight of 317 tons, but at busy summer week-ends this might be increased to 14 or even 15 bogie vehicles, to be taken non-stop over the 130·2 miles between Liverpool Street and North Walsham in 158 minutes down and 159 minutes up. The non-superheated "Claud Hamilton" 4-4-0s in use had 7 ft. driving wheels, 19 in. × 26 in. cylinders, 180 lb. pressure, and a weight in working order of 50½ to 51¾ tons (according to type); and only those familiar with the formidable difficulties of the route can realise what was involved in making such a run as that set out in Table 29, with locomotives of such proportions.

Suffice it to say that when, after considerable flourish of trumpets, the "East Anglian" express was put into commission by the L.N.E.R. in 1937, with a streamlined three-cylinder 4-6-0 locomotive of the latest type and six coaches of 219 tons, the allowance from Liverpool Street, including a 4-minute stop at Ipswich, to passing Trowse, 114 miles, was 132 minutes. Thirty years earlier the Great Eastern "Claud Hamiltons," innocent even of superheaters, were expected—without the Ipswich stop—to get through Trowse with a tare load of

317 to 371 tons, and occasionally even 398 tons (if 15 bogies were taken), in 134 minutes. At least one prominent L.N.E.R. operating official in 1937 refused to believe that the latter feat had ever been performed or had even been possible. But it should be emphasised that picked engines and engine-crews were reserved for the "Norfolk Coast Express," over which the G.E.R. authorities displayed the greatest solicitude.

The run in Table 29 was made in the up direction, with a load of 14 bogies, packed with passengers and weighing 400 tons all told; No. 1809 was the locomotive, in charge of Arthur Cage of Ipswich, a very competent driver. There is a sharp rise beyond Wroxham which cannot be taken at speed because of the slack round Wroxham curve; but this is nothing to the delays in the environs of Norwich, where the exceedingly severe slack round Wensum curve and over the swingbridge is followed by ¾-mile up at 1 in 84 to Trowse Upper Junction, and thence by grades generally adverse as far as Tivetshall. The 47½ m.p.h. minimum near Finningham was after a climb of 7½ miles, partly at 1 in 132 and 248 up. Then, attaining 74 m.p.h. down Haughley bank, Driver Cage continued at 70 m.p.h. down the Gipping Valley over almost level track.

TABLE 29

YEAR 1911

G.E.R. "CLAUD HAMILTON" CLASS (4-4-0)

Engine No. 1809

Load: 371 tons tare, 400 tons gross

Driver A. Cage (Ipswich)

Dist.		Sched.	Actual	Speeds
miles		min.	min. sec.	m.p.h.
0·0	NORTH WALSHAM ..	0	0 00	—
7·3	Wroxham ..	—	10 04	*45
15·3	Wensum Junction ..	21	21 35	*15
17·2	Trowse Upper Junction ..	—	26 08	—
29·6	Tivetshall ..	43	43 31	—
35·1	Diss	—	49 25	66
43·5	Finningham ..	—	59 14	47½
47·2	Haughley ..	62	63 30	—
49·5	STOWMARKET..	64	65 25	74
61·4	IPSWICH ..	76	76 25	*40
64·9	Belstead ..	—	81 39	31
70·6	MANNINGTREE ..	88	88 29	67/40½
78·4	COLCHESTER ..	98	97 20	*55
83·5	Mark's Tey ..	—	103 05	—
91·5	WITHAM ..	113	111 51	—
100·4	CHELMSFORD ..	123	121 46	—
109·9	SHENFIELD ..	134	134 09	—
110·8	Ingrave Summit ..	—	135 39	36
120·1	Chadwell Heath ..	144	144 20	†76½
			sigs.	
126·1	STRATFORD ..	151	150 40	*35
129·0	Bethnal Green ..	—	155 10	*25
130·1	LIVERPOOL STREET ..	159	157 24	—

Net time: 157 min.

* Service slack   † At Harold Wood

After Ipswich slack, the 31 m.p.h. at Belstead was the minimum up 2¼ miles at 1 in 125, and there was a fall from 67 through Manningtree to 40½ near Ardleigh up 2½ miles at 1 in 134. The time of 24 minutes 26 seconds over the sharp undulations from Colchester to Chelmsford, 22·0 miles, was excellent; and though on the long rise from Chelmsford to Shenfield and Ingrave a hardly-won 1¼ minutes was dropped, with 76½ m.p.h. at the bottom of Brentwood bank Cage recovered his loss. Service slacks on the old Great Eastern were noted for their rather extravagant severity, and they were taken with considerable indulgence on this run; but even so the net time of 157 minutes for the 130·2 miles, in such conditions of road and load, was a triumph for both engine and driver.

Before leaving the Great Eastern, reference is needed to the working of the Continental boat trains between Liverpool Street and Parkeston Quay. After the advent in 1911 of the 4-6-0 locomotives designed by Stephen Holden, later the L.N.E.R. Class "B12," the schedule of the down Hook of Holland express was cut to 82 minutes for the 68·9 miles to Parkeston Quay. Why this should have been done, when a few minutes more or less on the boat crossing would have been immaterial, has always been a mystery to me, for the task so laid on locomotives of but 63 tons weight, with the load imposed on them, was formidable to the last degree. Fortunately, on this short run, it was soon over. As with the summer "Norfolk Coast Express," picked engines and a small link of expert engine-crews alone made possible consistent timekeeping.

On the run set out in Table 30, I travelled on the footplate of No. 1566 with Harry Chapman, whose handling of the engine was a fine art. The load consisted of 11 bogies (including restaurant cars), two Pullmans, and a 6-wheeled van, 415 tons all told. Shortly after starting comes the 1 in 70 ascent of Bethnal Green bank; then, after the Stratford slack, the gradients are against the engine for 15 miles, mostly at 1 in 380-435 to beyond Harold Wood, and then for 3 miles averaging about 1 in 100 to Ingrave. Up the easier grades we maintained a steady 55 m.p.h., cutting off at 40 per cent. and with regulator wide open; then came a slight signal check on Brentwood bank proper, after which Chapman opened out to 60 per cent. cut-off, the engine rousing the echoes of the entire district with her thunderous exhaust. Yet the boiler found steam without difficulty,

TABLE 30

YEAR 1922
G.E.R "1500" CLASS (4-6-0)
Engine No. 1566
Load: 388 tons tare, 415 tons gross
Driver H. Chapman (Parkeston)

Dist.			Sched.	Actual	Speeds
miles			min.	min. sec.	m.p.h.
0·0	LIVERPOOL STREET	..	0	0 00	—
1·1	Bethnal Green	.. ..	—	3 25	—
4·0	STRATFORD	..	8	7 50	*40
7·3	ILFORD ..	.. ..	—	11 55	—
10·0	Chadwell Heath	..	15	14 50	55
15·0	Harold Wood	..	—	20 15	55
				sigs.	
18·2	Brentwood	.. ..	—	24 25	—
19·3	Ingrave Summit	..	—	26 25	33
20·2	SHENFIELD	..	28	27 40	—
23·6	Ingatestone	.. ..	—	31 00	71½
29·7	CHELMSFORD	..	38	36 30	*55
35·9	Hatfield Peverel ..	..	—	42 50	—
38·6	WITHAM ..	..	48	45 35	66
42·3	Kelvedon ..	..	—	49 10	—
46·6	Mark's Tey	..	—	53 40	†50
51·7	COLCHESTER	.. · ..	61	58 25	70½/*50
54·1	Parson's Heath	..	—	61 10	—
56·0	Ardleigh ..	..	—	63 35	—
59·5	MANNINGTREE..	..	70	67 20	67/*30
61·2	Mistley	.. ..	—	70 15	—
65·1	Wrabness ..	..	—	75 20	—
68·9	PARKESTON QUAY	..	82	80 15	—

Net time: 79¾ min.

* Service slack   † At Hill House box

and past Brentwood station, even up 1 in 85, we were doing a steady 33 m.p.h.

From Shenfield onwards the mile-a-minute average for the next 35·8 miles to Ardleigh was kept up with about 25 per cent. cut-off, and regulator varying from the second port (about one-quarter open) to three-quarters open on the short uphill stretches; actually there were frequent slight changes of both to suit the constant undulations of the road. Thus we gained nearly 2 minutes on the run. In the preceding week I had made a footplate trip on No. 1565, with Driver Osborne and a 420-ton train, on which very similar times were made, with a total of 81 minutes 5 seconds to Parkeston Quay; in the latter case the climb of Brentwood bank was made on a cut-off of 30 per cent. to Brentwood and 40 per cent. from there to Ingrave, and from Shenfield to Manningtree 30 per cent. cut-off and regulator from one-third to one-half open did all that was necessary.

Before the end of the Nineteenth Century Ivatt had built his first Atlantic locomotives, but it was the large-boilered series, beginning with No. 251 in 1902, that in the course of years established a locomotive reputation with few rivals among engines of equivalent dimensions and weight. As with many other British types, it was not until superheating had been added to the original design that its real merits became apparent. With the first superheated series, Nos. 1452 to 1461, Ivatt increased his cylinder diameter from 18¾ to 20 in., and in order not to add to the tractive effort and at the same time to reduce the cost of boiler maintenance, he reduced his boiler pressure from 175 to 150 lb. per sq. in. by way of balance. But this somewhat shortsighted measure was later rectified, and a pressure of 170 lb. was restored.

These engines have been responsible for some astonishing performance in relation to their modest tractive effort of 17,340 lb. The

TABLE 31

YEAR 1936
G.N.R. IVATT 4-4-2 (L.N.E.R. CLASS "C1")
Engine No. 4460
Load: 275 tons tare, 290 tons gross

Dist.		Sched.	Actual	Speeds
miles		min.	min. sec.	m.p.h.
0·0	KING'S CROSS	0	0 00	—
2·5	FINSBURY PARK ..	—	6 27	—
5·0	Wood Green	—	9 44	52
9·2	New Barnet	—	14 45	46½
12·7	Potter's Bar	—	19 25	44
17·7	HATFIELD	24	24 19	74
20·3	Welwyn Garden City ..	—	26 24	67
23·5	Woolmer Green	—	29 19	64
28·6	Stevenage	—	33 34	74
31·9	HITCHIN	37	36 05	86
35·7	Three Counties ..	—	38 38	90
37·0	Arlesey	—	39 32	87
41·1	Biggleswade	—	42 22	88
44·1	Sandy	—	44 56	82
47·5	Tempsford	—	46 52	80½
51·7	St. Neot's	—	50 02	77½
56·0	Offord	—	53 14	80½
58·9	HUNTINGDON	59	55 28	74
62·0	Milepost 62	—	58 10	64
63·5	Abbot's Ripton	—	59 34	66
69·4	Holme	—	63 56	83
72·6	Yaxley	—	66 36	63½
76·4	PETERBOROUGH ..	†77	†70 34	*

* Service slack, severe   † Passing time

finest chapter in their history, probably, was in the working of the Pullman services between King's Cross and Leeds. What an engine of this type could do with the seven-car "Queen of Scots," when a particularly fast performance was needed, is well seen in Table 31. A normal start was made, with speed dropping from 52 to 44 m.p.h. up the 1 in 200 from Finsbury Park to Potter's Bar, but from there onwards the speed was extraordinary; indeed, there was a gain of 6¾ minutes between Hatfield and Peterborough alone. A top speed of 90 m.p.h. was reached at Three Counties; over the 54·9 miles from Hatfield to Yaxley the average speed was 78·0 m.p.h., while over the 30·3 miles from Stevenage to Huntingdon the engine kept up an average of 83·0 m.p.h. The start from London had been behind time, but with this brilliant running the loss had been more than regained by Peterborough, and more normal travelling followed.

TABLE 32

YEAR 1939
G.N.R. IVATT 4-4-2 (L.N.E.R. CLASS "CI")
Engine No. 4401
Load: 366 tons tare, 385 tons gross

Dist.			Sched	Actual		Speeds
miles			min.	min.	sec.	m.p.h.
0·0	GRANTHAM	.. ..	0†	0	00‡	—
3·5	Great Ponton	..	—	7	53	37½
5·4	Stoke	.. ..	—	10	55	40
8·4	Corby	.. ..	—	14	17	64½
13·3	Little Bytham	..	—	18	21	76
16·9	Essendine ..	..	—	21	03	80½
20·7	Tallington	..	—	24	00	76
26·0	Werrington Junction		—	28	21	74
29·1	PETERBOROUGH	..	28†	31	51	*32
30·5	Fletton Junction	..	—	34	08	—
36·1	Holme ..	..	—	39	59	68½
43·5	Milepost 62	..	—	47	01	58
46·6	HUNTINGDON ..	..	46†	49	45	79½
53·8	St. Neot's..	..	—	55	21	72
61·4	Sandy	..	—	61	29	77/72
68·5	Arlesey	..	—	67	34	69
73·6	HITCHIN ..	..	70†	72	16	60
76·9	Stevenage..	..	—	76	05	51
82·0	Woolmer Green	..	—	81	25	58½
87·8	HATFIELD	..	84†	86	26	77
92·8	Potter's Bar	..	—	91	07	60
100·5	Wood Green	..	—	98	02	72½
103·0	FINSBURY PARK	..	—	100	29	—
105·5	KING'S CROSS ..	..	104†	104	35	—

* Service slack　† From passing Grantham
‡ From dead start

Some of the most exceptional efforts of the Ivatt Atlantics have been made when they have been compelled, at a moment's notice, to tackle heavy express trains on which Pacifics have failed. One such run, on the up "Yorkshire Pullman," appears in Table 32. This express, timed from Doncaster to King's Cross, 156 miles, in 155 minutes, had made an emergency stop at Grantham, and No. 4401 was called on to take over the 385-ton load from a Class "A3" Pacific which had run hot. Of such quality was the Atlantic's performance that the Pullman was worked from the dead start at Grantham to King's Cross in no more than 35 seconds over the 104 minutes allowed from pass to stop; from Peterborough to London there was a gain of 3¾ minutes. High lights of the journey were the 58 m.p.h. minimum up 4½ miles at 1 in 200 past Abbots Ripton, and 51 m.p.h. minimum at Stevenage, after the long climb up from Three Counties, much of it at 1 in 200. The average speed of 74·7 m.p.h. from Huntingdon to Arlesey, 21·9 miles, was another outstanding performance, as also was the average of 65·3 m.p.h. over the 97·6 miles from Stoke summit to Finsbury Park, Peterborough station slowing included. This run was timed by Mr. J. C. Thorne.

As to the run set out in Table 33, I might have regarded it as incredible had I not recorded the performance myself; so incredible, indeed, that more than once I rose from my seat and put my head out of the window, as we rounded the curves at Selby and elsewhere, to make certain that we had neither left any of the train behind nor attached a pilot. The train was the 1·20 p.m. from King's Cross to Edinburgh, with a 17-coach load of 585 tons, and again it was the running hot of an "A3" Pacific that made necessary an Ivatt Atlantic substitution, this time of No. 4404. Needless to say, the 69½-ton Atlantic, with her 40 tons of adhesion, took some time to get this vast train on the move at Grantham, and did so only after we had set back twice. With the slow start, we lost 2½ minutes on the first stage, to Newark. But by Doncaster we had recovered 4 minutes, and by Selby another 2 minutes; indeed, by Brayton Junction, Selby, the engine had achieved the almost miraculous feat of "even time" from the start—67·5 miles in 67 minutes 41 seconds. From Barkston to this point we had covered 63·3 miles at an average of 64·0 m.p.h.

Most outstanding of all the running, perhaps, was the 72½ to 75 m.p.h. maintained along the whole of the level and slightly falling section from Retford to Bawtry, whereby the 17·4 miles from Retford to Doncaster were completed in 15 minutes 4 seconds, instead of the 18 minutes allowed. When the large-boilered Atlantic design was

TABLE 33

YEAR 1936
G.N.R. IVATT 4-4-2 (L.N.E.R. Class "C1")
Engine No. 4404
Load: 546 tons tare, 585 tons gross
Driver Walker, Fireman Barrick (Gateshead)

Dist.		Sched.	Actual	Speeds
miles		min.	min. sec.	m.p.h.
0·0	GRANTHAM	0	0 00	—
4·2	Barkston	—	8 17	—
9·9	Claypole	—	13 23	74
14·6	NEWARK.. ..	15	17 23	—
20·9	Carlton-on-Trent ..	—	23 22	64¼
25·8	Dukeries Junction ..	—	28 30	48
28·2	Markham	—	31 31	48½
33·1	RETFORD	35	36 15	†77½
36·2	Sutton	—	38 49	72½
38·4	Ranskill	—	40 37	74
42·2	Bawtry	—	43 43	75
44·0	Piper's Wood ..	—	45 22	61
47·7	Black Carr Junction ..	—	48 38	72½
50·5	DONCASTER ..	53	51 19	*55
54·7	Shaftholme Junction ..	—	55 36	62½
57·5	Moss	—	58 15	64
60·5	Balne	—	61 02	65/60
64·3	Templehirst ..	—	64 42	66
67·5	Brayton Junction ..	—	67 41	—
68·9	SELBY	73	69 17	*30
73·0	Riccall	—	75 18	55
75·6	Escrick	—	78 04	59
78·5	Naburn	—	80 56	60
80·7	Chaloner's Whin Junction	—	83 09	—
			sigs.	
82·7	YORK	90	87 40	—

Net time, 86½ min.
* Service slack   † Speed before Retford

introduced in 1902, 350 tons was regarded as a heavy train, and 400 tons as abnormal; moreover, this express in those days was allowed 97 minutes from Grantham to York. Yet No. 4404 reduced the 97-minute schedule of 1902 and after, and the 90-minute booking of 1936, to an actual time of 87¾ minutes and a net time of 86½ minutes, with a load of 585 tons   Another striking feature of this run was that the driver, Walker of Gateshead, and his fireman, Barrick, were from the North Eastern Area of the L.N.E.R.; not only had they to take over a strange machine without warning or preparation, but in the normal course they could very rarely have handled an engine of this type previously. "Grand engines, these," Walker remarked, with quiet enthusiasm, when I went up to speak to him on alighting at Darlington.

70. An arduous locomotive task of earlier years—the "Norfolk Coast Express" on its 130-mile non-stop run to North Walsham, with 12 bogies headed by a 50-ton "Claud Hamilton" 4-4-0. (*F. R. Hebron.*)

71. Successor to the "Claud Hamiltons"—a Holden 4-6-0, later L.N.E.R. Class "B12," at speed with the "Eastern Belle" Pullman. (*F. R. Hebron.*)

LOCOMOTIVES OF THE ONE-TIME GREAT EASTERN RAILWAY

72. One of the most handsome past British designs—a Robinson Atlantic on the "Sheffield Special." (*F. E. Mackay.*)

73. A Robinson "Director" 4-4-0, *Princess Mary*, lent to the Great Northern Section to work the "Queen of Scots" Pullman. (*Courtesy, British Railways.*)

74. A Gresley "Sandringham" 3-cylinder 4-6-0, of L.N.E.R. Class "B17." *Ford Castle*, since rebuilt with two cylinders, is seen here at work on the Great Eastern Section. (*E. R. Wethersett.*)

STAGES IN GREAT CENTRAL MOTIVE POWER

— 14 —

PERFORMANCE—THE L.N.E.R. UNDER GRESLEY

WE come now to the Pacific classes of the late London & North Eastern Railway, with which, more than any other of the designs for which he was responsible, the late Sir Nigel Gresley made his unique reputation as a locomotive engineer. More than that, his was the supreme part played in helping the L.N.E.R. to the pinnacle of speed achievement in Great Britain that this company reached during the years from 1935 to 1939 inclusive. Although the first Pacific, No. 1470, *Great Northern*, had emerged from Doncaster Works in 1922, just before the London & North Eastern Railway was formed, it was not until the lessons of the 1925 exchange of locomotives with the Great Western Railway had been learned and applied that the Gresley Pacifics came into their own. With higher working pressures, long-lap valves and long-travel valve-motions, L.N.E.R. main-line drivers soon learned the art of short cut-off working, until at last, with the evolution of the "A4" streamlined Pacifics, Gresley put into their hands machines which may have equals, but certainly have had no superiors in this country in the realm of capable and efficient performance. The old Great Northern tradition referred to in the first paragraph of Chapter 13 was being well and truly carried on.

So far as speed is concerned, the principal exploits of the Gresley Pacifics have been those connected with the streamline trains introduced in 1935 and 1937. The first preliminary trial was made on November 30th, 1934, when No. 4472, *Flying Scotsman*, of the original "A1" series, in charge of the redoubtable William Sparshatt, made the run of 185·8 miles from King's Cross to Leeds in the record time of 151 minutes 56 seconds. True, the load was no more than four coaches of 145 tons tare and 147 tons gross, but even so such an average speed as 82·5 m.p.h. up the whole of the 10 miles to Stoke Summit, between mileposts 90 and 100, with an absolute minimum of 81 on the final 1 in 178, was a startling experience for the observers on the train. So also was the starting time of 17 minutes 3 seconds out to Hatfield. We had made our exit from platform No. 11 at King's Cross with such vigour that No. 4472 left some wheel-flange marks on parts of rails where normally they ought not to be visible, among the sharply-curved connections out into the Gasworks tunnel.

Hitchin was passed in 28 minutes 22 seconds, Huntingdon in 46 minutes 31 seconds, Peterborough in 60 minutes 39 seconds, Stoke

Box in 79 minutes 33 seconds, Grantham in 83 minutes 39 seconds, Newark in 94 minutes 38 seconds, Retford in 108 minutes 44 seconds, and the 153¾ milepost in precisely 2 hours from London—an average of 76·9 m.p.h. from the start. After passing Doncaster in 122 minutes 27 seconds (the fastest time ever recorded), *Flying Scotsman* tackled the heavy gradients through the West Riding with great *vim*, with minimum speeds of 77½ m.p.h. up two 1 in 150 stretches, and an acceleration from 40 to 55 m.p.h. up the 1 in 122 to Ardsley. So we reached Leeds in 13 minutes less than the 2¾-hour schedule laid down for the run—a time which still remains unbeaten. The maximum cut-off used on the uphill stretches was 40 per cent., and the maximum speed downhill was 93½ m.p.h.

For the return journey the load was increased by two coaches, making the train up to six vehicles, of 205 tons empty and 208 tons gross. This was worked back to London in 157 minutes 17 seconds, at speeds which included, for the first time in L.N.E.R. history, a maximum of exactly 100 m.p.h., attained in the descent of Stoke bank. To Peterborough, passed in 92 minutes from Leeds, 8 minutes had been gained on the test schedule, but the effects of this exacting round were now beginning to tell on Fireman Webster, and small wonder! No further gain in time was achieved on to London. In the complete trip that day, *Flying Scotsman* had covered 40 miles at 90 m.p.h., 250 miles at 80 m.p.h., and 371·6 miles in 309¼ minutes, at 72·1 m.p.h.; the total coal burned was about 9 tons.

Next came the trial of March 5th, 1935, from King's Cross to Newcastle and back, which preceded the introduction of the "Silver Jubilee." For this a six-coach train of 213 tons tare and 217 tons gross had been made up, with the "A3" class Pacific No. 2750, *Papyrus*, at the head. The actual times of the runs call for no special remark, for they became a daily performance after the "Silver Jubilee" went into service; but the outstanding feature was that the one locomotive in a a single day covered 500 miles of line, all service slacks included, in 423 minutes 57 seconds, or (allowing for out-of-course checks), in 412½ minutes net, equal to 72·7 m.p.h.; moreover, 300 miles of the day's round were completed at an average of 80 m.p.h. In descending Stoke bank, again with Sparshatt at the regulator, *Papyrus* averaged 100·6 m.p.h. for 12¼ miles and reached a top speed of 108 m.p.h.

Such feats as these pale into insignificance, however, in comparison with the exploit of *Silver Link*, first of the famous "A4" series of Gresley streamlined Pacifics, on the trial trip of the "Silver Jubilee." The run took place on September 27th, 1935—one hundred and ten years to the day after George Stephenson drove *Locomotion No.* 1 over the

Stockton & Darlington course on the opening day of the world's first public railway. This was the first public appearance of a locomotive of the "A4" type, and it was indeed an auspicious *début*. Directors, officials, guests and pressmen filled the train; the three articulated sets of coaches, seven vehicles in all, weighed 230 tons.

Up the 1 in 200 from Wood Green to Potter's Bar Driver Arthur Taylor steadily increased his speed from 70 to 75 m.p.h.; once over the "Northern Heights" the engine crossed the 100 m.p.h. line at milepost 30, and from then onwards to milepost 55, for 25 miles continuously, the speed at no point fell below 100 m.p.h. The mean speed over this length was 107·5 m.p.h.; at two separate points we reached 112½ m.p.h.; and for 43 miles on end an average of 100 was maintained. Over the 70 miles from Wood Green to Fletton Junction, including all the climbing between Wood Green and Knebworth, the average was 91·8 m.p.h. On passing Peterborough, in no more than 55 minutes 2 seconds from King's Cross, *Silver Link* already had gained 8½ minutes on the new "Silver Jubilee" schedule, and was so much ahead of time that signal checks now brought the record-breaking to an end. The run is set out in detail in Table 34.

TABLE 34

YEAR 1935

L.N.E.R. CLASS "A4" STREAMLINED 4-6-2

Engine: No. 2509, *Silver Link*

Load: 220 tons tare, 230 tons gross

Driver A. J. Taylor, Fireman Luty (King's Cross)

Dist.			Sched.	Times		Speeds
m.	ch.		min.	min.	sec.	m.p.h.
0	00	KING'S CROSS ..	0	0	00	—
2	41	Finsbury Park	—	4	42	—
4	04	Hornsey	—	6	22	—
4	78	Wood Green	—	7	11	70
6	35	New Southgate ..	—	8	26	71½
9	12	New Barnet	—	10	43	72
10	46	Hadley Wood	—	11	53	74
12	57	Potter's Bar	—	13	36	75
17	55	HATFIELD	18½	17	07	94½
20	25	Welwyn Garden City..	—	18	46	98
22	00	Welwyn North ..	—	19	52	90
23	39	*Woolmer Green* ..	—	20	52	88
25	03	Knebworth	—	21	55	93½
28	46	Stevenage	—	24	13	90
30	00	*Milepost 30*	—	25	06	100
31	74	HITCHIN	29½	26	14	107
35	56	Three Counties ..	—	28	20	109½
37	03	Arlesey	—	29	03	112½
41	12	Biggleswade	—	31	22	105
44	10	Sandy	—	32	59	112½
47	41	Tempsford	—	34	50	109½
51	58	St. Neot's	—	37	13	104½
55	00	*Milepost 55* ..	—	39	03	109½
55	76	Offord	—	39	41	*85
58	70	HUNTINGDON ..	48½	41	41	88
62	00	*Milepost 62* ..	—	43	53	83½
63	42	Abbot's Ripton ..	—	44	58	—
69	29	Holme	—	48	50	93½
72	48	Yaxley	—	51	08	80½
74	78	*Fletton Junction*.. ..	—	52	55	—
76	29	PETERBOROUGH ..	†63½	†55	02	*20

* Speed reduced by brakes † Passing time

To claim that this run was as enjoyable as it was exciting would be rather wide of the mark. There had been no special preparation of the track for these enormously high speeds; curves in general were canted for speeds of 70 m.p.h. and were reasonably comfortable at 85, to which *Silver Link* was adding in places all but another 30 m.p.h. The new springing that Gresley had devised for his streamline stock made the coaches alarmingly lively, with severe jarring from side to side as we struck the sharper curves; the engine, however, was riding perfectly, and those on the footplate had no idea of the sensations to which we were being subjected in the train. The designer himself was completely imperturbable, as ever; but not so those of his passengers whose minds dwelt uneasily on the slightly over one-inch depth of steel flanges that was keeping the flyer to the track!

It should be added, however, that the curves throughout the route were promptly taken in hand, and with the help of spiral development and improvement of super-elevation they were adjusted to provide for the much higher speeds that were now contemplated; also, in the light of experience, the springing of the train was improved to give smooth and comfortable riding. Moreover, during the short time that the three L.N.E.R. streamliners ran, up to the outbreak of the Second World War, none of them was ever involved in a major mishap, so the risks on the trial trip were doubtless more imaginary than real.

For the distance concerned, the "Silver Jubilee" trial trip is easily the fastest run that has been performed in British railway annals, even though its maximum of 112½ m.p.h. has since been exceeded. Its principal purpose was to ascertain what margin the new locomotive might be expected to have in hand on the new schedule, when normal running began on the following Monday, three days later. Until that Friday, *Silver Link*, then only three weeks out of the shops, had had no more than routine running-in on moderately-timed trains. It says a great deal for the excellence of Doncaster locomotive building that for the next fortnight, until the second engine of the class became available, *Silver Link* shouldered the entire burden of working the "Silver Jubilee," five days a week in each direction, which meant 2,683 miles of streamline speed weekly and 2,323 miles of the total actually timed at 70·4 m.p.h., an outstanding feat of British locomotive endurance.

Although there was a nominal limit of 90 m.p.h. to the speeds of the L.N.E.R. streamline trains, this has been exceeded on a number of special occasions, chiefly in the descent of Stoke bank. On August 27th, 1936, with the dynamometer car added to the "Silver Jubilee" set and making up the weight of the train to 270 tons, near Essendine *Silver Fox* reached a maximum of 113 m.p.h.—probably the highest speed ever attained by an express in Great Britain carrying ordinary passengers. On June 30th, 1937, the trial trip of the then new "Coronation" stream-liner took place, with its considerably heavier gross load of 320 tons, and "A4" Pacific *Dominion of Canada* reached 109½ m.p.h. at the same point. On a regular run of the "Coronation," timed by Mr. O. S. Nock, *Commonwealth of Australia*, hauling 325 tons, not only reached

106 m.p.h. at Essendine, but continued running at from 105 to 106 m.p.h. for 6¾ miles during which the gradient flattens from 1 in 200 to 264, 440, 528, and then to level. Driver Walker of Gateshead, already mentioned in connection with the exploit of Ivatt Atlantic No. 4404, was in charge of the engine and told Mr. Nock, at the end of the run, that the engine was being worked on no more than 15 per cent. cut-off, with full regulator.

But the maximum speed achievement of an "A4" was that of July 7th, 1938, when one of these engines reached what is believed to be the highest speed ever yet attained with steam. The occasion was the climax of a series of brake tests, which were being made with six coaches out of one of the "Coronation" streamline sets, and the dynamometer car, weighing 240 tons all told. It is significant that the locomotive employed, No. 4468, *Mallard*, was one of the Pacifics which enjoys the benefit of the Kylchap double blast-pipe and chimney; and the freedom of steaming and exhaust so obtained doubtless had no small influence on the maximum speed reached. On this particular run, it is an open secret that the brake trials were merely incidental to the determination of Sir Nigel Gresley to achieve a record for the L.N.E.R. and for one of his locomotives that would stand in no fear of challenge for a considerable time to come. The *venue* of the test, of course, was the customary long stretch of downhill track from Stoke Summit southwards towards Peterborough. Driver J. Duddington, of Doncaster, was at the regulator.

TABLE 35

YEAR 1938

L.N.E.R. CLASS "A4" STREAMLINED 4-6-2

Engine No. 4468, *Mallard*

Load: 237 tons tare, 240 tons gross

Driver J. Duddington, Fireman T. H. Bray (Doncaster)

RECORD SPEED LENGTH ON TEST RUN

Distance	Station or Milepost	Actual Time (p.m.)			Speeds*
miles‖		hr.	min.	sec.	m.p.h.
105½	GRANTHAM‡	4	24	19	24
105	*Milepost*	4	25	13	32
104	,, ...	4	26	32	52¼
103	,, ...	4	27	36½	59¾
102	Great Ponton ..	4	38	35½	63½
101	*Milepost*	4	29	30	69
100·1	*Stoke Box*	4	30	16	—
100	*Milepost*	4	30	20½	74½
99	,, ...	4	31	05	87½
98	,, ...	4	31	44½	96½
97·1	*Corby*	4	32	17	—
97	*Milepost*	4	32	20¼	104
96	,, ...	4	32	54½	107
95	,, ...	4	33	27½	111½
94	,, ...	4	33	59½	116
93	,, ...	4	34	30	119
92¾	,, ...		—		119¼
92½	,, ...		—		120¾
92¼	Little Bytham ..	4	34	52½	122¼
92	*Milepost*		—		122½
91¾	,, ...		—		122¼
91½	,, ...		—		123
91¼	,, ...		—		124½
91	,, ...	4	35	29½	124¼
90¾	,, ...		—		123½
90½	,, ...		—		124
90¼	,, ...		—		§125
90	,, ...	4	35	58½	124¼
89¾	,, ...		—		†123
89¼	,, ...		—		113
89	,, ...	4	36	29	—
88·65	Essendine	4	36	40	107½

* Actual speed on passing each milepost indicated
† Steam shut off; brakes applied at milepost 89½
‡ Passing time
§ 126 m.p.h. for a very short distance near here
‖ Miles from King's Cross

The train passed Grantham at 24 m.p.h., with 5¼ miles of line ahead rising at 1 in 200. With regulator full open, and 40 per cent. cut-off for 2½ miles, speed rose to 59¾ m.p.h.; then came an interlude of 30 per cent. for 1½ miles (milepost 103 to 101½), with a rise to 69 m.p.h.; and the final 1½ miles of the climb were again on 40 per cent., and produced 74½ m.p.h. on passing Stoke Summit. Apart from a brief 45 per cent. between mileposts 94¼ and 93 inclusive, 40 per cent. was then continued down the bank, still with full regulator, and at the end of successive miles from milepost 100, speeds were 87½, 96½, 104, 107, 111½, 116, and 119 m.p.h. by milepost 93. Then the "120" line was crossed, and at mileposts 92½, 92, 91½, 90½, and 90¼ respectively speeds were 120¾, 122½, 123, 124¼, and 125 m.p.h. For a very short distance the enormous

TABLE 36

L.N.E.R. 100 M.P.H. RECORDS, 1934–1938

Date		30/11/34		5/3/35		27/8/36		30/6/37		3/7/38	
4-6-2 Locomotive Class		‡A1		A3		A4		A4		†A4	
,, ,, Number		4472		2750		2512		4489		4468	
,, ,, Name		*Flying Scotsman*		*Papyrus*		*Silver Fox*		*Dominion of Canada*		*Mallard*	
Load, No. of Vehicles		6		6		8		9		7	
,, tons tare		205¼		213½		254		312		236¾	
,, ,, gross		207½		217		270		320		240	
Dist.	Timing Points	Times	Speeds	Times	Speeds	Times	Speeds	Times	Speeds	Times	Spee
miles		min. sec.	m.p.h.	min. sec.	m.p.h.	min. sec.	m.p.h.	min. sec.	m.p.h.	min. sec.	m.p.
0·0	*Stoke Summit Box* .. pass	0 00	68½	0 00	69¼	0 00	68½	0 00	69	0 00	74
3·0	Corby .. .. .. ,,	2 17	85¾	2 12	91	2 17	85	2 18	86½	2 01	96
7·9	Little Bytham .. ,,	5 31	95½	5 13	106	5 23	104¾	5 19	102½	4 36½	122
		—	100	—	108	—	—	—	—	—	126
11·5	Essendine .. .. ,,	7 44	98	7 16	102	7 23	109¾	7 19	109½	6 24	*107
		—	—	—	—	—	113	—	—	—	—
15·3	Tallington .. .. ,,	10 16	86½	9 32	98½	9 27	—	9 50	—	—	—
18·2	*Helpston Box* .. .. ,,	12 20	84	11 27	—	11 20	—	11 49	92	—	—
20·6	*Werrington Junction* .. ,,	14 06	80½	13 10	—	13 10	*64	13 35	*63	—	—

* Speed reduced by brakes † With Kylchap exhaust and double chimney ‡ Later Class "A10"

speed of 126 m.p.h.—the maximum usually quoted—appeared on the dynamometer car roll.

Between mileposts 94 and 89 five miles were covered in 2 minutes 29½ seconds, at an average of 120·4 m.p.h.; and speed was at or above the 120 m.p.h. mark for the three miles from post 92¾ to post 89¾, where a reduction was made for brake test purposes. At this speed the driving wheels were rotating at more than 500 times a minute, and it is astonishing indeed that the boiler was able to supply steam for no less than 40 per cent. cut-off and with full regulator at such a speed. Table 35 sets out the details of this record of records; and in Table 36 there are compared the chief occasions on which 100 m.p.h. speeds have been attained in the descent of Stoke bank. It should be noted how maximum speed capacity advanced with the advance in design between Pacific classes "A1" (later "A10"), "A3" and "A4," and, lastly, with the application of the Kylchap exhaust to an engine of the "A4" class.

Actually the working of the "Silver Jubilee," with its 235-ton normal load (increased later to 270 tons when an eighth coach was added permanently to the formation) was not a difficult proposition for the locomotives. In a Presidential address to the Institution of Mechanical Engineers, Sir Nigel Gresley revealed that the average drawbar horse-power needed for the run was not more than 620, nor the average coal consumption more than 39 lb. to the mile. On a test run with the down train, with the 270-ton load, on August 27th, 1936, on which I was present in the dynamometer car, Driver Sparshatt never required to extend the engine beyond 18 per cent. cut-off, except on starting and recovering from slacks; with full regulator this was sufficient to take the train up the 15·3 miles from Tallington to Stoke Summit at an average speed of 82·7 m.p.h. With the most scrupulous observance of service slacks we covered the 232·3 miles from King's Cross to Darlington in 194 minutes 43 seconds, so arriving 3¼ minutes ahead of time.

Incidentally, the fastest journey that I ever made on this train in normal conditions was one in which *Silver Link*, with 235 tons, ran to Darlington in 194 minutes 40 seconds, notwithstanding a dead stop for adverse signals and a permanent-way relaying check. At eleven different locations speed reached or exceeded 90 m.p.h., up to a maximum of 98 m.p.h., and this included sections of level track covered at from 93 to 93½ m.p.h. The average speed from Tallington up to Stoke was 84·9 m.p.h., and Stoke Summit was cleared at 76½ m.p.h. From Potter's Bar to Naburn, near York, allowing for the two out-of-course checks, but not for the severe service slacks through Peterborough and Selby, the engine averaged 80 m.p.h. for 171·3 miles continuously. The net time to Darlington, 232·3 miles, was 187¼ minutes, or 10¾ minutes less than that scheduled; and this was at the time when speed over the perfectly aligned stretch from York to Darlington was held down to 70 m.p.h., owing to the limitations of the automatic signalling then in use.

As showing that the art of continuous high speed running has not been lost during the years of the Second World War, I give in Table 37 details of a run from Newcastle to York—the fastest on record over this length—which formed part of a high speed test trip from London to Edinburgh and back in May, 1946. The load was certainly light— 207 tons all told behind the tender—but in view of the various slacks through the colliery area of County Durham, the time of just over

68 minutes made by *Silver Fox* from Newcastle to York (7 minutes less than that allowed the pre-war "Coronation" streamliner) was noteworthy. The most striking part was the perfectly even 90 to 93½ m.p.h. maintained by Driver Leonard for mile after mile of the level course south of Northallerton, with the engine cutting off at 35 per cent.; it was indeed an exhilarating post-war experience to those of us who were in the train. Later in the same journey *Silver Fox* touched 102 m.p.h. in the descent of Stoke bank; and on the previous day the northbound York to Newcastle run was completed in 70 minutes 2 seconds from start to stop.

Equally distinguished work has been performed by the "A4" class engines with extremely heavy trains. On April 5th, 1940, the wartime 1 p.m. from London to Edinburgh left King's Cross with the colossal load of 25 vehicles, weighing 750 tons tare and fully 830 to 850 tons gross, behind engine No. 2509, *Silver Link*. It took 16 minutes to get this vast assemblage through Finsbury Park, but the 100½ miles thence to Grantham were run in 123 minutes, which involved a loss of 11 minutes to Grantham on the schedule then in force. From there onwards, with 64 minutes allowed to Doncaster, 43 minutes from Doncaster to York, 52 minutes on to Darlington, and 50 minutes thence to Newcastle, the engine lost no more than 4 minutes in running. On the same day, incidentally, one of the original "A1" Pacifics, with 180 lb. pressure—No. 2549, *Persimmon*—worked a train of 24 bogie coaches, weighing 759 tons tare, and 850 tons gross, over the 76·4 miles from Peterborough to King's Cross in 96 minutes, within 2 minutes of the schedule at that time of the up Leeds express concerned.

In more normal conditions of peace-time running the "A4" Pacifics

TABLE 37

YEAR 1946
L.N.E.R. CLASS "A4" STREAMLINED 4-6-2
Engine No. 2512, *Silver Fox*
Load: 204 tons tare, 207 tons gross
Driver J. Leonard

Dist.		Sched.	Actual		Speeds
miles		min.	min.	sec.	m.p.h.
0·0	NEWCASTLE	0	0	00	—
0·6	*King Edward Bridge Junc.*	—	1	58	—
2·5	Low Fell	—	4	12	72½
5·4	Birtley	8½	6	33	75
8·2	Chester-le-Street ..	—	8	53	74
10·1	Plawsworth	—	10	38	*30
12·6	*Newtonhall Junction* ..	—	13	51	64
14·0	DURHAM	18	15	26	*26
15·0	*Relly Mill Junction* ..	—	17	21	37
18·2	Croxdale..	—	20	18	74/72½
23·1	FERRYHILL	28	24	26	76½
25·9	Bradbury	—	26	40	75/*72
30·6	Aycliffe	—	30	37	75/*64
36·0	DARLINGTON	39½	35	01	85
38·6	Croft Spa	—	36	55	83½
41·2	Eryholme	44	38	52	82
42·9	Cowton	—	40	06	—
46·4	Danby Wiske	—	42	23	92/*62
50·1	NORTHALLERTON ..	51½	45	34	79
53·5	Otterington	—	47	59	90
57·9	THIRSK	57½	50	52	92½
62·1	Sessay	—	53	37	90
64·0	Pilmoor	—	54	54	92
66·7	Raskelf	—	56	40	93½
68·9	Alne	—	58	05	92
74·6	Beningbrough	—	61	52	88
77·1	*Skelton Bridge*	—	63	32	92
78·5	*Skelton Junction*	—	64	45	*60
80·1	YORK	†75	‡68	04	—

* Speed reduced by brakes   † Passing time ("Coronation" schedule)   ‡ To dead stop can do almost anything required by the timetables on 15 per cent. cut-off, save only on starting, in recovering from slacks, and up the steepest grades. In his book, *The Locomotives of Sir Nigel Gresley*, Mr. O. S. Nock mentions the attainment by No. 4498, *Sir Nigel Gresley*, with cut-off fixed at this modest percentage, of no less than 79 m.p.h. on the level with a 510-ton train. On another journey, No. 4902, *Seagull*, one of the series with the Kylchap exhaust, accelerated so rapidly down a 1 in 200 grade with 16 per cent. cut-off and partly-closed regulator as to raise the speed from 84 to 95 m.p.h. in three miles.

Shortly after the beginning of the Second World War, I received from the Rev. G. C. Stead details of an astonishing trip with No. 4901 of the Kylchap engines, then named *Capercaillie*, in which, with a train of 21 coaches weighing 665 tons tare and 730 tons gross, the engine averaged no less than 75·9 m.p.h. over the 25 level miles from Otterington to Poppleton Junction, north of York. The beginning and end of the run suffered from signal checks, but the relevant portion appears in Table 38; over this stretch the continuous drawbar-horsepower output must have been in the region of 2,200. It should be added here that after the new and exceedingly weighty air-conditioned stock was

TABLE 38

YEAR 1940
L.N.E.R. CLASS "A4" STREAMLINED 4-6-2
Engine No. 4901, *Capercaillie*
Load: 665 tons tare, 730 tons gross

Dist.		Times		Average Speeds	Max. and Min. Speeds
miles		min.	sec.	m.p.h.	m.p.h.
0·0	Otterington	*0	00	—	71
4·4	THIRSK	3	34	74·0	74½
8·6	Sessay	6	59	73·8	74
10·5	Pilmoor ..	8	32	73·7	75
13·2	Raskelf	10	40	76·6	78½
15·4	Alne	12	21	77·4	77½
16·9	Tollerton ..	13	31	76·4	77½
21·1	Beningbrough	16	47	77·1	76½
25·0	*Poppleton Junction*	*19	57	73·9	†76

* Passing times   † Before shutting off steam

brought into use on the "Flying Scotsman" in 1938, the up train was required to make the run of 105·5 miles from Grantham to King's Cross in 105½ minutes, start to stop, with loads never less than 500 tons and often nearer 600 tons—a task with which the "A4" Pacifics seldom failed to cope adequately, but it left little to spare.

Though probably less efficient as regards coal consumption, the "A3" Pacifics, when extended, have shown capabilities in performance but little inferior to those of their more celebrated "A4" sisters. On two occasions in the same week in March, 1939, engines of the former class were commandeered at a moment's notice to take over the up "Coronation" at Newcastle from streamlined locomotives which had developed minor faults; in both cases the times of this difficult assignment were improved on considerably by Driver Nash and Fireman Gilbey. On the first run No. 2595, *Trigo*, completed the journey of 268·3 miles in 229 minutes, or 225 minutes net; on the second, with No. 2507, *Singapore*, the even more remarkable time of $227\frac{1}{2}$ minutes gross and $222\frac{1}{2}$ minutes net was achieved. The latter, requiring an overall average of 72·3 m.p.h., was $14\frac{1}{2}$ minutes less than schedule and in all probability the fastest overall time ever made from Newcastle to London.

A very brilliant performance of an "A1" appears in Table 39. The train concerned was the "Scarborough Flyer," on a day when the start from King's Cross was delayed by 3 minutes owing to an unexpected rush of passengers. Not only so, but near Hatfield an alert signalman noticed that the end of one of the carriage headboards had come adrift, and had the train stopped at Welwyn Garden City for the trouble to be rectified. As a result, Hitchin was passed $10\frac{3}{4}$ minutes late. Yet, on this 62·7 m.p.h. schedule, with a load 50 per cent. heavier than that of the "Silver Jubilee," Driver Duddington (who also drove *Mallard* on the 1938 record run) coaxed *Solario* into keeping the streamliner's schedule exactly from Hitchin to Selby.

It is hardly surprising that the "Jubilee" booking over the uphill section from Peterborough to Grantham could not be maintained, with a train of all but 400 tons weight; though even then minima of 60 m.p.h. at the top of the 1 in 200 to Corby, and $57\frac{1}{2}$ on the 1 in 178 to Stoke, were astonishing enough; but what of the time of

TABLE 39

YEAR 1936
L.N.E.R. CLASS "A1" 4-6-2
Engine No. 4473, *Solario*
Load: 371 tons tare, 395 tons gross
Driver J. Duddington (Doncaster)

Dist.		Sched.	Actual		Speeds
miles		min.	min.	sec.	m.p.h.
0·0	KING'S CROSS	0	0	00	—
2·5	FINSBURY PARK	—	6	16	—
5·0	Wood Green	—	9	11	—
12·7	Potter's Bar	—	17	37	—
17·7	HATFIELD	22	21	55	77
			sig. stop		
23·5	*Woolmer Green*	—	35	20	$51\frac{1}{2}$
28·6	Stevenage	—	40	04	72
31·9	HITCHIN	35	42	38	$80\frac{1}{2}$
37·0	Arlesey	—	46	04	91
44·1	Sandy	—	51	02	$85\frac{1}{2}$
51·7	St. Neot's	—	56	41	76
56·0	Offord	—	59	51	81
58·9	HUNTINGDON	56	62	07	74
62·0	*Milepost 62*	—	64	49	$65\frac{1}{2}$
69·1	Holme	—	70	30	$83\frac{1}{2}$
			sigs.		
75·0	*Fletton Junction*	—	75	21	38
76·4	PETERBOROUGH	73	77	23	*26
79·5	*Werrington Junction*	—	81	27	60
84·8	Tallington	—	86	18	—
88·6	Essendine	—	89	36	68
92·2	Little Bytham	—	92	47	—
97·1	Corby	—	97	30	60
100·1	*Stoke Summit*	—	100	27	$57\frac{1}{2}$
105·5	GRANTHAM	102	104	40	$81\frac{1}{4}$
109·7	Barkston	—	107	49	—
115·4	Claypole	—	111	40	90
120·1	NEWARK	114	114	56	85
126·4	Carlton	—	119	33	82
133·7	*Markham Summit*	—	125	45	64
138·6	RETFORD	132	129	40	†84
143·9	Ranskill	—	133	31	$81\frac{1}{2}$
147·7	Bawtry	—	136	19	—
149·5	*Piper's Wood Summit*	—	137	48	71/$83\frac{1}{2}$
156·0	DONCASTER	147	142	55	*67
160·2	*Shaftholme Junction*	151	146	20	—
166·0	Balne	—	150	51	76
169·8	Templehirst	—	153	48	—
174·4	SELBY	164	157	53	*34
178·5	Riccall	—	162	31	62
184·0	Naburn	—	167	14	72
186·2	*Chaloner's Whin Junc.*	—	169	08	—
188·2	YORK	180	172	06	—

Net time: 163 minutes

* Service slack   † Speed before Retford

38 minutes 15 seconds over the 50·5 miles from Grantham to Doncaster? On passing Doncaster the express had been restored to schedule; York was reached 5 minutes before time. It is fortunate that so experienced a recorder as Mr. R. E. Charlewood happened to be on the train, so that full details of this superb feat were obtained. The net time from King's Cross to York was 162 minutes, exceeding by no more than 5 minutes the schedule of the down "Coronation," of which, even with the observation car, the gross weight never exceeded 325 tons.

Brief reference may be made here to another outstanding run with a Gresley locomotive, though unhappily the engine no longer exists in its original form. This was the 2-8-2 locomotive *Cock o' the North*, as originally built with poppet-valve motion. On a test run with a 19-coach train weighing 650 tons, on which no high downhill speeds were attempted, the 15·3 miles from Tallington up to Stoke Summit were run at an average of 60·3 m.p.h. Up the 4½ miles at 1 in 200 to Corby speed fell from 63 to 56 m.p.h., and up the final 3 miles at 1 in 178 from 60 to 56½ m.p.h.; drawbar-horsepower never fell below 1,800, and reached a maximum of 2,090. On 1 in 440-264 up, speed had been

TABLE 40

YEAR 1945
L.N.E.R. "GREEN ARROW" CLASS (2-6-2)
Engine No. 4786
Load: 630 tons tare, 690 tons gross
Driver J. W. Handley (Grantham)

Dist.		Sched.	Actual		Speeds
miles		min.	min.	sec.	m.p.h.
0·0	GRANTHAM.. ..	0	0	00	—
5·4	Stoke	—	12	21	26
8·4	Corby	—	16	20	54
16·9	Essendine	—	23	57	71
20·7	Tallington	—	27	10	71
26·0	Werrington Junction ..	—	31	55	60
29·1	PETERBOROUGH ..	36	35	30	*
30·5	Fletton Junction ..	—	38	20	—
36·1	Holme.. ..	—	44	55	60
42·7	Milepost 62¼ ..	—	52	37	40½
46·6	HUNTINGDON ..	†57	57	00	68
53·8	St. Neot's ..	—	63	40	61
61·4	Sandy	—	70	55	65
68·5	Arlesey	—	78	20	54
73·6	HITCHIN	†99	84	30	48
76·9	Stevenage ..	—	89	50	36
80·5	Knebworth ..	—	94	35	—
83·5	Welwyn North ..	—	98	10	—
87·8	HATFIELD	116	102	00	67
92·8	Potter's Bar ..	—	107	00	55
100·5	Wood Green ..	—	114	10	67
103·0	FINSBURY PARK ..	—	116	40	—
105·5	KING'S CROSS ..	141	121	20	—

* Service slack, severe   † Schedule from Huntingdon to Hitchin included 11 min. recovery time.

maintained at 62½ to 60 m.p.h. with 15 per cent. cut-off; cut-off was then advanced to 20 and 25 per cent. up the 1 in 200, and to 30 per cent. for the final 4¼ miles. On the return journey the locomotive gave a similar demonstration of her ability by climbing the 8·4 miles from Arlesey to Stevenage at an average of 61 m.p.h., on 30 per cent. cut-off, and with a maximum drawbar-horsepower of 2,100, the highest figure reached on the day's test. Downhill the engine ran with such freedom that, if the poppet-valves were lifted off their seats, it was possible to maintain speeds of over 60 m.p.h. down continuous 1 in 200 gradients without any steam at all.

Two other Gresley designs require mention before this chapter is concluded. The first is his highly successful" V2" 2-6-2, which despite wheels of no more than 6 ft. 2 in. diameter, has proved interchangeable with the Pacifics on almost every main-line duty, with the exception of the streamline trains. Yet in emergency even the latter have had 2-6-2 haulage. On one such occasion, No. 4789 was faced at short notice with the haulage of the "West Riding Limited" express from King's Cross to Leeds, and covered the 185·8 miles in a net time of 167 minutes, with the usual 295-ton load. This was 4 minutes only in excess of the train's schedule. Engines of this type were used regularly for the "Yorkshire Pullman" in each direction between King's Cross and Doncaster, with its schedule of 156 minutes down and 155 minutes up for the 156 miles. On one run with this express, timed by Mr. J. C. Thorne, No. 4817, with Driver Sherriff in charge, and a 380-ton train, covered the 17·6 miles from Corby to Werrington at an average speed of 86·2 m.p.h., maintaining an average of 90·2 for 7½ miles and reaching a maximum of 93 m.p.h.

TABLE 41

YEAR 1938
L.N.E.R. "SANDRINGHAM" CLASS "B17" (4-6-0)
Engine No. 2848, *Arsenal*
Load: 437 tons tare, 465 tons gross
Driver Webb, Fireman Hayes (Leicester)

Dist.		Sched.	Actual		Speeds
miles		min.	min.	sec.	m.p.h.
0·0	LEICESTER	0	0	00	—
4·7	Whetstone	—	7	45	50
9·2	Ashby	—	13	55	42
13·1	Lutterworth	—	18	59	†73½
19·9	RUGBY	—	25	12	63
24·6	Braunston	—	29	23	70
27·9	*Staverton Road*	—	32	42	—
31·6	Charwelton	—	37	17	44
34·0	WOODFORD	37	39	53	69¼
37·0	Culworth	—	42	40	60
40·6	Helmdon	—	45	58	—
43·8	Brackley	—	48	46	79
48·6	Finmere	—	52	37	69
54·3	Calvert	—	57	03	80½/72
56·3	*Grendon Underwood Jc.*	56	58	45	*63
59·0	Quainton Road	59	61	14	71
65·2	AYLESBURY	65	66	37	69
67·4	Stoke Mandeville	—	68	49	—
69·8	Wendover	—	71	54	—
71·9	*Milepost 31¼*	—	75	05	39
74·3	Great Missenden	76	77	37	71
79·5	Amersham	—	82	33	55
81·5	Chalfont	83	84	26	80
85·9	RICKMANSWORTH	87½	88	11	*
89·4	Northwood	—	92	45	46
			p.w.s.		
93·9	HARROW	97	98	47	*
98·0	*Neasden Sth. Junction*	101¼	103	12	68
100·1	Brondesbury	—	105	21	49
103·1	MARYLEBONE	109	110	06	—

Net time: 109 min.

* Service slack   † Beyond Shawell box

As might be expected, the work of the "Green Arrow" 2-6-2s with heavy loads is of no less merit, as is apparent in the wartime run set out in Table 40, timed by Dr. R. H. Dale. The schedule of this Sunday express at that time had a time recovery margin of 11 minutes from Huntingdon to Hitchin, but even so Driver J. W. Handley succeeded in gaining another 9 minutes, making the run of 105·5 miles in 121 minutes 20 seconds. The finest feat was probably that of running the 27·0 miles from Huntingdon to Hitchin in 27½ minutes, against the rising tendency of the road, with a train of no less than 690 tons behind the tender.

Finally, there are the "B17" class three-cylinder 4-6-0 engines, the star performances of which have been achieved, probably, over Great Central metals. Of these the most remarkable of which I have ever seen a record was one timed by Mr. J. H. Colyer-Fergusson in 1939 (Table 41), when No. 2848, *Arsenal*, was faced with the task of working a 13-coach express, of 465 tons gross weight, from Leicester to Marylebone, 103·1 miles, in 109 minutes. It needs a close acquaintance with this difficult road to realise the nature of the task set this moderately-dimensioned 77-ton locomotive. Long stretches of 1 in 176 gradient were surmounted at minima of 42 to 44 m.p.h.; but the biggest power output was on the 1 in 117 climb from Aylesbury up into the Chilterns, the 6 miles of which were begun at 60 and finished at 39 m.p.h. Despite a permanent-way check, a single minute only was dropped on schedule.

Like most of the later Gresley designs, the "B17" 4-6-0s can do a large part of their work on 15 per cent. cut-off. Mr. O. S. Nock recorded a footplate journey on the morning "Newspaper," loaded to 300 tons, on which No. 2841, *Gayton Hall*, ran the 19·9 miles from Rugby to Leicester in 19 minutes 2 seconds start to stop; with 25 per cent. cut-off and full regulator Driver Simpson reached 66 m.p.h. in $1\frac{3}{4}$ miles of downhill at 1 in 176, and mounted 4 miles of 1 in 176 at a minimum of $57\frac{1}{2}$ m.p.h.; later, with 15 per cent. and partly-open regulator the engine accelerated from 75 to 90 m.p.h. down 5 miles at the same inclination.

It only remains to add that the late Sir Nigel Gresley achieved a notable triumph, even if posthumously, in the extensive locomotive exchange trials of 1948. For his A4 Pacifics, unaltered from the original 1935 design other than by the provision of double exhaust pipe and double chimney, showed a lower coal and water consumption, relatively to power output, than all the other thirteen types of locomotive under test, whether express passenger, mixed traffic or freight.

15

PERFORMANCE—THE G.W.R. UNDER
CHURCHWARD AND COLLETT

IN dealing with locomotive performance on the Great Western Railway since the beginning of the century, there is no need, as with the two northern groups, to devote separate chapters to the pre-grouping and the post-grouping periods. For Great Western locomotive practice, and with it the potential output of its locomotives, continued with very little change for four decades. In 1948 express engines were still being built to a design first evolved in 1923, practically unchanged during the intervening 25 years. Since the year 1902, when he succeeded to the post of Chief Mechanical Engineer at Swindon, the influence of George Jackson Churchward, as described in Chapter 1, has continued to pervade the G.W.R. It was Churchward who put into the company's hands locomotives capable of continuous steaming at high speeds, by the use of which the operating authorities were able, in their timetables, to give a lead in speed to the entire country.

The century had barely opened before the Great Western had made certain runs which put completely in the shade all previous performances either by 4-2-2 or 4-4-0 locomotives in Great Britain. Of these the first was on July 14th, 1903, when the then Prince and Princess of Wales—later King George V and Queen Mary—were making a trip to Cornwall, and it had been intimated in high quarters that the Royal party would like "a good run." In view of the extraordinary care which normally is lavished on Royal journeys (and even more so in those days, when the working notices relating to Royal specials usually included precise passing times at every station along the route), it is still a matter of the utmost astonishment that such a run as this should have been attempted in these conditions. So "good" was it, in fact, that the Prince and Princess were brought into North Road station at Plymouth no less than 37 minutes ahead of time!

To make up a reasonable load, a two-coach advance section of the 10·40 a.m. down "Cornishman" was added to the three Royal saloons, making five vehicles in all, of 130 tons gross weight. The engine was No. 3433, *City of Bath*, a 4-4-0 which had emerged from Swindon shops a few months previously, and one of the first engines to be built under Churchward's superintendence. Burden, one of the most competent G.W.R. drivers of his day, was at the regulator.

This, of course, was well before the opening of the Westbury route, and the train had to travel *via* Bristol, by-passing Temple Meads station by the tortuous avoiding line between St. Anne's Park and Pylle Hill junction. The journey to Plymouth was thus 20 miles longer than it is to-day. Moreover, between Dawlish and Teignmouth the line was still single, and severe slacks were therefore necessary at both these stations for the exchange of single-line tokens. Notwithstanding these handicaps, Burden brought his train to rest in North Road station in 233 minutes 35 seconds from Paddington, 6½ minutes less than the non-stop timing, up to the outbreak of the Second World War, of the "Cornish Riviera Limited," by the shorter Westbury route.

Details of the run are set out in Table 42. Three miles from the start the train was doing a mile-a-minute; 70 m.p.h. was attained by West Drayton, and 73 before Reading. Between West Drayton and Bathampton, for over 91 miles speed barely fell below the 70 m.p.h. level, and a maximum of 87½ was reached down Dauntsey bank; the average speed over 101·2 miles from Ealing Broadway to Bath was 71·8 m.p.h. Had the special been running into Bristol, Temple Meads could have been reached easily in less than

TABLE 42

YEAR 1903
G.W.R. "CITY" CLASS (4-4-0)
Engine No. 3433, *City of Bath*
Load: 130 tons
Driver Burden

Dist.		Time	Speed
miles		min. sec.	m.p.h.
0·0	PADDINGTON	0 00	—
1·3	Westbourne Park	2 47	—
5·7	Ealing Broadway	7 32	62
9·1	Southall..	10 35	67
13·2	West Drayton ..	14 13	70
18·5	SLOUGH	18 32	73
24·2	Maidenhead	23 26	70½
31·0	Twyford	29 14	73
36·0	READING	33 26	†70
41·5	Pangbourne	38 07	72½
48·5	Cholsey..	43 50	73
53·1	DIDCOT	47 33	77
60·4	Wantage Road ..	53 40	71
66·5	Uffington	58 56	69
71·6	Shrivenham	63 12	70½
77·3	SWINDON	68 01	72
82·9	Wootton Bassett	72 44	71
87·7	Dauntsey	76 31	87½
94·0	CHIPPENHAM	81 10	75
98·3	Corsham	84 54	67
101·9	Box	87 41	77
104·6	Bathampton	89 55	—
106·9	BATH ..	92 02	*
111·3	Saltford..	96 42	66
117·0	*Bristol East Depot*	101 52	*
118·4	*Pylle Hill Junction*	104 42	*
123·9	Flax Bourton	110 46	—
130·0	YATTON	115 45	77
133·6	Worle ..	119 32	75½
138·2	Bleadon..	122 17	75½
144·9	Highbridge	127 36	76
151·2	BRIDGWATER	132 45	72½
157·0	Durston	137 31	72½
162·8	TAUNTON	142 39	†
164·8	Norton Fitzwarren	144 58	—
169·9	Wellington	150 03	62
173·7	*Whiteball*	154 27	50
178·7	Tiverton Junction	158 58	—
181·0	Cullompton	160 57	72
186·4	Silverton	165 44	68
190·2	Stoke Canon	169 12	64
193·6	EXETER	172 34	*
198·4	Exminster	178 32	—
202·1	Starcross	181 54	67
205·8	Dawlish..	185 32	*
208·6	Teignmouth	190 15	*
213·7	NEWTON ABBOT	195 51	*
217·6	*Dainton*	201 28	30
222·5	Totnes ..	206 46	†
227·0	*Rattery*	213 24	36
229·3	Brent	216 12	—
231·5	Wrangaton	218 45	51½
234·8	Ivybridge	222 11	—
238·9	Hemerdon	226 25	—
241·6	Plympton	228 54	—
245·6	PLYMOUTH (N. ROAD)	233 35	—

* Service slack, severe
† Service slack, slight

104 minutes, as compared with the 105-minute booking of the "Bristolian," introduced with much *éclat* some 32 years later. From Ealing to Taunton, including the severe slack at Bath and the worse one round the Bristol curves, *City of Bath* maintained an average of 69·8 m.p.h. for just over 157 miles—a wonderful performance for a 54½-ton 4-4-0 with 18 in. × 26 in. cylinders, no more than 20·6 sq. ft. of firegrate, and 195 lb. per sq. in. working pressure.

The uphill work was equally meritorious—such speeds as 50 m.p.h. at Whiteball summit, after 1¼ miles at 1 in 90 and a mile at 1 in 81, or the minimum of 30 up the final 1 in 43 to Dainton summit, or of 36 on the tremendous climb out of Totnes—a mile at 1 in 70, 1¾ miles at 1 in 50, and 1½ miles at 1 in 90, approximately—were all first-class feats, especially coming, as they did, near the end of this hard steaming over so long a distance. It may be added that the only stretch taken under easy steam was from Whiteball summit down to Exeter; here the Royal party were at lunch, and the engine-crew were notified that some moderation of speed was desirable. Otherwise Plymouth might have been reached in 231 minutes from London.

The following year, 1904, was one of great note in G.W.R. speed annals. Transatlantic steamers had begun to make calls at Plymouth; their passengers were brought up to London by the London & South Western Railway and their mails by the Great Western; and the two companies were competing strongly for the distinction of being the first to reach the Metropolis. It was, in fact, a race, carried on through the month of April and reaching its climax on May 9th, 1904. On that day the G.W.R. time from Millbay Crossing, Plymouth, to Paddington, including a stop of 3¾ minutes at Pylle Hill, Bristol, where engines were changed, was cut to 226¾ minutes. The equivalent non-stop time from North Road to Paddington *via* Bristol, allowing also for the severe slowing over a bridge under repair at Swindon, would be about 218 minutes. From Plymouth to Bristol, with five heavily-laden mailvans, the load of 148 tons was hauled by another "City" class 4-4-0, No. 3440, *City of Truro*; at Bristol one van was detached, and the train was taken on by No. 3065, *Duke of Connaught*, a Dean 4-2-2 single-driver. The runs, as recorded by the late Charles Rous-Marten, appear in Tables 43 and 44.

In running the 31·9 miles from North Road, Plymouth, to Newton Abbot in 33 minutes 35 seconds, Driver Clements made a record which is never likely to be challenged. Little has been revealed as to the downhill speeds over this sinuous stretch of line, which must have been considerably less cautious than usual—the average speed down from Wrangaton to Totnes, for example, was 68·7 m.p.h.—but the uphill work was certainly superlative. The latter included an average speed of 40·2 m.p.h. for the 2·7 miles from Plympton up to Hemerdon, of which the renowned Hemerdon bank, for 2 miles at 1 in 42, forms a part; and then came the average of no less than 57·5 m.p.h. from Totnes up to Dainton summit, of which the final 1½ miles steepen from 1 in 76 to 1 in 37. From the slowings through Newton Abbot, Teignmouth and Dawlish, lightning recoveries were made, and then came a fine sustained speed up the long rise from Exeter to Whiteball, with a minimum of 52 m.p.h. on the final 2 miles at 1 in 115.

About what happened next a great deal of controversy has raged. In the descent of Wellington bank, Rous-Marten claimed, a mile was covered at 96 m.p.h., of which one-half was at 100 m.p.h., with a peak of 102·3 m.p.h.; and the claim has been sufficient to earn for *City of Truro* a place in the York Railway Museum as the first British locomotive ever to cross the three-figure line in speed. Unfortunately, the figures that Rous-Marten left behind him were both few and contradictory, and there is some reason to suspect that he misread a milepost.

Much of the confusion arose from the thoughtlessness of some platelayers,

TABLE 43

YEAR 1904
G.W.R. "CITY" CLASS (4-4-0)
Engine No. 3440, *City of Truro*
Load: 148 tons
Driver Clements

Distance				Time	
miles				min.	sec.
0·0	MILLBAY CROSSING	..		0	00
0·9	PLYMOUTH (N. ROAD)..		..	3	07
4·9	Plympton	..	..	7	31
7·6	*Hemerdon*	..	..	11	54
11·7	Ivybridge	..	..	16	29
15·0	Wrangaton	..	..	19	48
17·2	Brent..	..	..	21	43
24·0	Totnes	..	..	27	39
28·9	*Dainton*	..	..	32	40
32·8	NEWTON ABBOT*	..	..	36	42
37·9	Teignmouth*	..	..	41	59
40·7	Dawlish*	..	..	45	54
44·4	Starcross	..	..	50	14
48·1	Exminster	..	..	54	09
52·0	St. Thomas	..	..	57	49
52·9	EXETER*	..	..	59	02
56·3	Stoke Canon	..	..	62	54
60·1	Silverton	..	..	66	26
65·5	Cullompton	..	..	71	13
67·8	Tiverton Junction	..	..	73	32
72·8	Whiteball	..	..	78	31
76·6	Wellington	..	..	81	38
81·7	Norton Fitzwarren..		..	85	19
83·7	TAUNTON	..	..	86	51
89·5	Durston	..	..	91	42
95·3	BRIDGWATER	..	..	96	10
101·6	Highbridge	..	..	101	09
108·3	Bleadon	..	..	106	26
112·9	Worle	..	..	109	11
116·5	YATTON	..	..	113	01
122·6	Flax Bourton	..	..	118	11
127·7	Bedminster	..	..	122	19
128·1	PYLLE HILL JUNCTION	..	..	123	19

* Service slack, severe

who stood obstinately on the track until the train was almost on them, causing Driver Clements to brake sharply just as he had reached his top speed. The fiery temperament of the recorder was a matter of common knowledge; so it would not be surprising if this happening, just at the precise moment of attaining his life's ambition, upset the accuracy of his timing. That the speed was in the neighbourhood of 100 m.p.h. there is, of course, no doubt; if the 102·3 m.p.h.

M

was actually reached, it was destined to remain as the British record for just over 30 years.

After the Wellington slack, which was to about 60 m.p.h., *City of Truro* soon recovered speed; the average speed from Whiteball summit to Bedminster was 74·8 m.p.h. Thus the 128·1 miles from Millbay Crossing and the 127·2 miles from North Road to Pylle Hill junction were run in 123 minutes 19 seconds and 120 minutes 12 seconds respectively—times which have never been equalled or even approached since.

TABLE 44

YEAR 1904

G.W.R. DEAN SINGLE-DRIVER (4-2-2)

Engine No. 3065, *Duke of Connaught*

Load: 120 tons

Driver Underhill

Dist.		Time		Speed
miles		min.	sec.	m.p.h.
0·0	PYLLE HILL JUNCTION	0	00	—
1·4	*Bristol East Depot*	3	39	*
4·7	Keynsham	7	21	—
7·1	Saltford..	9	32	66
11·5	BATH	13	38	*
13·8	Bathampton	16	00	—
16·5	Box	18	28	68
20·1	Corsham	22	01	52
24·4	CHIPPENHAM	25	48	71½
30·7	Dauntsey	30	49	76
35·5	Wootton Bassett	35	06	67
41·1	SWINDON	39	37	
		p.w.s.		10
46·8	Shrivenham	45	19	
51·9	Uffington	49	17	77½
58·0	Wantage Road.. ..	53	47	81
65·3	DIDCOT	59	08	83
69·9	Cholsey..	62	35	81
76·9	Pangbourne	67	52	76½
82·4	READING	72	09	78
87·4	Twyford	76	00	75
94·2	Maidenhead	80	58	87
99·9	SLOUGH	85	03	85
105·2	West Drayton	88	53	80
109·3	Southall..	92	04	79
112·7	Ealing Broadway	94	35	81
117·1	Westbourne Park	98	01	—
118·4	PADDINGTON	99	46	—

* Service slack, severe

Another record was to follow, for Driver Underhill, with the 4-2-2 engine *Duke of Connaught*, for the first time in history brought Bristol within less than 100 minutes of Paddington. Notable ascents were made of the short 1 in 100 banks, the first through Box tunnel, and the second up from Dauntsey; then, after the dead slowing over the Cricklade bridge at Swindon, the single-driver, as Rous-Marten wrote, "blazed forth in all her glory." For the time at which it was made it was indeed a glorious performance. From Shrivenham to Westbourne Park the speed averaged precisely 80 m.p.h. for 70·3 miles, with this 120-ton train. Had the run been made from Temple Meads station at Bristol, and unchecked, it would have taken a little over 98 minutes, as compared with the 105 minutes allowed the "Bristolian" 31 years later. From Swindon, passed very slowly, the train took 9 seconds over the hour, as compared with the "Cheltenham Flyer's" 65-minute schedule from 1932 onwards. A notable feature of the single's performance was that it was accomplished on a coal consumption of no more than 32 lb. to the mile. May 9th, 1904, was certainly a day to be remembered in Great Western history.

From this it is fitting that we should pass to the record runs connected with the acceleration of the train last-mentioned to its 65-minute schedule from Swindon to Paddington. It was in 1923 that the G.W.R. wrested from the L.N.E.R. the distinction of tabling the fastest daily start-to-stop run in Great Britain, by booking an afternoon express from Cheltenham to run from Swindon to Paddington, 77·3 miles, in 75 minutes—61·8 m.p.h. as compared with the L.N.E.R. 61.5 m.p.h. from Darlington to York. In July, 1929, the Swindon-Paddington timing came down to 70 minutes; in September, 1931, to 67 minutes; and finally, in September, 1932, to 65 minutes, raising the start-to-stop average to 71·4 m.p.h. With each successive acceleration new feats of speed were attempted; and there could be no more ideal course in the country for such a purpose—almost perfectly level throughout, with any slight tendency of grading in favour of the engine, and so perfectly aligned as to permit unrestricted speed from start to finish.

TABLE 45

YEARS 1932 & 1937
G.W.R. "CASTLE" CLASS (4-6-0)

	5006	5039
Engine No.	5006	5039
" Name	*Tregenna Castle*	*Rhuddlan Castle*
Load, tons tare	186	223
" " gross	195	235
Driver	*Ruddock	*F. W. Street
Fireman	*F. H. Thorpe	—

Dist.		Sched.	Time		Speed	Time		Speed
miles		min.	m.	s.	m.p.h.	m.	s.	m.p.h.
0·0	SWINDON	0	0	00	—	0	00	—
1·3	*Milepost* 76	—	2	26	56½	2	38	—
2·3	" 75	—	3	29	64½	3	43	59
3·3	" 74	—	4	22	69	4	37	66
5·3	" 72	—	5	56	79	6	15	—
5·7	Shrivenham	—	6	15	80	6	35	80½
7·3	*Milepost* 70	—	7	24	82½	7	44	—
9·3	" 68	—	8	50	85	9	10	—
10·8	Uffington	—	9	51	85	10	10	90
13·4	Challow	—	11	42	87	11	57	90
16·9	Wantage Road	—	14	05	89	14	12	94
20·8	Steventon	18½	16	40	90	16	45	95
24·2	DIDCOT	21	18	55	91	18	57	90½
28·8	Cholsey	—	21	59	91½	21	58	91
32·6	Goring	—	24	25	92	24	25	88
35·8	Pangbourne	—	26	33	‡89	26	40	‡86½
38·7	Tilehurst	—	28	28	91½	28	40	90
41·3	READING	34	30	11	91½	30	27	86½
46·3	Twyford	—	33	31	89	33	50	90
53·1	Maidenhead	—	38	08	88	38	17	93
54·8	Taplow	—	39	24	86	39	27	90
58·8	SLOUGH	47	42	10	87	42	08	90½
61·1	Langley	—	43	42	86	43	38	86
64·1	West Drayton	—	45	51	84	45	47	84
68·2	SOUTHALL	54½	48	51	81½	48	46	†82
69·8	*Milepost* 7½	—	50	01	83½	49	59	eased
71·6	Ealing Broadway	—	51	17	84½	51	40	—
73·0	Acton	—	52	20	84½	53	15	—
75·3	*Milepost* 2	—	53	56	†82½	—		—
76·0	Westbourne Park	61	54	40	—	57	40	—
77·3	PADDINGTON	65	56	47	—	61	07	—

† Steam shut off ‡ Slight speed reduction resulting from taking water at Goring troughs * Old Oak Common shed

The culminating performance was that of June 6th, 1932. The engine *Tregenna Castle*, with a train of 195 tons, cut the time to 56 minutes 47 seconds, and for the first time on record made a journey of which the start-to-stop average exceeded 80 m.p.h.—to be precise, 81·7 m.p.h. The times and speeds set out in Table 45 were recorded jointly by Mr. Humphrey Baker and myself. With a brilliant acceleration, Driver Ruddock worked his engine up to 56½ m.p.h. in the first 1¼ miles from the start, to 69 m.p.h. in 3¼ miles, and to 79 m.p.h. in 5¼ miles; 90 m.p.h. was reached in 17¼ miles, and from then onwards, speed continued unbrokenly at above the "90" level for 28 miles, save for the slight reduction to 89 caused by taking water at Goring troughs. Over the 70 miles between mileposts 72 and 2, the mean speed was 87·5 m.p.h.   Starting from Swindon with full cut-off and partially opened regulator, as is customary in Great Western driving practice, by Shrivenham Ruddock had his regulator opened to full, and the cut-off back to 17 per cent.   This setting was used for most of the run, except for an increase to 18 per cent. from Goring to Maidenhead, and again from Southall until steam was shut off at milepost 2.

That such a performance is by no means merely an extreme possibility with one of these most capable engines is proved by the second run which is included in the same table.   It features the driving of F. W. Street, of Old Oak Common—one of the most able enginemen that the G.W.R. has yet produced—with *Rhuddlan Castle*.   The run was made in the week of June, 1937, in which the L.M.S.R. and L.N.E.R. were making records on the trial trips of their "Coronation Scot" and "Coronation," and Street had evidently determined that the two bigger companies should not have all the limelight.   The upshot was that, with one coach more than the six vehicles of *Tregenna Castle's* 1932 record, he passed Shrivenham within 20 seconds of the latter's time, and then tied with it by Cholsey; after that he fell 19 seconds behind to Twyford, only to overhaul and beat *Tregenna Castle* by 5 seconds to Southall, where *Rhuddlan Castle* was eased drastically to avoid too early an arrival.   At Steventon, on but little easier than level track, Street worked his engine up to 95 m.p.h., and 93 was reached again at Maidenhead; between mileposts 70 and $17\frac{1}{2}$ an average speed of 90 m.p.h. was maintained continuously for $52\frac{1}{2}$ miles.   It would have been perfectly easy to repeat the 1932 timing of $56\frac{3}{4}$ minutes from Swindon to Paddington, given a clear road.   This run was recorded by the Rev. J. E. T. Phillips.

We must now return to June 6th, 1932, for the day's records were not at an end with the arrival of the "Cheltenham Flyer" at Paddington at 4·45 p.m., 10 minutes early (this run was made when the 67-minute timing was still in force).   The Great Western operating authorities had made all arrangements to attempt another record, this time in the down direction, with the 5 p.m. from Paddington to Cheltenham, which was to be stopped specially at Swindon for the purpose.   To the latter, therefore, Mr. Humphrey Baker and I transferred ourselves, in order to record the paces of *Manorbier Castle*.   Due to the use of heavier stock than on the up journey, the load behind the tender (though the number of coaches was the same) totalled 210 tons.   In this direction the slightly inclined tendency of the route was against the engine; it is barely perceptible until after Didcot, where there begins the gradual rise, 23 miles long, at between 1 in 754 and 880, that continues almost to Swindon. The run is set out in Table 46.

At 2¼ miles from the start we were doing 60 m.p.h., at 4½ miles 70 m.p.h., and at 9 miles 80 m.p.h., after which speed rose gradually to 86½ at Slough, the highest of the journey. The 70 miles between mileposts 6 and 76 were covered at an average of 82·0 m.p.h., with fluctuations between 86½ m.p.h. at Slough, 79 m.p.h. at Twyford, 85½ m.p.h. at Didcot, 77½ m.p.h. up the 1 in 754 to milepost 69, and an acceleration to 84 m.p.h. up the 1 in 834 to milepost 76. Drawing slowly round into the back platform line at Swindon, Burgess stopped his train in one hour out of Paddington (*plus* a single second) for the 77·3 miles. As to the engine working, the regulator was opened gradually to full by Ealing Broadway, after which cut-off was 23 per cent. to Southall, 20 per cent. on to Slough, 19 per cent. thence to Reading, 20 per cent. from Reading to Goring and 19 per cent. from there to Didcot, 20 per cent. from Didcot to Uffington, and 21 per cent. from Uffington to milepost 76, where steam was shut off. The response of these remarkable engines to the change of a single unit per

TABLE 46

YEAR 1932
G.W.R. "CASTLE" CLASS (4-6-0)
Engine No. 5005, *Manorbier Castle*
Load: 199 tons, 210 tons gross
Driver G. Burgess, Fireman G. Gibson (Old Oak Common)

Dist.				Sched.	Actual	Speeds
miles				min.	min. sec.	m.p.h.
0·0	PADDINGTON	..		0	0 00	—
1·3	Westbourne Park	..		—	2 34	—
3·0	*Milepost 3*	..		—	4 31	62
5·7	Ealing Broadway	..		—	6 52	73¼
9·1	Southall	..		11	9 25	81
13·2	West Drayton	..		—	12 26	84½
18·5	SLOUGH	..		20	16 03	86½
22·5	Taplow	..		—	18 55	83
24·2	Maidenhead	..		25½	20 14	82
31·0	Twyford	..		31½	25 17	79
36·0	READING	..		37	29 02	82
38·6	Tilehurst	..		—	30 58	83½
41·5	Pangbourne	..		—	33 01	82½
44·7	Goring	..		—	35 23	82½
48·5	Cholsey	..		—	38 03	84
53·1	DIDCOT	..		53	41 25	85½
56·5	Steventon	..		56½	43 47	83½
60·4	Wantage Road	..		—	46 35	81¼
63·9	Challow	..		—	49 13	80½
66·5	Uffington	..		—	51 13	78½
71·6	Shrivenham	..		—	54 59	†77½
76·0	*Milepost 76*	..		—	58 15	‡84
77·3	SWINDON	..		*77	60 01	—

* Scheduled passing time   † At milepost 69
‡ At milepost 75

cent. in the cut-off, as mentioned already in Chapter 10, is most noteworthy.

Even yet the speed-making was not at an end. To return Mr. Baker and myself to London, the 5·15 p.m. two-hour express from Bristol to London was stopped at Swindon, and made a magnificent run up in 66 minutes 33 seconds, notwithstanding a slight signal check at Didcot and a slowing through the platform road at Reading to slip a coach. The engine, No. 4091, *Dudley Castle*, in charge of Driver A. Drury, had a more substantial train of 280 gross tons from Swindon to Reading and 240 tons on to London, but managed to attain

81½ m.p.h. at Steventon and 82½ m.p.h. through Ealing, and covered the last 36 miles from passing Reading slowly to the Paddington stop in 29 minutes 58 seconds. Between 3·48 and 7·12 p.m., therefore, the recorders made three journeys between Paddington and Swindon, with 15 minutes to make the London connection, and just under 6 minutes for that at Swindon. The average duration of each of the three runs of 77½ miles was a shade over 61 minutes, and within the overall compass of 2 hours 24 minutes, three "Castle" class 4-6-0 engines had covered in all 220 miles at an average speed of 80 m.p.h.

It is obvious from the foregoing runs that a "Castle" class locomotive should have no difficulty in reaching 100 m.p.h. with some slight assistance from gravity. Actually, since the war, a speed of 96½ m.p.h. has been reached on the level by No. 5056, *Earl of Powis*, with a four-coach train of about 130 tons.

The only record of a 100 m.p.h. maximum with one of these engines was on a falling gradient, during a run down the Worcester line, timed by Mr. R. E. Charlewood in 1939. No. 4086, *Builth Castle*, driven by Tidball, was the engine, with a load of 255 tons. The stretch of line concerned is one ideally laid out for record-breaking, with 4½ miles of 1 in 100 down, well aligned, from Campden tunnel, flattening out with easier grades in the ensuing 3 miles. The relevant part of the run appears in Table 47, which shows in a striking way the possibilities of acceleration down such a grade. Actually the descent begins at milepost 97¼, where the train was doing 67 m.p.h.; subsequent miles were covered at average speeds of 70, 81¾, 85¾, 92¼, 100, 97¼, 94¾, and 94¾ m.p.h. The 100 was exactly at the foot of the 1 in 100 inclination, after which the speed fell with the easing of the grade until brakes were applied beyond Littleton station. There was nothing of particular note about the remainder of this run.

The journey set out in Table 48, also recorded by Mr. R. E. Charlewood, demonstrates that the earlier Great Western 4-6-0 classes are equally capable of high sustained speeds when occasion requires.

TABLE 47

YEAR 1939
G.W.R. "CASTLE" CLASS (4-6-0)
Engine No. 4086, *Builth Castle*
Driver Tidball (Worcester)
Load: 243 tons tare, 255 tons gross

					Times	Speeds*
					min. sec.	m.p.h.
KINGHAM..	..	..	..	..	0 00	—
Milepost 96	..	..	..	..	14 04	—
,, 97 (Campden) ..		..	..	..	14 58	66·7
,, 98¼	..	..	..	..	16 15	70·1
,, 99	..	..	..	..	16 37	81·8
,, 100	..	..	..	..	17 19	85·7
,, 101	..	..	..	..	17 58	92·3
,, 101¾ (Honeybourne)		..	..	..	18 25	100·0
,, 102	..	..	..	..	18 34	100·0
,, 103	..	..	..	..	19 11	97·3
,, 104	..	..	..	..	19 49	94·7
,, 105 (slack)	..	..	..	20 27	94·7
,, 106	..	..	..	..	21 10	69·2

* Average between mileposts

In this case the particular need arose from the failure, at Reading, of the "King" class engine working the down "Bristolian." In consequence, two-cylinder 4-6-0 No. 2937, *Clevedon Court*, which was standing pilot, had to be commandeered at a moment's notice, and most ably succeeded in keeping, from Reading start to Bristol stop, the "Bristolian's" pass-to-stop schedule, and this in spite of three signal checks and a permanent way slowing. At Goring, 8¾ miles from the start, the train was travelling at 78 m.p.h.; from the 55 m.p.h. check beyond Steventon Driver Jones worked his engine up to 75 m.p.h. on the 1 in 754 inclination, and then to 83½ on the 1 in 834 from Shrivenham, so tieing with the speed of *Manorbier Castle* with 210 tons, on the record run in Table 46.

A maximum of 90 m.p.h. down Dauntsey bank was spoiled by the signal check at Chippenham, notwithstanding which the driver accelerated to 72½ m.p.h. up the 1 in 660 to Corsham. There was no very high speed through the Box tunnel, and scrupulous attention was paid to the Bath service slack; then came a final maximum of 76½ through Keynsham, again on level track. The net time of 69 minutes for the 82¼ miles from Reading to Bristol—almost exactly 72 m.p.h. from start to stop—was about 5½ minutes less than the "Bristolian" booking demanded of its more powerful locomotives, and the behaviour of the 28-year-old locomotive concerned, without any previous preparation for such an exploit, was praiseworthy indeed.

TABLE 48

YEAR 1938
G.W.R. "SAINT" CLASS (4-6-0)
Engine No. 2937, *Clevedon Court*
Driver Jones(Old Oak Common)
Load: 216 tons tare, 225 tons gross

Dist.		Sched.	Actual	Speeds
miles§		min.	min. sec.	m.p.h.
0	READING	†0	‡0 00	—
5½	Pangbourne	—	6 32	—
8¾	Goring	—	9 15	78
12½	Cholsey	—	12 09	77½
17¼	DIDCOT	13½	15 53	76
		—	sigs.	60
20½	Steventon	16½	18 35	—
		—	sigs.	55
24½	Wantage Road ..	—	22 32	—
28	Challow	—	25 34	75
30½	Uffiington	—	27 34	76½
35½	Shrivenham	—	31 21	82
39½	*Milepost* 75½	—	34 16	83½
41¼	SWINDON	33½	35 34	78
47	Wootton Bassett ..	—	39 57	80
51¾	Dauntsey	—	43 19	90
56	*Milepost* 92	—	46 18	83½
		—	sigs.	46½
58	CHIPPENHAM ..	47	48 18	—
62¼	Corsham	—	52 15	72½
65	*Milepost* 101	—	54 28	76½
70	„ 106	—	58 28	—
70⅞	BATH	58½	59 29	*34
75¼	Saltford	—	63 55	72
77¾	Keynsham	—	65 55	76½
		—	p.w.s.	40
80¾	St. Anne's Park ..	—	68 50	—
		—	sigs.	—
82¼	BRISTOL	72	72 28	—

Net time: 69 minutes

* Service slack † Passing time ‡ From dead start
§ Timings taken to mileposts in each case

Table 49 introduces the working of the "Cornish Riviera Limited," which in the last decade before the Second World War, in the down direction, constituted one of the most onerous propositions of locomotive haulage in the country. Moreover, the route includes in its length the greatest extremes of gradient found on any main line in Great Britain. Out of London it begins with the perfection of Brunel's original Bristol line, as nearly dead level as makes no matter. At the western end, beyond Newton Abbot, there are the mountainous inclinations resulting from the intersection of the deep valleys draining the southern slopes of Dartmoor. Between Newton Abbot and Totnes, in the Dart valley, comes the gable of Dainton summit, approached by a 2-mile climb which begins at 1 in 98 and then steepens to a final mile at from 1 in 46 to 1 in 36; similarly the first mile westwards from the summit is down at between 1 in 37 and 1 in 43.

From Totnes there is a 9-mile ascent to Wrangaton, beginning with a mile at about 1 in 70 and continuing with 1¾ miles at 1 in 46-56 as far as Tigley box, whence the grade flattens out to about 1 in 90 for 1¾ miles to Rattery. The remaining 4½ miles to Wrangaton are on easier inclinations. Finally, there is the abrupt descent from Hemerdon to Plympton, which for 2¼ miles averages 1 in 42. Between Reading and Newton Abbot the locomotives must negotiate the summits at Savernake, milepost 122¾ (13 miles west of Westbury) and Whiteball, in the Blackdown Hills beyond Taunton, all approached by long and gradual climbs except Whiteball, going west, to which there is a sharp ascent, of 3 miles at 1 in 90, 86, 80 and 127.

In the pre-war working of the down "Limited," except during the summer months, reduction of the train by means of the detaching of slip portions at various intermediate points nicely proportioned the train's weight to each progressive increase in the steepening of the gradients. Thus the locomotive, leaving Paddington with 14 vehicles, of all but 500 tons tare weight, lost two of them at Westbury and two more at Taunton, before tackling the ascents to milepost 122¾ and to Whiteball respectively; at least two more would come off at Exeter, reducing the tare to not more than 300 tons for the extremely difficult stretch from Newton Abbot to Plymouth. To-day, however, with no slip portions and a considerably heavier train to be worked through, a stop is made invariably at Newton Abbot for pilot assistance.

In all the circumstances, with the total change in the physical characteristics of the route west of Newton Abbot, it is, perhaps, surprising that this town, rather than Plymouth, should not have been made the locomotive changing point, with a small-wheeled type of engine, far more suited to the gradients of South Devon and Cornwall, substituted at Newton Abbot for the run through to Penzance.

Three runs with the down "Limited" figure in Table 49. The first happened also to be the first that I had ever made on the train

TABLE 49

YEARS 1921, 1925 and 1928

G.W.R. "STAR," "CASTLE," AND "KING" 4-6-0 CLASSES

Distance		Schedule						
	Engine No.		4003		4074		6011	
	,, Name		*Lode Star*		*Caldicot Castle*		*King James I*	
	Driver		Springthorpe		Rowe		W. Wright	
	Load from Paddington, tons..		406/425		498/530		492/525	
	,, ,, Westbury ,, ..		341/355		426/455		421/450	
	,, ,, Taunton ,, ..		282/295		363/385		357/380	
	,, ,, Exeter ,, ..		249/260		292/310		253/270	
miles		min.	min. sec.	m.p.h.	min. sec.	m.p.h.	min. sec.	m.p.h.
0·0	PADDINGTON	0	0 00	—	0 00	—	0 00	—
1·3	Westbourne Park	—	3 15	—	3 15	—	3 05	—
5·7	Ealing Broadway	—	9 40	—	9 08	—	—9 10	—
9·1	Southall.. ..	11	13 20	55½	12 42	59	12 45	59
13·2	West Drayton ..	—	17 40	62	16 41	66	16 55	65
18·5	SLOUGH ..	20	22 35	65	21 26	68½	21 35	70½
			p.w.s.	25				
24·2	Maidenhead	25½	29 50	—	26 36	65½	26 40	66
31·0	Twyford	31½	37 10	62½	32 49	67	32 55	65
36·0	READING	37	42 15	*45	37 25	*	37 30	*40
			p.w.s.	20				
37·8	*Southcote Junction* ..	—	44 50	—	39 31	—	40 00	*45
41·2	Theale	—	49 40	—	42 57	62	43 35	61
44·8	Aldermaston	—	52 30	—	46 20	62	46 55	66/*60
49·6	Thatcham	—	58 45	55	51 06	59½	51 30	63
53·1	NEWBURY	56	62 30	57½	54 38	58	54 55	61
58·5	Kintbury	—	68 15	59	60 05	60½	60 10	62½
61·5	Hungerford	—	71 25	55½	63 12	56/58	63 15	57½/61½
66·4	Bedwyn..	—	76 30	57½	68 17	57	68 15	58½
							p.w.s.	20
70·1	SAVERNAKE	73½	80 40	46½	72 25	46	73 35	—
75·3	Pewsey	—	85 50	72½	77 25	—	79 05	75
81·1	Patney	—	91 15	—	82 16	—	83 50	77½
			p.w.s.	25	—	—	p.w.s.	20
86·9	Lavington	—	98 25	—	87 00	77½	88 35	—
91·4	Edington	—	102 05	75	93 08	—	94 10	68
			p.w.s.	25				
95·6	WESTBURY‡	97½	107 50	*30	94 40	*	98 35	*35
98·5	*Milepost 112¾*	—	111 40	—	98 13	—	102 05	54
101·3	Frome	—	115 10	*35	101 40	*	105 30	*35
106·6	Witham..	—	121 55	53	108 03	53½	112 00	53½
108·5	*Milepost 122¾*	—	124 10	49	110 24	46	114 15	50½
111·9	Bruton	—	127 10	82	113 25	75	117 15	83½
115·3	Castle Cary	120	130 00	*69	116 18	*	120 00	*50
120·2	Keinton Mandeville ..	—	134 00	—	120 26	70/66½	124 55	67/64½
125·7	Somerton	—	138 45	77½/72½	125 28	70½/65	129 45	75/70½
131·0	*Curry Rivell Junction* ..	—	142 55	79	130 09	72	134 05	79
134·9	Athelney	—	146 05	74	133 30	68½	137 15	74
							p.w.s.	10
137·9	*Cogload Junction* ..	144	148 30	72½	136 06	68	140 55	—
142·9	TAUNTON‡	149	152 45	69	140 30	67	147 45	58½
144·9	Norton Fitzwarren ..	—	154 30	70½	142 22	68	149 45	62½/64
150·0	Wellington	—	159 15	60	147 17	57½	154 40	58½
153·8	*Whiteball*	—	164 00	39½	152 12	41	159 25	42½
158·8	Tiverton Junction ..	—	168 35	—	156 46	—	164 05	76½
161·1	Cullompton	—	170 25	79	158 38	76½	165 55	80½
165·3	Hele	—	173 45	75	161 58	—	169 10	77½
170·2	Stoke Canon	—	177 30	80½	166 00	—	173 05	76½
173·7	EXETER‡	180	180 55	*30	169 10	*	175 55	70
178·4	Exminster	—	186 15	70½	174 40	—	179 40	82
							p.w.s.	10
182·2	Starcross	—	189 40	*60	178 00	—	185 20	—
							p.w.s.	20/54
185·9	Dawlish..	—	193 25	—	181 50	—	190 50	—
							p.w.s.	5/52½
188·7	Teignmouth	—	196 20	*45	184 54	—	195 25	*40/65
193 9	NEWTON ABBOT ..	203	202 20	*35	190 25	—	201 25	*25/50½
					p.w.s.			
197·7	*Dainton*	209½	208 20	30½	197 40	—	207 50	24½/60
202·5	Totnes	215½	213 40	*60	203 00	—	213 35	*50
205·3	*Tigley*	—	217 25	32½	206 55	—	217 50	29
207·1	*Rattery*	223	220 25	37	210 25	—	221 15	36
209·4	Brent	225	223 30	60	213 28	—	224 10	54
							p.w.s.	*25
211·6	Wrangaton	—	226 00	52½	215 40	—	226 40	—
							p.w.s.	25
214·9	Ivybridge	—	229 20	*52	219 10	—	231 10	50
219·0	*Hemerdon*	237	233 30	64½	223 10	—	235 55	60/68
221·7	Plympton	—	236 00	70½	225 41	—	238 30	*50
			sigs.	20				
224·2	*Lipson Junction*	245	239 25	—	p.w.s.	—	241 20	—
			sigs.	5			sigs.	5
225·7	PLYMOUTH (N. ROAD) ..	247	244 50	—	231 58	—	245 35	—
225·7	Net times (minutes)	247†	232	—	230¼	—	228	—

* Service slack † Schedule 240 min. on third run (Engine No. 6011) ‡ Coach or coaches slipped

personally, and it was an electrifying experience. This was in 1921, with a "Star" class four-cylinder 4-6-0 at the head, at a time when 12 coaches from London, 10 from Westbury, 8 from Taunton, and 7 from Exeter sufficed to carry the traffic. The second was probably the most outstanding run of its kind that has ever been made by a "Castle" class 4-6-0; the occasion was the last day of the historic fortnight in 1925 in which the G.W.R. and the L.N.E.R. were exchanging locomotives for trial purposes; and the Great Western enginemen were very much on their mettle. The final run, with a "King" class 4-6-0, was one on which I was privileged to travel on the footplate; it was hampered throughout by permanent way slowings, but notwithstanding eight of these and a signal check in addition, the old 247-minute schedule was more than kept. The work performed, however, was in no degree superior to that of the memorable "Castle" performance just mentioned.

On the first run, William Springthorpe, an Old Oak Common driver of very high reputation, who was at the regulator of *Lode Star*, had little chance as far as Westbury, owing to fog in the Thames Valley and a succession of four permanent-way relaying checks; as a result, schedule time to Westbury was exceeded by 10½ minutes. But from there onwards, by some glorious running, he gained 16 minutes on his booked time from Westbury to Lipson Junction, Plymouth. The 65·2 miles from milepost 122¾ to Exeter were run at an average of 68·9 m.p.h., including the climb to Whiteball; after this came some most energetic climbs to Dainton and Rattery, with 30 m.p.h. minimum speed over Dainton summit, 32½ at Tigley box, and an acceleration to 37 at Rattery. With due allowance for delays, Springthorpe thus achieved a net time of 232 minutes for the run, 15 minutes less than the schedule then operative.

On the second run, *Caldicot Castle* had to tackle 100 tons more of train as far as Taunton, 90 tons more from there to Exeter, and 50 tons more from Exeter, 14, 12, 10 and 8 vehicles respectively on the four stages of the run. Heavier stock had come into use by now, and this accounts for the greater average weight per vehicle. Except at the extreme end, this run was unchecked throughout, and Driver E. Rowe brought his train into Plymouth 15 minutes ahead of time. The handling of the locomotive throughout was brilliant. On the level this 530-ton load was worked up to a speed of 68½ m.p.h. at Slough; up the long and gradual rise of the Kennet valley speed was kept at between 56 and 60½ m.p.h. save for the drop to 46 on the final pitch to Savernake —2 miles at 1 in 180 and a last mile steepening to 1 in 145-106. A second magnificent climb, now with 385 tons, was that to Whiteball summit, with no greater fall in speed than from 68 to 41 m.p.h.

Unfortunately, no records are available as to the speeds between Exeter and Plymouth; Mr. A. V. Goodyear, who was responsible for the timing to Exeter, was in the Exeter slip coach and alighted at that station; the times west of Exeter were obtained from another source. Both permanent-way checks were slight; the net time therefore works out at 230¼ minutes—16¾ minutes less than the schedule then in force, and 9¾ minutes less than the 4-hour timing of later years.

As previously mentioned, on the run with *King James I* I was on the footplate. Throughout this journey Fireman Hounslow had no difficulty in maintaining the full boiler pressure; even on the hardest climbs it did not fall below 230 lb. (save for a momentary 225 lb. at Savernake), and for most of the journey it was consistently at 240 to 245 lb. per sq. in, just below blowing-off point. Starting with the full cut-off of 75 per cent., Driver Wright had linked up to 23 per cent. by Westbourne Park, 20 per cent. by Acton, and 18 per cent. by Hanwell, while at the same time the regulator was being advanced from one-half to full open. Full regulator and 18 to 20 per cent. cut-off took us up the Kennet valley, save for a brief 30 per cent. in recovering from a permanent-way slowing before Savernake. On the downhill lengths after Savernake, 16 per cent. was the minimum cut-off setting, mostly with the regulator about one-half open; 20 per cent. and full open was used from Westbury up to milepost 122¾.

The dead slowing over Cogload Junction came at a particularly bad place, with the climb from Taunton to Whiteball immediately ahead; after the slack, the regulator was opened to full, and cut-off was advanced to 20 per cent., then at Wellington station to 25 per cent., and finally at milepost 173 to 30 per cent., which took us over the summit, with a 380-ton train, at a minimum of 42½ m.p.h.—a fine performance. The least impressive part of this run was after the discouraging series of checks from Exminster onwards—two underline bridge reconstructions which brought us down to 10 and 5 m.p.h., and an intervening permanent-way relaying slack to 20 m.p.h.

To Dainton, Wright used 20 per cent. cut-off from Newton Abbot, 25 from milepost 16, and 35 per cent. for the last mile; from Totnes we gradually advanced from 20 to 35 per cent. at Tigley box, and then came back to 25 from Rattery and 20 from Wrangaton. But the times on these ascents were longer than those of *Lode Star* with an almost equal load, and *Caldicot Castle* made a better time from Totnes up to Brent with a load heavier by 40 tons. This is no disparagement, however, of the fine run made by *King James I*. With an allowance for all delays the net time from Paddington to Plymouth was 228 minutes, 19 minutes less than the original 247-minute schedule, and 12 minutes less than the booking in force at the time the run was made.

Some of the finest performances of the "Kings" have been on the North road between Paddington and Wolverhampton, both under the *aegis* of Old Oak Common shed and in the hands of a very keen top link of enginemen at Wolverhampton. The run set out in Table 50, timed by the late Mr. G. P. Antrobus, is as fine an example of maximum "King" capacity as could be found. The train was the heavy 6·10 p.m. "diner" from Paddington, loaded to 510 tons as far as Bicester, and then reduced by successive slips to 475 tons from there and 405 tons from Banbury. The stiffest test of this run was that of keeping time to Princes Risborough, with the handling of the full load over Saunderton summit in the Chilterns.

After the usual slowing at Old Oak Common West Junction, the engine reached 65 m.p.h. by Denham, in preparation for the 6-mile climb to Seer Green—2 miles at 1 in 175 and the rest at 1 in 264—which was surmounted at a minimum of 56½ m.p.h. After the High Wycombe slowing, Driver Jay accelerated his engine to 52 m.p.h. up the 1 in 164 past Saunderton—a most

TABLE 50

YEAR 1938
G.W.R. "KING" CLASS (4-6-0)
Engine No. 6008, *King James II*
Driver Jay (Wolverhampton)
Load from Paddington: 476/510 tons
,, ,, Bicester: 445/475 ,,
,, ,, Banbury: 374/405 ,,

Dist.		Sched.	Actual	Speeds
miles		min.	min. sec.	m.p.h.
0·0	PADDINGTON	0	0 00	—
			sigs.	
3·3	Old Oak Common West ..	7	6 43	*40
5·0	Park Royal ..	—	9 00	47
7·8	Greenford	—	12 01	61
10·3	Northolt Junction ..	15½	14 36	58
14·8	Denham	—	19 04	65
17·4	Gerrard's Cross ..	—	21 46	57½
21·7	Beaconsfield ..	—	26 22	56½
24·2	Tyler's Green ..	—	28 33	75
26·5	HIGH WYCOMBE ..	32	30 44	*40
28·8	West Wycombe ..	—	33 40	—
31·5	Saunderton ..	—	37 04	52
34·7	PRINCES RISBOROUGH	41	40 28	75
40·1	Haddenham ..	—	44 30	90
44·1	Ashendon Junction..	49	47 35	*60
47·4	Brill	—	50 58	58
50·4	Blackthorn ..	—	53 30	76
53·4	BICESTER† ..	58	55 58	67
57·2	Ardley	—	59 37	62
62·4	Aynho Junction ..	67	64 19	*64
67·5	BANBURY† ..	72	69 12	66
			p.w.s.	38
71·1	Cropredy ..	—	73 31	52
76·2	Fenny Compton ..	—	79 01	80
81·2	Southam Road ..	—	83 02	68
83·6	Fosse Road.. ..	—	84 59	80
			sigs.	
87·3	LEAMINGTON	91	89 23	—

Net time: 86¾ minutes

* Service slack   † Coach or coaches slipped

remarkable feat. Full advantage was taken of the falling grades from the summit to Ashendon Junction, on which speed touched 90 m.p.h.; then, after the Ashendon slack, and an acceleration to 76 m.p.h. at Blackthorn, the 5½ miles at 1 in 200 up to Ardley were completed without the speed falling below 62 m.p.h.—another notable effort. In the middle of this climb came the reduction of the load from 510 to 475 tons by the Bicester slip.

Notwithstanding a permanent-way check beyond Banbury, and adverse signals before Leamington, Jay brought his train to rest at the latter station in 89 minutes 23 seconds from Paddington, or 86¾ minutes net for the 87·3 miles of arduous gradients and awkward speed restrictions—a superlatively fine piece of work. That this was not an isolated example of Wolverhampton driving talent is proved by another run on the same express, also timed by Mr. Antrobus, in which, with identical loads and the same engine, Driver Lewis of Wolverhampton made the run with three severe checks in 91 minutes 8 seconds, or 86½ minutes net.

16

PERFORMANCE—THE S.R. UNDER MAUNSELL AND BULLEID

FOR various reasons the Southern Railway and its pre-grouping constituent companies seldom attempted officially to make speed records, like certain of those described in the preceding chapters. Few of the Southern main lines are well adapted to high continuous speeds; and although Dugald Drummond of the London & South Western Railway once contemplated the provision of water-troughs and actually fitted some of his tenders with water-scoops, the troughs did not materialise, and non-stop runs much exceeding 100 miles in length have not been possible. No record exists of any Southern locomotive having attained a maximum speed of 100 m.p.h.; though there is no doubt that the Bulleid "Merchant Navy" Pacifics could do so with little difficulty over a favourable stretch of line.

Long before the formation of the Southern group, a notable run was staged by the London, Brighton & South Coast Railway from Victoria to Brighton and back. In the year 1903, a Bill was promoted for the construction of an electric railway between London and Brighton, by which, it was claimed, 50-minute runs would be made possible. The L.B.S.C.R. therefore set out to prove that they could achieve the same time, if necessary, with steam power. A train of three Pullman cars and two vans, weighing 130 tons, was made up; the engine was No. 70, *Holyrood*, a Billinton 4-4-0 with 6 ft. 9 in. driving wheels, 19 in.× 26 in. cylinders, and 180 lb. pressure, with Driver Tompsett at the regulator. The date was July 26th, 1903.

As with several other outstanding performances of this early period, it is unfortunate that Charles Rous-Marten, who recorded the times and speeds, left on record so few details of the running. All that we know about this occasion is that the journey of 50·9 miles from Victoria to Brighton was completed in a start-to-stop time of 48 minutes 41 seconds, of which 1 minute 52 seconds was spent in getting up the initial 1 in 64 to Grosvenor Road; speed up the long 1 in 264 to Coulsdon was a steady 62½ to 64 m.p.h., with a fall to about 58 on the 1 in 165 to Quarry tunnel; maximum speeds were 80½ m.p.h. at Horley and 90 m.p.h. at Haywards Heath, with minima of 66½ up to Balcombe tunnel and about 69 at the exit from Clayton tunnel, in both cases up 1 in 264. Of the return journey all the information available is that the run was made in 50 minutes 21 seconds start-to-stop—again at an average of over a mile-a-minute—and that the maximum speed attained was 85 m.p.h. Though over short distances only, these were notable performances for the period.

In the following year came the contest between the London & South Western and Great Western Railways for the passenger and mail traffic from Plymouth to London, off the Transatlantic steamers making Plymouth calls, already mentioned in Chapter 15. The best L.S.W.R. run appears to have been on April 23rd, 1904, when the journey of 230 miles from Stonehouse Junction, Plymouth, to Waterloo was made in 4 hours 3 minutes 51 seconds, including stops at Exeter (St. Davids) and Templecombe, totalling exactly 4 minutes. The total running time, therefore, was almost exactly 4 hours.

The scanty details left by Rous-Marten appear in Tables 51 and 52. It was intended to make the run of 117·8 miles from Plymouth to Templecombe without a stop, but the conditions under which the L.S.W.R. (and also the later S.R.) exercised running powers over the G.W.R. between Cowley Bridge Junction and St. Davids station gave the owning company the right to stop the competitor's trains in St. Davids, and

TABLE 51

YEAR 1904
L.S.W.R. 6 ft. 4-4-0 Class "S11"
Engine No. 399
Load: 105 tons gross

Distance		Times
miles		min. sec.
0·0	STONEHOUSE JUNCTION.. ..	0 00
0·3	DEVONPORT	1 21
2·8	St. Budeaux	4 48
16·3	Tavistock	21 27
32·6	OKEHAMPTON	42 44
47·0	Yeoford..	56 13
		sigs.
50·7	Crediton	59 47
56·3	*Cowley Bridge Junction* ..	*
57·6	}EXETER (ST. DAVIDS) .. {	67 28
0 0		0 00
0·6	EXETER (QUEEN STREET).. ..	2 25
12·8	Sidmouth Junction	16 12
24·4	Seaton Junction	28 55
49·5	YEOVIL JUNCTION*	54 24
60·2	TEMPLECOMBE	66 50

* Service slack

this right the G.W.R. was determined to exercise, even though the enforced stop lasted no more than 35 seconds.

On this run the train has to be lifted over an altitude of 950 ft. at a point 3¼ miles west of Okehampton. Up the long approach grades to this summit, for many miles at between 1 in 73 and 1 in 78, the engine climbed steadily at between 40 and 42 m.p.h., with one momentary minimum of 36 m.p.h.; the entire climb of 23½ miles from near Tamerton Foliot (5½ miles after starting, and practically at sea level) to the summit, took a couple of seconds under 31 minutes. East of Exeter, the 1 in 90 to Honiton tunnel was climbed at a minimum of 55½ m.p.h. and the 1 in 80 from Sherborne at 47½ m.p.h. But all the downhill speeds were very restrained; the maximum reached at any point was

70 m.p.h. While the uphill running was most praiseworthy, the times, especially from Exeter to Templecombe, might have been cut considerably had more advantage been taken of the well-aligned downhill stretches.

There was no such restraint, however, with the 6 ft. 7 in. Drummond 4-4-0 used from Templecombe to Waterloo. Here again the details of the running available are lamentably few; the only note concerning speed is that the minimum up the rising grades from Andover was 64 m.p.h. It will be seen from Table 52 that No. 336, with Driver F. Gare in charge, covered the 83·8 miles from Salisbury to Waterloo in 76 minutes 30 seconds—an amazing piece of work for these early days. From Basingstoke to Clapham Junction, 43·9 miles, the average speed was as high as 70·5 m.p.h. A fairly high speed must have been run, not only through Clapham Junction, but also for most of the distance between there and Waterloo, to permit the time for the 3·9 miles to the dead stand at Waterloo to be cut to 4 minutes 56 seconds, as compared with the normal 7 minutes or so to-day.

TABLE 52

YEAR 1904
L.S.W.R. 6 ft. 8 in. 4-4-0 Class "T9"
Engine No. 336
Load: 105 tons gross
Driver F. Gare

Distance		Times	
miles		min.	sec.
0·0	TEMPLECOMBE	0	00
28·4	SALISBURY	28	03
45·8	ANDOVER JUNCTION	45	09
64·4	BASINGSTOKE	62	00
79·0	Farnborough	74	13
87·8	WOKING	81	49
100·2	SURBITON	92	30
108·3	CLAPHAM JUNCTION	99	39
112·2	WATERLOO	104	33

Similarly, there is little doubt that the speeds of these boat-trains through Salisbury were incautiously high, for two years later there came the disastrous Salisbury derailment, over a reverse curve at the London end of Salisbury station, of an up boat special from Plymouth, which brought the non-stop running to an abrupt end. For this and other reasons it is difficult to believe Rous-Marten's contention that the curve through Salisbury, including the sharp reverse at the London end of the station, was taken "at full speed," on certain of these runs that he timed, which very likely would mean 70 m.p.h. or more.

Relatively to their dimensions and weight, the 81-ton "King Arthur" 4-6-0 engines, of which the design originated on the London & South Western Railway, share with the later Southern Railway "Schools" 4-4-0 engines the credit for some of the finest locomotive performances in Southern history. As regards speed with a moderate load, the "King Arthur" run set out in Table 53 is probably the most notable ever made on Southern metals by an engine of this type.

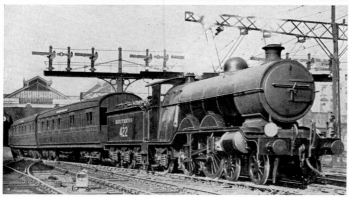

86. Brighton Pullman express at speed. The 4-4-0 engine, *Siemens*, is of the same class as *Holyrood*, which made the record Victoria-Brighton runs in 1903. (*F. E. Mackay.*)

87. The "Sunny South Express," headed by one of the Marsh "13" 4-4-2 tanks which were largely instrumental in introducing locomotive superheating into Great Britain. (*O. J. Morris.*)

88. One of the superheated Marsh Atlantics leaving Victoria for Brighton in the days of the overhead suburban electrification. (*F. E. Mackay.*)

DEVELOPMENT OF "BRIGHTON" PASSENGER POWER

89. The "Royal Engine"—an ex-London and South Western Drummond 4-4-0 kept in spotless condition for working light Royal specials between London and the South Coast. (O. J. *Morris*.)

90. Most powerful 4-4-0 type in Britain—*Marlborough*, one of the capable Southern Region 3-cylinder "Schools" class designed by Maunsell. (M. W. *Earley*.)

SOUTHERN REGION 4-4-0 LOCOMOTIVES

91. The 2-cylinder "King Arthur" class—*Sir Galagars* at speed with a train of 13 bogie coaches. (*Rev. A. C. Cawston.*)

92. The 4-cylinder "Lord Nelson" class—*Lord Hawke*, with a 14-coach train, on the up journey near Winchfield. (*M. W. Earley.*)

SOUTHERN REGION 4-6-0s WITH THE "ATLANTIC COAST EXPRESS"

93. Calais boat express leaving the Gare du Nord, Paris, with de Glehn 4-cylinder compound Pacific No. 3.1224. (*W. H. C. Kelland.*)

94. Leaving Paris for Calais with one of the later Collin 4-cylinder compound super-Pacifics, No. 3.1254. (*Cecil J. Allen.*)

95. The "Golden Arrow" at full speed on the Reine Blanche viaduct with standard Chapelon 4-cylinder compound Pacific No. 231.E.41. (*C. R. Gordon Stuart.*)

THREE STAGES IN POWER ON THE CALAIS-PARIS BOAT TRAINS

96. 3-cylinder simple 4-6-4 No. 05.002, German State Railways.

97. 4-cylinder compound 4-6-4 No. 232.S.001, French National Railways. (*C. R. Gordon Stuart.*)

98. 3-cylinder simple 4-8-4, No. 242.A.1 (converted from Etat 4-8-2), French National Railways. (*C. R. Gordon Stuart.*)

99. 3-cylinder simple 4-8-4 No. 06.001, German State Railways.

RECENT STREAMLINED FRENCH AND GERMAN EXPRESS LOCOMOTIVES

100.   2-8-2 Mixed traffic locomotive, No. 41.166, German State Railways.

101.   Class "02" Pacific locomotive, No. 02.010, German State Railways.

102.   South Eastern Region 2-4-6-2 freight locomotive, French National Railways, the equivalent of a 4-cylinder compound 2-10-2 but with divided drive. (*C. R. Gordon Stuart.*)

103.   New standard 2-8-2 mixed traffic locomotive, South Eastern Region, French National Railways. (*C. R. Gordon Stuart.*)

SOME STANDARD FRENCH AND GERMAN LOCOMOTIVE TYPES

104. Last stages in the erection of a streamlined 4-6-4 tank locomotive, German State Railways. The boiler casing remains to be applied.

105. Lifting a 4-8-4 passenger locomotive in the erecting shop. The overhead crane requires to have a capacity of over 200 tons. (*Courtesy, Canadian National Railways.*)

ERECTING SHOP WORK

106. Eight-wheel corridor tender built by the L.N.E.R. for the 393-mile non-stop run of the "Flying Scotsman" between King's Cross and Edinburgh. (*W. J. Reynolds.*)

107. Ready for the "Twentieth Century Limited"—New York Central 4-6-4, with typical American twelve-wheel tender. (*Rail Photo Service, Boston, Mass., W. J. Pontin.*)

108. Twelve-wheel tender of the Vanderbilt type, Great Northern Railway, U.S.A., with circular water tank and coal hopper above. (*Rail Photo Service, Boston, Mass., B. F. Cutler.*)

HIGH CAPACITY LOCOMOTIVE TENDERS

With ten bogies of heavy main-line stock behind the tender of his engine, Driver Alderman succeeded in cutting his 90-minute schedule from Salisbury to Waterloo by no less than 17¼ minutes, and thereby achieved a start-to-stop average speed of 69.2 m.p.h. From Grateley to Wimbledon, for 65·5 miles, including the long climb from Andover to Oakley, the average was 79·6 m.p.h., with a minimum speed of 70½ m.p.h. up 3 miles at 1 in 176 from Andover to milepost 62½. From Worting to Esher speed averaged no less than 82·7 m.p.h. for 35·5 miles, much of which is no easier than level, and it was but momentarily, up the slight rise to milepost 31, that speed fell below the "80" mark. The time of precisely 17 minutes from Basingstoke to Woking was a "record of records" indeed over this stretch, where so much fast running has been done.

As an example of "King Arthur" capacity with a heavy load over a more steeply-graded route, it would be difficult to select a finer run than that set out in Table 54. On this occasion, *Sir Balin* had to tackle a load of 13 bogie vehicles, crammed with passengers and luggage, over the formidable gradients between Salisbury and Exeter. Fortunately, this section is so well aligned that there are no service slacks whatever in the westbound direction, and Driver Young therefore made the utmost use of the impetus derived from high downhill speeds in order to carry his train well up the succeeding ascents. In consequence, maximum speeds of from 82 to 86½ m.p.h. were reached at six well-separated points.

Note should be taken of the minimum speeds on the climbs—50 m.p.h. before Milborne Port (after 2½ miles up at 1 in 80-100); 37 m.p.h. at milepost 133¼ (after 2¾ miles at 1 in 80); and 26½ m.p.h. on entering Honiton tunnel (after 1½ miles at 1 in 100 and 4½

TABLE 53

YEAR 1936
S.R. "KING ARTHUR" CLASS (4-6-0)
Engine No. 777, *Sir Lamiel*
Load: 328 tons tare, 345 tons gross
Driver Alderman (Nine Elms)

Dist.		Sched.	Actual	Speeds
miles		min.	min. sec.	m.p.h.
0·0	SALISBURY	0	0 00	—
1·1	*Tunnel Junction*	3	3 04	—
5·5	Porton	—	8 22	53
11·0	Grateley	—	14 00	66
17·4	ANDOVER JUNCTION ..	22	18 43	70½/76½
22·7	Hurstbourne	—	22 52	70½/76½
24·6	Whitchurch	—	24 24	72½
28·2	Overton	—	27 20	72½
31·4	Oakley	—	29 54	79
33·5	*Worting Junction* ..	39	31 33	75
36·0	BASINGSTOKE	41½	33 26	83½
41·6	Hook	—	37 25	88½/80
44·1	Winchfield	—	39 15	82
47·3	Fleet	—	41 33	85
50·6	Farnborough	—	44 00	80½
55·8	Brookwood	—	47 56	76½/83½
59·4	WOKING.. ..	62½	50 26	88½
62·1	Byfleet	—	52 15	90
64·7	Weybridge	—	54 05	82
69·0	Esher	—	57 18	80½
71·8	SURBITON	—	59 28	76½
74·0	Malden	—	61 14	74
76·5	Wimbledon	—	63 20	69
78·2	Earlsfield	—	64 46	72½
79·9	CLAPHAM JUNCTION ..	83	66 27	*
82·5	Vauxhall	—	69 32	*
83·8	WATERLOO	90	72 41	—

* Service slack

continuously at 1 in 80); and to show that the engine was in no way winded by the last-mentioned effort, there was a recovery to 32 m.p.h. on the 1 in 132 through the tunnel. It may be added that the working timetable laid down a maximum tare load of 355 tons for this timing; yet Driver Young regained 6 minutes on schedule with 66 tons (two coaches) over the maximum—a most exceptional feat.

It is doubtful if the four-cylinder "Lord Nelson" 4-6-os—the first new express passenger design after the formation of the Southern Railway—have ever displayed tractive powers equal to those of the "King Arthurs" at their best. As originally built, the four-cylinder engines were indifferent in their steaming, and it was not until Mr. O. V. Bulleid, in later years, rearranged the front end, and fitted the Lemaître type of multiple-jet exhaust, with large-diameter chimney, that the engines began to show their true capabilities. The run with the up "Bournemouth Belle" Pullman train, shown in Table 55, was one on which 4-6-0 No. 865, *Sir John Hawkins*, was handled by Driver Fred J. Payne, one of the most outstanding experts that Nine Elms shed has produced. Hauling twelve Pullmans of all but 500 tons weight, the engine gave a fine exhibition of hard steaming up the 16½ miles from Allbrook Junction (Eastleigh) to Litchfield, with its continuous average gradient of 1 in 252, accelerating gradually from 49 to 55½ m.p.h. Then followed some good steady high-speed work, by which the speed over the 40·5 miles from Basingstoke to Wimbledon, with maxima of 75½ to 76½ m.p.h., averaged 72·7 m.p.h. Had the train not been stopping at Southampton, the run of 107·9 miles from Bournemouth to Waterloo might have been made in 113 minutes.

With little doubt the most successful of the designs evolved by

TABLE 54

YEAR 1934
S.R. "KING ARTHUR" CLASS (4-6-0)
Engine No. 768, Sir Balin
Load: 421 tons tare, 460 tons gross
Driver Young (Salisbury)

Dist.		Sched.	Actual		Speeds
miles		min.	min.	sec.	m.p.h.
0·0	SALISBURY	—	0	00	—
2·5	Wilton	—	6	15	44
8·2	Dinton	—	13	05	59
12·5	Tisbury	—	17	50	53
17·5	Semley	—	23	50	42
21·6	Gillingham	—	27	30	82
23·9	*Milepost 107½* ..	—	29	19	64
26·2	*Milepost 109¾* ..	—	31	09	82
28·4	TEMPLECOMBE	—	32	55	65
30·8	Milborne Port ..	—	35	30	50
34·5	Sherborne	—	38	45	85
39·1	YEOVIL JUNCTION ..	43	42	10	77
41·3	Sutton Bingham	—	44	05	62
42·7	*Milepost 126¼* ..	—	45	30	54
47·9	Crewkerne	—	50	15	71†
49·7	*Milepost 133¼* ..	—	52	45	37
55·9	Chard Junction ..	—	58	25	80
61·0	Axminster	—	62	00	86½
64·2	Seaton Junction	—	64	30	71
67·4	*Milepost 151* ..	—	68	20	35
69·0	*Tunnel Entrance* ..	—	71	30	26¼
69·8	*Tunnel Exit* ..	—	73	07	32
71·2	Honiton	—	74	50	62
74·4	*Milepost 158*	—		—	82
75·8	SIDMOUTH JUNCTION ..	83	78	35	65‡
79·5	Whimple	—	81	50	76
83·2	Broad Clyst	—	84	30	83
86·9	*Exmouth Junction*	93	87	45	—
88·0	EXETER	96	90	00	—

† At 130 milepost   ‡ At 161¼ milepost

Mr. R. E. L. Maunsell, during his *régime* as Chief Mechanical Engineer of the South Eastern & Chatham and the Southern Railways, was the three-cylinder "Schools" class 4-4-0. Though no more than 67 tons in weight (without tenders), these most capable engines, by an easy margin the most powerful of this wheel arrangement ever built in Great Britain, have done work equal to, and, indeed, more than equal to, that of many 4-6-0 locomotives of considerably more ample dimensions. The running of *King's Wimbledon* set out in Table 56, indeed, might almost be classed with that of one of the Pacific-hauled streamline trains on the Northern lines.

Driver Silk was on the verge of retirement, and was evidently determined to make the best of his opportunity; he was fortunate to obtain a perfectly clear road for his exploit, except at the very end of the run. The recorder of this journey did not obtain any maximum and minimum speeds, though these can be deduced with fair accuracy from the running times. It may be assumed that speed rose to 77-78 m.p.h. past Byfleet, and that the long and gradual rise to mile-post 31 was surmounted at a minimum of about 70 m.p.h.; on the level past Fleet and in

TABLE 55

YEAR 1935
S.R. "LORD NELSON" CLASS (4-6-0)
Engine No. †865, *Sir John Hawkins*
Load: 462 tons tare, 495 tons gross
Driver H. Payne (Nine Elms)

Dist.		Sched.	Actual	Speeds
miles		min.	min. sec.	m.p.h.
0·0	BOURNEMOUTH C...	0	0 00	—
3·6	Christchurch ..	—	6 26	65½/*57
6·9	Hinton Admiral	—	10 10	46
12·4	Sway ..	—	16 16	62/60
14·2	*Lymington Junction*	—	18 03	65
15·1	BROCKENHURST	19	18 56	66
19·8	Beaulieu Road ..	—	23 28	58
22·5	Lyndhurst Road	—	26 02	70
26·0	Redbridge ..	—	29 40	*40
28·7 }	SOUTHAMPTON C. }	35 }	33 30	—
0·0 }		0 }	0 00	—
1·1	*Northam Junction*	—	3 23	*20
3·3	Swaythling ..	—	7 20	40½
5·6	EASTLEIGH ..	9	10 22	48
9·5	Shawford ..	—	14 52	52½
12·6	WINCHESTER..	—	18 24	53
14·7	*Winchester Junction*	—	20 48	53½
17·4	Wallers Ash ..	—	23 53	54
21·1	Micheldever ..	—	27 49	54½
22·9	*Litchfield*	—	29 51	55½
28·9	*Worting Junction*	37	35 36	67/*60
31·4	BASINGSTOKE ..	—	37 49	76½
37·0	Hook	—	42 21	72
42·7	Fleet	—	46 54	76
46·0	Farnborough ..	—	49 35	74
48·2	*Milepost 31*	—	51 26	70½
51·2	Brookwood ..	—	53 52	75
54·8	WOKING.. ..	60	56 46	75½
57·5	Byfleet	—	58 54	75½
60·1	Weybridge ..	—	60 59	68
62·1	Walton	—	62 44	73½
65·9	SURBITON ..	—	65 56	67½
71·9	Wimbledon ..	—	71 13	69
74·2	*Milepost 5* ..	—	73 23	60
75·3	CLAPHAM JUNCTION	79	74 54	*30
77·9	Vauxhall ..	—	78 33	—
79·2	WATERLOO	86	81 10	—

* Service slack   † With multiple-jet exhaust and large-diameter chimney

the slight dip beyond Hook the maximum was 81 or 82 m.p.h., and the minimum up the 1 in 249 to Worting Junction (5 miles) was about 62-63 m.p.h. On the descent to Hurstbourne the engine probably reached 90 m.p.h., and the speed just before Andover was 87-88 m.p.h. Up the 1 in 264-165 to Grateley (4½ miles) speed fell to about 57 or 58 m.p.h.

Then came Nemesis in the shape of a stop for adverse signals at Porton; and small wonder, for the train was now at least 12 minutes ahead of time, and, moreover, on a summer Saturday! For 60·8 miles from Surbiton through to Grateley the speed had averaged almost precisely 75 m.p.h.—a startling performance indeed for a 4-4-0 locomotive with this load. Unchecked, Driver Silk should have been into Salisbury in 74 minutes from Waterloo, or very slightly over, on a schedule allowing 88 minutes for the run.

TABLE 56

YEAR 1939

S.R. "SCHOOLS" CLASS (4-4-0)

Engine No. ‡931, *King's Wimbledon*

Load: 288 tons tare, 305 tons gross

Driver Silk (Nine Elms)

Dist.				Sched.	Actual	†Speeds
miles				min.	min. sec.	m.p.h.
0·0	WATERLOO	..		0	0 00	—
1·3	Vauxhall	..		—	3 40	24·0
3·9	CLAPHAM JUNCTION*			7	7 10	42·5
5·5	Earlsfield	..	—		9 05	53·1
7·3	Wimbledon	..	..	—	10 55	55·7
9·8	Malden	..		—	13 25	60·0
12·0	SURBITON	..	..	—	15 20	68·7
14·4	Esher	..	..	—	17 15	75·0
17·1	Walton	..	..	—	19 30	72·0
19·1	Weybridge	..	..	—	21 15	68·5
21·7	Byfleet	..	..	—	23 20	75·0
24·4	WOKING..	..	..	30	25 30	74·3
28·0	Brookwood	..		—	28 30	72·0
33·2	Farnborough	..		—	32 45	73·4
36·5	Fleet	..	..	—	35 15	79·2
39·7	Winchfield	..	..	—	37 00	79·4
42·2	Hook	..	..	—	39 35	78·3
47·8	BASINGSTOKE	..	..	53	43 50	79·0
52·4	Oakley	..	..	—	48 00	66·1
55·6	Overton	..	..	—	50 45	70·0
59·2	Whitchurch	..	..	—	53 40	73·9
61·1	Hurstbourne	..	..	—	55 00	85·7
66·4	ANDOVER	..	..	—	58 45	84·8
72·8	Grateley	..	..	—	64 00	73·1
					sigs.	
78·3	Porton	..	.. {	—	71 20	—
				—	74 30	—
					sigs.	
83·8	SALISBURY	..	..	88	81 50	—

Net time: 74 minutes

* Service slack   † *Average* speeds from station to station
‡ With multiple-jet exhaust and large-diameter chimney

Too late for inclusion in tabular form, details have reached me of another high speed "Schools" run which certainly deserves a place among the "immortals." The year was 1939, and Driver Rice, with No. 937, *Epsom*, had to bring up a 12-coach load of 387 tons tare and probably 410 tons gross from Salisbury to Waterloo. His running, as timed by Mr. Frank E. Box, was brilliant indeed. Maintaining 44 m.p.h. up Porton bank, and passing Amesbury Junction at 55½, Rice went through Andover at 85, and averaged over 70 up the whole of the long rise to Oakley. Worting Junction was passed at 79 m.p.h., and Basingstoke at 82; from 85 before Hook speed fell away gradually to 75 at Farnborough, and was just reaching the 80 mark once again when adverse signals were sighted, with the result that the train was pulled up dead at Woking. From the start, Porton had been passed in 9 minutes 35 seconds, Grateley in 15 minutes 47 seconds, Andover in 20 minutes, 36 seconds, Whitchurch in 26 minutes 19 seconds, Worting Junction in 33 minutes 41 seconds, and Basingstoke in 35 minutes 31 seconds—just inside "even time." The 19·8 miles from Basingstoke to Brookwood were run in 15 minutes 16 seconds, making 50 minutes

47 seconds for the 55·8 miles from the Salisbury start, as compared with *Sir Lamiel's* time of 47 minutes 56 seconds, with 65 tons (two coaches) less of train, in Table 53.

To the Woking stop, 59·4 miles from Salisbury, *Epsom* took 55 minutes 19 seconds. Getting away again, Driver Rice reached 69 m.p.h. by Weybridge and 79 by Surbiton, passing Weybridge, 5·3 miles, in 6 minutes 50 seconds, Surbiton, 12·4 miles, in 12 minutes 27 seconds, and Wimbledon, 17·1 miles, in 16 minutes 11 seconds. Then came a slow to 37 m.p.h. through Clapham Junction, and the usual cautious running into Waterloo; the 24·4 miles from Woking to Waterloo took 25 minutes 36 seconds start to stop. With an unchecked run through Woking, it is certain that Rice could have made the journey from Salisbury to Waterloo in 76¼ minutes for the 83·8 miles. This astounding feat for a 4-4-0 locomotive with a 410-ton train compares more than favourably with the 72 minutes 41 seconds of the "King Arthur" 4-6-0 with 345 tons set out in Table 53.

Equally astonishing, though this time in the realm of weight haulage, was the run from Waterloo to Southampton with *Blundells* in Table 57. This schedule had a nominal limit of 400 tare tons (12 bogies), but

TABLE 57

YEAR 1939
S.R. "SCHOOLS" CLASS (4-4-0)
Engine No. 932, *Blundells*
Load: 473 tons tare, 510 tons gross
Driver Allen (Bournemouth)

Dist.		Sched.	Actual	Speeds
miles		min.	min. sec.	m.p.h.
0·0	WATERLOO	0	0 00	—
3·9	CLAPHAM JUNCTION	7	8 13	—
7·3	Wimbledon	—	13 07	47
12·0	SURBITON	—	18 40	58/65½
19·1	Weybridge	—	25 24	60/67
24·4	WOKING	29	30 22	59
28·0	Brookwood	—	34 18	53
31·0	*Milepost 31*	—	37 52	48½
36·5	Fleet	—	43 34	65½
42·2	Hook	—	49 03	59/65½
47·8	BASINGSTOKE	54	54 20	59
50·3	*Worting Junction*	57	57 08	50½
52·6	*Wootton*	—	59 55	47½
58·1	Micheldever	—	65 52	64
66·5	WINCHESTER	—	72 34	82
73·6	EASTLEIGH	79½	77 52	*60
77·3	St. Denys	—	81 26	62
78·1	*Northam Junction*	84½	83 20	*15
79·2	SOUTHAMPTON C.	87½	86 32	

*Service slack

Driver Allen was taking three more than this, 15 bogies in all, and a very crowded train at that. Nevertheless, he more than succeeded in keeping time. From Wimbledon to Wootton, a stretch of hard and unbroken "collar-work," the engine steamed grandly, keeping up an average of 58·1 m.p.h., and not falling below 48½ m.p.h. at milepost 31 or 47½ m.p.h. up the 7 miles at 1 in 249 to Wootton. Then came a lively sprint downhill, with a top speed of 82 m.p.h. through Winchester. As a result, over the entire 70 miles from Wimbledon to St. Denys Driver Allen maintained an average of 61·5 m.p.h., notwithstanding the fact that his 67-ton locomotive was hauling—tender included—fully eight times her own weight.

But the best performances of the "Merchant Navy" Pacifics easily eclipse those of any of their predecessors. By the kindness of Mr. O. V. Bulleid, Chief Mechanical Engineer of the late Southern Railway, I have been supplied with details of certain of the test runs which have been made with these locomotives, and these are set out in Tables 58 to 60 inclusive. There are first (Table 58) two runs from Exeter to Salisbury, both of which include times far faster than any made previously over this route. Indeed, if the time of 41 minutes 55 seconds made by *Blue Funnel* from Exeter to Sutton Bingham be added to the 36 minutes 33 seconds of *Nederland Line* from Sutton Bingham to Salisbury, the almost unbelievable total of 78 minutes 22 seconds is obtained over the 88 miles of this heavily-graded switchback.

The first trip was made with a train of 12 bogie vehicles, and had a severe signal check through Crewkerne; but for this, *Nederland Line* would have completed the run, probably, in 81½ minutes. Some of the uphill work was magnificent, particularly the average of 69·2 m.p.h. maintained up the long climb from Axminster to Hewish box; other notable figures were 58·4 from Whimple up to the west end of Honiton tunnel, 63·4 m.p.h. from Sherborne up to Milborne Port, and 63·1 m.p.h. from Gillingham up to Semley. Some of the fastest downhill running was from Semley onwards, with an average of 77·4 m.p.h. over the 10·0 miles from Tisbury to Wilton, where the usual slack was made for the curve. Before the Second World War, with tare loads limited to 355 tons, the "King Arthur" 4-6-0s were allowed 98 minutes on the fastest schedules from Exeter to Salisbury; *Nederland Line*, with one coach more, cut this time to 86 minutes gross and 81½ minutes net.

TABLE 58

YEARS 1946–1947
S.R. "MERCHANT NAVY" CLASS (4-6-2)

Dist.	Engine No. .. .. ,, Name .. .. Load: tons tare ,, ,, gross ..	21C14 *Nederland Line* 389 415	21C13 *Blue Funnel* 325 345
miles		min. sec.	min. sec.
0·0	EXETER CENTRAL ..	0 00	0 00
1·1	*Exmouth Junction* ..	3 32	3 25
2·9	Pinhoe	6 02	5 51
4·8	Broad Clyst	7 47	7 30
8·5	Whimple	11 12	10 50
12·2	SIDMOUTH JUNC. ..	15 20	14 40
16·8	Honiton	19 38	18 37
18·2	*Honiton Tunnel W. End* ..	21 10	20 04
23·8	Seaton Junction ..	26 04	24 11
27·0	Axminster	28 44	26 35
32·1	Chard Junction ..	32 58	30 33
37·5	*Hewish Siding*	37 50	35 10
		sigs.	
40·1	Crewkerne	42 15	37 15
		sigs.	
46·7	Sutton Bingham ..	49 33	41 55
48·9	YEOVIL JUNCTION ..	pass	{ 44 14 }
		51 20	{ 0 00 }
53·5	Sherborne	55 05	6 32
57·2	Milborne Port	58 35	10 28
59·6	TEMPLECOMBE ..	60 45	12 46
			p.w.s.
66·4	Gillingham	66 31	21 13
70·5	Semley	70 25	26 23
75·5	Tisbury	74 55	31 16
79·8	Dinton	78 14	34 52
85·5	Wilton*	82 40	39 53
			p.w.s.
88·0	SALISBURY	86 06	44 51
88·0	Net times (minutes)	81½	44¼ + 39¾

* Service slack

With a 10-coach train of 325 tons tare and 345 tons gross, *Blue Funnel* gave an electrifying performance indeed. Down the short 1 in 100 past Pinhoe the engine reached 74 m.p.h.; the 5-mile climb to milepost $161\frac{1}{4}$ (1 in 170-135-145-100) was taken at a minimum of 58 m.p.h., and after the $4\frac{1}{2}$ miles up to Honiton tunnel, all at 1 in 100-90, the engine actually entered Honiton tunnel at 62 m.p.h. —an unheard-of speed at this point. Caution was shown in the early part of the descent of Seaton bank, but then the speed was allowed to reach 96 m.p.h.; the rate was eased to 78 through Seaton Junction, but rose again to 86 at the bottom of the dip. Up from Axminster to Hewish an average of 73·4 m.p.h. was maintained throughout; even the final 1 in 200-120-160 did not pull the speed below 67 m.p.h. Down Crewkerne bank there was a 90 m.p.h. maximum.

By Hewish siding *Blue Funnel*, with two coaches less, was 2 minutes 40 seconds ahead of *Nederland Line*, but the former had then to stop at Yeovil Junction, as this was a normal passenger service. The 55-minutes schedule had been cut to the extraordinary figure of 44 minutes 14 seconds. The remainder of the run was of less interest, as two perma-

TABLE 59

YEAR 1945

S.R. "MERCHANT NAVY" CLASS (4-6-2

Engine No. 21C2, *Union Castle*

Load: 517 tons tare, 520 tons gross

Dist.		Sched.	Actual		Speeds
miles		min.	min.	sec.	m.p.h.
0·0	WATERLOO	0	0	00	—
3·9	CLAPHAM JUNCTION	7	7	30	*42
5·6	Earlsfield	—	9	44	56
7·3	WIMBLEDON	—	11	44	64
9·8	Malden	—	14	18	68
12·0	SURBITON	—	16	21	66
14·4	Esher	—	18	22	75
17·1	Walton	—	20	29	77
19·1	Weybridge	—	22	09	72
21·7	Byfleet	—	24	11	77
			sigs.		28
24·4	WOKING	—	27	00	—
28·0	Brookwood	—	31	29	48
31·0	Milepost 31	—	35	00	54
33·2	Farnborough	—	37	16	64
36·5	Fleet	—	40	18	68
39·7	Winchfield	—	43	00	69
42·2	Hook..	—	45	00	75
47·8	BASINGSTOKE	—	49	31	64
50·3	*Worting Junction*	54	52	03	*46
58·1	Micheldever	—	60	00	76
64·5	*Winchester Junction*	—	65	02	80
66·6	WINCHESTER	—	66	45	74
69·7	Shawford	—	69	31	70
73·6	EASTLEIGH	$75\frac{1}{2}$	72	30	70
77·3	St. Denys	—	75	44	65
78·1	*Northam Junction*	$80\frac{1}{2}$	77	15	*13
79·2	SOUTHAMPTON C.	83	79	31	*24
80·1	Millbrook	—	81	02	45
			sigs.		36
82·6	Totton	—	84	29	42
85·4	Lyndhurst Road	—	88	30	52
88·1	Beaulieu Road	—	91	31	54
92·8	BROCKENHURST	—	96	00	70/*50
93·7	*Lymington Junction*	100	97	16	42
95·5	Sway	—	99	32	55
98·5	New Milton	—	102	30	64
101·0	Hinton Admiral	—	104	28	76
104·3	CHRISTCHURCH	—	107	29	*56
106·2	Pokesdown	—	109	59	44
106·8	Boscombe	—	111	00	38
107·9	BOURNEMOUTH C.	116	112	46	—

Net time: 109 minutes

* Service slack

nent-way checks were experienced, and obviously the engine was being run under easier steam; but even in these conditions, the 51-minute schedule was pared to 44 minutes 51 seconds, or not more than 40 minutes net.

A third run (Table 59) was made to Bournemouth, and was notable, not only for the fact that a 17-coach train of 517 tare tons was taken down in well under the pre-war 116-minute booking (which was enforced only with loads restricted to 365 tons), but that the engine completed this task on a tender water supply of 5,000 gallons, with no chance of replenishment over this 108-mile route. The locomotive, *Union Castle*, soon got into her stride; before Esher the speed on virtually level track was up to 75 m.p.h., and over the undulations to Byfleet an average of 74·3 m.p.h. was maintained.

TABLE 60

YEAR 1945
S.R. "MERCHANT NAVY" CLASS (4-6-2)
Engine No. 21C2, *Union Castle*
Load: 454 tons tare, 460 tons gross

Dist.				Sched.	Actual		Speeds
miles				min.	min.	sec.	m.p.h.
0·0	VICTORIA ..	..	..	0	0	00	—
3·2	Brixton	..	..	—	5	40	—
4·0	HERNE HILL	..	..	8	6	40	*30
5·7	Sydenham Hill	..		—	9	11	47
7·2	Penge East	..	..	—	11	06	*44
8·7	BECKENHAM JUNCTION	..		16	12	38	—
10·9	BROMLEY SOUTH	..		—	14	46	60
12·6	*Bickley Junction*	..	..	—	16	54	*23
14·9	ORPINGTON	..	..	26	20	38	38
16·4	Chelsfield	..		—	22	40	—
17·7	Knockholt	..		—	24	26	48
					sigs.		20
21·7	Dunton Green	..	..	—	30	05	—
23·2	SEVENOAKS	..	..	36	32	00	45
28·1	Hildenborough	..		—	37	04	78
30·6	TONBRIDGE	..	..	43½	39	23	*32
					p.w.s.		20
35·9	Paddock Wood	..	..	49	45	16	—
40·5	Marden	..	..	—	48	46	81
43·0	Staplehurst	..		—	50	44	77
46·3	Headcorn	..		—	53	01	83
51·5	Pluckley	..		—	56	43	86
57·2	ASHFORD	..	..	68	60	57	85
61·5	Smeeth	..		—	64	21	80
65·3	Westenhanger	..		—	67	33	69
66·5	Sandling Junction	..	..	77	68	44	*30
					p.w.s.		15
71·0	FOLKESTONE JUNCTION			82	75	16	50
					sig stop		—
78·0	DOVER MARINE ..		..	90	84	55	—

Net time: 77½ minutes
* Service slack

The check through Woking, costing a little over 3 minutes, was unfortunate, as it spoiled the engine's effort up the long rise to milepost 31. Along the level stretch from Farnborough to Hook speed mounted again to the 75 m.p.h. level, with an average of 71·5 from Farnborough to Basingstoke. Down the long incline from Litchfield to Eastleigh no exceptional speeds were run, but Northam Junction, where the usual severe speed restriction was observed, was passed in 77 minutes 15 seconds, or 74 minutes net, from Waterloo. Before the war the non-stop "Bournemouth Limited" was allowed 80½ minutes to this point. There were no other features of exceptional note, and the total time from Waterloo to Bournemouth, 107·9 miles, was 112 minutes 46 seconds, or 109 minutes net.

Another test run of great merit (Table 60) was that made by *Union Castle* from Victoria to Dover Marine in August, 1945, with a train of ten Pullmans and four bogie coaches weighing 454 tons all told, on a special schedule of 90 minutes for the 78·0 miles, much of which at the London end is slack-infested and very heavily graded. For this reason an allowance of 18 minutes had been given for the 10·9 miles from Herne Hill up to Orpington, which the locomotive cut to 13 minutes 58 seconds.   Up the 1 in 101 from Herne Hill to Sydenham Hill the speed averaged 40·6 m.p.h.; up the 1 in 95 from Bromley South to Bickley Junction 47·8 m.p.h.; and up the 1 in 120 from Orpington to Knockholt 44·2 m.p.h.; in each case the speeds would have been higher but for service slacks in their immediate vicinity.

Bad signal and permanent-way checks were experienced near Dunton Green and after Tonbridge, but from Paddock Wood the engine got away finely, maintaining an average of 78·6 m.p.h. continuously over the undulating and ultimately rising grades from Paddock Wood to Westenhanger, a total of 29·4 miles.   The maximum speed, on practically level track, was but little short of 90 m.p.h.; the mean speed from Staplehurst to Headcorn was 86·7 m.p.h.   A further string of permanent-way and signal checks beset the train through Folkestone and on to Dover, notwithstanding which the arrival was 5 minutes early.   Net time for the 78·0 miles from Victoria to Dover Marine was not more than 77½ minutes.

As showing that the exceptional capacity of the "Merchant Navy" Pacifics is not by any means confined to runs in exceptionally favourable test conditions, some of the exploits of these engines with the heavy Pullman trains during the summer of 1947 are worth quoting.   At busy week-ends, the "Devon Belle" was made up to 14 Pullman cars, with a tare weight of 545 tons, and a gross weight of fully 575 tons.   On one down journey with this load, timed by Mr. A. J. Baker, 21C7, *Aberdeen-Commonwealth*, touched 86 m.p.h. at Gillingham, 87 before Templecombe, 90 at Sherborne, 80 at Yeovil Junction, 82 after Axminster, and 80 before the Sidmouth Junction stop; minimum speeds were 57 m.p.h. up 2½ miles at 1 in 80-100 past Templecombe, 40 up Crewkerne bank (2¾ miles at 1 in 80), and 28 up the formidable Seaton bank— 1 in 100 for 1½ miles and 1 in 80 for 4¼ miles—until the engine began to slip, a mile from the tunnel, and speed dropped to 22 m.p.h.

The rising start from Wilton (just west of Salisbury, where engines were changed) caused the train to take 20 minutes 54 seconds for the first 15·0 miles, from Wilton to Semley; the 46·7 miles from Semley to Seaton Junction were then run with this tremendous load in 39 minutes 46 seconds; and the final 11·6 miles over Honiton summit into Sidmouth Junction took 17 minutes 39 seconds—total 78 minutes 19 seconds for the 73·6 miles from Wilton, as against 83 minutes booked.   On another run with the same engine and load, timed by Mr. P. W. B. Semmens, the starting time from Wilton to Semley was cut to 19 minutes 29 seconds, and with no slipping on Seaton bank, the Seaton Junction to Sidmouth Junction time came down to 14 minutes 25 seconds.   This means that the top of the 1 in 80 must have been reached at 33-34 m.p.h.—a very fine achievement—even though there was a fall to 27 m.p.h. on the greasy rails in the tunnel. Intermediately the speeds were not quite so high as before, but the considerably faster times at the two ends of the run brought the total Wilton-Sidmouth Junction time down to 74 minutes 37 seconds, nearly 8½ minutes less than schedule.

In comparing the performances just described with those of previous Southern Railway express locomotive classes, it should be remembered that, without tender, the 94¾ tons weight of a "Merchant Navy" Pacific exceeds that of a "Lord Nelson" 4-6-0 by 11¼ tons only, and a "King Arthur" 4-6-0 by 13¾ tons. The development of power has been out of all proportion to this modest increment. Designed and built as they were during the war, in war conditions and since the Southern Pacifics have had but little chance of showing their paces to full advantage. But the quality of the running reviewed in this chapter shows the potentialities of the Bulleid engines to be in no degree inferior to those of the Gresley and Stanier Pacifics of the late L.M.S.R. and L.N.E.R.; and this ability has been confirmed during the exchange tests of 1948. But the dynamometer records show the Southern 4-6-2s to have been considerably heavier on coal and water than their rivals.

In these exchanges, also, the feats of the considerably smaller "West Country" Pacifics have fallen but little short of those of the "Merchant Navy" engines. I cannot trace any comparable performance by an *ex*-L.N.E.R. engine over the Great Central main line, for example, to that of the Southern light Pacific *Bude*, as handled by Driver Swain of Nine Elms shed. With a 380-ton train he accelerated from 27 to 45 m.p.h. up the 1 in 105 from Rickmansworth and from 20 to 50 m.p.h. up the 1 in 164 from Hucknall to Annesley; another startling performance was the time of 31 minutes 24 seconds for the 31·2 miles from Aylesbury to Woodford, start-to-stop, including long stretches of 1 in 176 gradient mounted at a steady 59-64 m.p.h. Again, the acceleration from the dead start at Aylesbury, now with a 395-ton train, to 48 m.p.h. up the 1 in 117 to Wendover, was unprecedented. The drawbar horsepower outputs recorded by the dynamometer car ranged from 1,639 to 1,962. Thus, on a power-weight basis, no less than in overall thermal efficiency, Great Britain to-day has no cause to be dissatisfied with the performances of her principal modern steam locomotive classes.

17

PERFORMANCE—FRANCE AND GERMANY

ON the mainland of Europe, with little doubt it is in France that the steam locomotive has reached its highest degree of technical development. From the opening of the century, the four-cylinder De Glehn compound Atlantics introduced on the Northern Railway of France in 1900 by its Chief Mechanical Engineer, Du Bousquet, began to earn a reputation which spread far beyond the country of their origin. As mentioned in Chapter 1, this reputation was sufficient to encourage the Great Western Railway in our own country, in 1903 and 1904, to purchase three of these locomotives, built in France, for trial on their own system.

From the Atlantics there later developed the four-cylinder compound Pacific and super-Pacific designs of the Nord, which did such magnificent work over the three main lines of that company, including the Paris-Boulogne and Paris-Calais boat trains, and, in later years, the non-stop runs over the 226·7 miles between Paris and Liége and the 193·1 miles between Paris and Brussels, the latter on 3-hour schedules at 64·4 m.p.h. These were the longest regular non-stop runs on the European mainland with steam haulage.

On practically every main line in France, from the start of the century onwards, the standard of locomotive performance was very high, and the more so, perhaps, in that the fuel in general has consisted of a mixture of briquettes and slack. In general, the tendency has been towards compound rather than simple propulsion, and for reasons explained earlier, the training and mentality of French enginemen has caused them to thrive on the complications of their locomotives, and to make the most of their possibilities. A controlling factor in French express locomotive performance, until quite recent years, has been the statutory restriction of maximum speeds to 120 km.p.h. (74½ m.p.h.), which has encouraged brilliant uphill running in order that high average speeds might be maintained.

Space does not permit me to go in detail into the locomotive practice of each of the French railways prior to the formation of the French National Railway system in 1938, but it will perhaps serve the purpose if I concentrate on the work of the French designer who probably has achieved greater distinction than any other. This is M. André Chapelon, at first associated with the Paris-Orleans Railway, and later appointed to take charge of design for the National system.

The effect of his locomotive research has been felt, not merely throughout France, but in other countries as well.

In the year 1931, a compound Pacific locomotive of the Paris-Orleans, No. 3566, was rebuilt to Chapelon's directions. With further modifications, the rebuilding of a series of these engines was begun in the following year. While the original locomotives had no features of note in their design or performance, the modified engines set up standards both of work and of overall thermal efficiency that never previously had been attained in France. The designer's aim was both to improve the steaming capacity of the boiler, and also the efficiency of the steam distribution; and in both aims he was successful.

Beginning with the firebox, he fitted Nicholson thermic syphons to improve the circulation. The ashpan openings were increased in size,

TABLE 61

MODERN FRENCH COMPOUND LOCOMOTIVE TYPES—LEADING DIMENSIONS

Original Owning Railway	Nord	Paris-Orleans-Midi		French National	
Type	Collin Super-4-6-2	Chapelon rebuilt 4-6-2	Chapelon rebuilt 4-8-0	Series 232-S 4-6-4	Chapelon rebuild of Est 4-8-2 as 4-8-4
Cylinders, h.p., diameter ..	(2) 17¼ in.	(2) 16½ in.	(2) 17¼ in.	(2) 17⅞ in.	(1) 23⅝ in.
,, ,, stroke ..	26 in.	25½ in.	25½ in.	27½ in.	28¼ in.
,, l.p., diameter ..	(2) 24½ in.	(2) 25¼ in.	(2) 25¼ in.	(2) 26¾ in.	(2) 26¾ in.
,, ,, stroke ..	27 in.	25½ in.	25½ in.	27½ in.	30 in.
Driving Wheels, diameter ..	6 ft. 3 in.	6 ft. 3 in.	5 ft. 11 in.	6 ft. 6¾ in.	6 ft. 4¾ in.
Combined Heating Surface	2,928 sq. ft.	2,771 sq. ft.	2,975 sq. ft.	2,788 sq. ft.	4,011 sq. ft.
Firegrate Area	37·7 sq. ft.	49·0 sq. ft.	40·5 sq. ft.	55·9 sq. ft.	54·0 sq. ft.
Working Pressure, per sq. in.	242 lb.	227 lb.	284 lb.	284 lb.	284 lb.
Tractive Effort	37,830 lb.	—	45,930 lb.	—	—
,, ,, ...	50,770 lb.	—	57,470 lb.	—	—
Adhesion Weight	55·9 tons	—	74·3 tons	67·9 tons	82·8 tons
Total Engine Weight ..	99·0 tons	98·0 tons	104·6 tons	128·6 tons	145·8 tons

to permit more ample ingress of air. Next, the main steampipe was enlarged, and the superheater was increased in size from 24 to 32 elements, to ensure a steam temperature of from 750° to 770° F. In view of this high temperature, it was decided to substitute poppet-valves for piston-valves in the first rebuilds, with oscillating cam drive; but in certain of the later reconstructions the highly efficient Willoteaux piston-valve was used instead, with some advantage to the performance of the engines. Finally, the exhaust was carried from the cylinders to twin blast-pipes, with a double chimney above—the first of its kind. This had the effect both of reducing back-pressure in the cylinders and also of improving draught.

In effect, Chapelon had streamlined the flow of the steam from its generation to the moment of ejection as exhaust, and had proved that the secret of sustained high-speed steaming, with efficiency, lies more in this realm than in any other. The leading dimensions of these engines are given in Table 61. In working order each locomotive, without tender, weighed 99 tons, or slightly less than that of an L.M.S.R. or L.N.E.R. Pacific. On test, No. 3566 showed her mettle by working a train of 567 tons weight from St. Pierre-des-Corps to Angoulême, 133·0 miles, at a start-to-stop speed of 68·3 m.p.h., and by returning with a 656-ton load at 55·9 m.p.h.

By degrees, further improvements were made to the Chapelon rebuilds, including larger superheater elements, even larger steampipes, and poppet-valves to the low-pressure cylinders. A remarkable test run with No. 231.726, one of the later streamlined conversions, appears in Table 62; it was recorded by M. Orget and Baron Vuillet, two well-known authorities on French locomotive performance. The train concerned was the southbound "Sud Express," which for the purpose of the test had been made up to 615 tons.

The run started briskly, but it was not until after leaving Poitiers that the engine was really opened out. Some 7½ miles beyond Poitiers, No. 231.726 accelerated on the level to 75 m.p.h., and there was a

TABLE 62

YEAR 1937

PARIS-ORLEANS-MIDI RAILWAY

CHAPELON REBUILT 4-6.2 TYPE‡

Engine No. 231.726

Load: 615 tons gross

Dist.			Actual		Speeds
miles			min.	sec.	m.p.h.
0·0	ST. PIERRE-DES-CORPS	..	0	00	†56
8·5	Monts ..	..	11	13	75
14·2	Villeperdue ..	..	15	59	70
15·4	Kilometre 260 (summit)	..	16	56	—
42·3	CHATELLERAULT ..	..	39	01	75
62·8 }	POITIERS	..	{ 56	24	—
0·0 }			{ 0	00	—
2·7	St. Benoit ..	..	5	07	—
4·6	Ligugé.. ..	..	6	55	—
8·4	Iteuil	..	10	06	75½
12·0	Vivonne ..	..	12	55	79½
17·8	Anché-Voulon	..	17	24	77
20·9	Couhé-Verac ..	..	19	51	72½/77
24·0	Kilometre 375 (summit)	..	22	19	74
26·4	Epanvilliers ..	..	24	14	
32·0	ST. SAVIOL ..	..	28	39	
35·4	Voulême ..	..	31	17	} 76/77
40·7	Ruffec ..	..	35	33	
46·8	Salles-Moussac	..	40	19	
52·0	Luxe	..	44	23	77
58·4	St. Arnaud ..	..	49	36	70
61·7	Vars	..	52	05	76
69·3	Kilometre 448	..	58	02	—
70·1 }	ANGOULEME	..	{ 59	22	—
0·0 }			{ 0	00	—
4·7	La Couronne ..	..	6	36	} 66½/69
8·8	Mouthiers ..	..	10	10	
13·2	Charmant ..	..	14	07	
			p.w.s.		75/35
50·7	COUTRAS ..	..	46	50	*55
60·8	LIBOURNE ..	..	55	46	*35
			p.w.s.		—
82·3	Bordeaux-Benange ..	..	76	18	—
83·5	BORDEAUX-ST. JEAN	..	80	01	—

* Service slack   † Attained up 1 in 200 from start
‡ Streamlined

further increase to 79½ before the 10-mile ascent to km. 375 was begun. On this bank, a stretch at 1 in 333 was mounted at 75 to 77 m.p.h. and the minimum speed up two lengths of 1 in 200 gradient were 72½ and 74 m.p.h. The engine here was cutting off at 59 per cent. in the high-pressure and 54 per cent. in the low-pressure cylinders; pressure in the high-pressure chest was 228 lb., and in the low-pressure 84 lb. per sq.

in.; the recorded drawbar-horsepower was 2,500 and the indicated horsepower 3,700. On a later ascent of 4 miles at 1 in 200-250, the fall in speed was no more than from 77 to 70 m.p.h. From Ligugé, a distance of 64·7 miles was run at an average of 76 m.p.h. and the 70·1 miles from Poitiers to Angoulême were completed in 59 minutes 22 seconds start-to-stop, at an average of 70·7 m.p.h.

The final section, from Angoulême to Bordeaux, was delayed by service slacks and signal checks. Over the whole 216·4 miles, the 99-ton locomotive with this very heavy train, equal to about 18 British corridor coaches, had taken a net time of no more than 191¾ minutes, which works out at 67·6 m.p.h. Coal consumption averaged 2·49 lb. per drawbar-horsepower-hour, or 49·7 lb. per train-mile; water consumption per drawbar-horsepower-hour was 1·88 gallons. Many more runs with these notable locomotives might be quoted, with loads rising to maxima of all but 800 tons, but with substantial gains on schedule.

The next Chapelon achievement, designed to obtain the advantage of the previous conversions, but with increased adhesion weight, was the rebuilding of a series of Pacific locomotives with the 4-8-0 wheel arrangement. The same general principles as before were followed, including Nicholson thermic syphon and rocking grate in the firebox, but with working pressure raised to 290 lb. per sq. in.; large steam-pipes and passages; a reversion to oscillating-cam poppet-valves for all cylinders, actuated by Walschaerts motion; large superheaters giving a superheat temperature of 750° F.; and Kylchap double blast-pipe and chimney. From the dimensions of the rebuilt 4-8-0 engine in Table 61, it will be seen that the driving wheels were of 5 ft. 11 in. diameter only. The engine weight of 104½ tons was almost exactly equal to that of one of the L.N.E.R. "A4" streamlined Pacifics.

The rebuilt 4-8-0 proved itself capable of amazing work. On some of the earliest tests, a train of 787 tons was taken up a 1 in 200 gradient at 59 m.p.h.; of 566 tons up a 1 in 167 gradient at 68 m.p.h.; and of 541 tons up a 1 in 100 gradient, with curves of 25 chains radius, at 53 m.p.h. Maximum indicated horsepower readings of all but 4,000 were obtained, and continuous indicated horsepower outputs of 3,450, so that the engine was capable of developing 1 h.p. for every 68 lb. of its own weight. With a cut-off of 55 per cent. in the high-pressure cylinders, it was found possible to develop 3,060 i.h.p. at 75 m.p.h.

A later test of an engine of this type, No. 4707, was made in 1935 over the Northern main line between Calais and Paris, with a train made up to 635 tons—the maximum ever likely to be worked on one of the boat services. For the occasion the 120 km.p.h. speed limit was waived, though at that time it might hardly have been expected that a locomotive with eight-coupled driving wheels of less than 6 ft. diameter would be likely to travel at much over 75 m.p.h. The actual performance, however, at one point added over 20 per cent. to this limit. The details of the run are set out in Table 63.

The first obstacle after leaving Calais is the climb up to Caffiers, on the high ground behind Cap Gris Nez. This 6¾-mile bank, which is at 1 in 125, exactly equal to the northern approach to Shap, begun by the 4-8-0 at 58½ m.p.h., was completed at 51 m.p.h. On the climb, the engine, cutting off at 50 per cent. in the high-pressure and 55 per cent. in the low-pressure cylinders, was steadily maintaining the 290 lb. boiler pressure, with from 72 to 80 lb. in the low-pressure receiver; the drawbar-horsepower varied between 2,550 and 3,000. The regulator was full open, and the drop in pressure between boiler and high-pressure steam chest was seldom more than 7 lb. per sq. in.—a tribute to the efficient design of the steam passages. The 4-8-0 next proceeded to attain 85 m.p.h. on the descent to Boulogne. After the usual slowing through Boulogne, the engine attained 74 m.p.h. on the level at Hesdigneul, and then rushed the 1 in 133-143 ascent past Neufchatel at a minimum of 64 m.p.h. Next came some magnificent running along the level stretch after Etaples, where the locomotive actually maintained an average speed of 79·7 m.p.h. for 46·6 miles from Rang-du-Fliers-Verton to Ailly-sur-Somme, inclusive of a 65 m.p.h. slowing through Abbeville.

On the lower part of the long 1 in 333 ascent to Gannes, after Amiens slack, speed was 76 m.p.h., but it increased to 79½ before the summit was breasted; here the cut-offs were 40 per cent. in the high-pressure

TABLE 63

YEAR 1935
PARIS-ORLEANS-MIDI RAILWAY
CHAPELON REBUILT 4-8-0 TYPE
Engine No. 4707
Load: 635 tons gross

Dist.		Actual		Speeds
miles		min.	sec.	m.p.h.
0·0	CALAIS MARITIME	0	00	—
1·6	CALAIS VILLE ..	3	33	—
2·8	Les Fontinettes ..	4	58	62
6·1	Fréthun ..	8	15	58¼
11·7	Caffiers ..	14	20	51
16·8	Marquise-Rinxent	18	45	—
23·2	Wimille-Wimereux	23	40	85
26·2	BOULOGNE-TINTILLERIES	25	50	*65
32·1	Hesdigneul	31	30	74
36·2	Kilometre 238 (summit)..	34	20	64
43·5	ETAPLES..	39	55	*65
50·5	Rang-du-Fliers-Verton ..	45	10	80
60·5	Rue	52	20	84
75·1	ABBEVILLE	63	20	*65
90·0	Hangest ..	74	50	81
97·1	Ailly-sur-Somme	80	15	78¼
102·9	AMIENS ..	85	32	—
0·0		0	00	—
2·8	Longueau	4	32	62
16·4	La Faloise	15	50	73½
26·9	Gannes (summit)	23	57	79
31·7	St. Just ..	27	30	—
40·6	Clermont	33	47	89¼
49·8	CREIL ..	40	53	*59
55·7	Chantilly..	46	00	68
59·4	Orry-la-Ville	49	12	69
63·7	Kilometre 28 (summit) ..	53	00	71
69·0	Goussainville	56	52	91
77·3	St. Denis..	63	25	—
80·8	LA CHAPELLE ..	70	25	—

* Service slack

and 45 per cent. in the low-pressure cylinders, with the regulator seven-eighths open. The drawbar-horsepower attained was 2,500. A maximum of 89 m.p.h. on the descent to Creil was cut short by the 59 m.p.h. slack through that station. Then followed a glorious climb of the 1 in 200 to Survilliers, with speed maintained throughout at between 68½ and 71 m.p.h., and a drawbar-horsepower of 2,600; finally, there was an acceleration to no less than 91 m.p.h.—with eight-coupled driving wheels of 5 ft. 11 in. diameter —down the 1 in 200 before the outskirts of Paris were reached. It will be seen that the start-to-stop times of 85 minutes 32 seconds for the 102·9 miles from Calais to Amiens, and of 70 minutes 25 seconds for the 80·8 miles from Amiens to the La Chapelle depot at Paris, required average speeds of 72·1 and 68·8 m.p.h. respectively.

The 79·7 m.p.h. maintained by the French 4-8-0 on the level for 46·6 miles after Étaples (equivalent to a little over 80 m.p.h. if allowance be made for the Abbeville slack), with a train of 635 tons, compares in striking fashion with the 75·9 m.p.h. of the L.N.E.R. "A4" Pacific, *Capercaillie*, kept up for 25 miles on the Darlington-York run with a 730-ton train, as described in Chapter 14 and set out in Table 38, the two engines concerned being almost identical in weight. The L.N.E.R. locomotive had the advantage of a very slightly falling gradient for most of the distance concerned. But the French compound obviously was putting out an even greater effort from Amiens onwards, and even for France the run set up some new standards of locomotive performance.

Since then, in addition to the numerous rebuilds, new locomotives have been built by the French National Railways to the Chapelon designs, and much has been done, also, in the modernisation of locomotives of the pre-nationalisation Nord, Est and P.L.M. Railways to ensure equally capable and efficient performances by other 4-6-0, 4-6-2 and 4-8-2 classes. For the Nord main lines, new 4-6-4 express locomotives were built in 1940 and 1941, Series "232 S" with four-cylinder compound and Series "232 R" with three-cylinder simple expansion; these are included in Table 61. A post-war Chapelon conversion has been of an experimental Etat 4-8-2 locomotive, which never was a conspicuously successful machine, into an even larger three-cylinder compound 4-8-4 weighing no less than 145·8 tons without tender. The leading dimensions of this engine also are shown in Table 61. It is equipped for mechanical firing, and for the first time in French practice has a triple blast-pipe of the Kylchap type.

Already the locomotive last-mentioned, No. 242 A1, has put up some remarkable performances. With a 604-ton train it has attained 62 m.p.h. in 3 km. from a dead start on the level, taking 3 minutes

10 seconds for this 1·9 miles. With 818 tons behind the tender, the same speed was reached in 6 minutes 45 seconds from the start. On the level with 935 tons the rate rose to 75 m.p.h., while some speeds attained uphill during the tests were 59 m.p.h. with 639 tons up 1 in 125 continuously, and 40½ m.p.h. with 590 tons up a long bank at 1 in 71. At 60 m.p.h. on the level, No. 242 A1 has developed a maximum drawbar-horsepower of 4,200, which suggests that the indicated horse-power must have been 5,000 at least. Based on experience with this locomotive, a new standard 4-8-4 design has been prepared, with 6 ft. 4¾ in. driving wheels; also a 7 ft. 2½ in. 4-6-4 for high-speed work, a 5 ft. 9 in. 2-8-4 for mixed traffic, and a 5 ft. 5 in. 2-10-4 for heavy freight, all three-cylinder compounds with triple blast-pipes and chimneys. Locomotive development in France thus is very much alive.

Past records include little of spectacular interest in the performance of steam locomotives on the German railways. It is not that the later German designs have not been capable of first-class work but rather that, until the advent of the first diesel-electric streamline units in 1932, the Germans had never been as speed-conscious as their French neighbours. In the interests, no doubt, of keeping down the costs of maintenance, German locomotives, though of ample dimensions, were seldom worked as hard as the French; and solicitude for the track no doubt also helps to explain why up to the end of 1932 there were no runs in Germany timed at as much as a mile-a-minute from start to stop, and no more than 18 at over 55 m.p.h. Indeed, it was not until 1937 that the maximum speed limit over German main lines in general was raised from 62 to 75 m.p.h. From 1933 onwards, however, there was a rapid advance in schedule speeds. On the "Special Class" main lines, which were rebuilt, realigned and recanted to permit, wherever possible, the 100 m.p.h. maximum speeds of the diesel streamline trains, the maximum speed allowed with steam power went up to 84 m.p.h., and over certain well-aligned routes to 93 m.p.h.

Some of the fastest running in Germany has been between Berlin and Hamburg, where apart from about 16 miles near the Hamburg end of the route, with very slight gradients of 1 in 500 to 714, the line is practically dead level throughout. Midway between the terminals, at Wittenberge, there was a speed restriction of 35 m.p.h.; over the first 8 miles from Berlin, to Spandau West, and the final 17 miles from Friedreichsruh into Hamburg, there were limits of 50 and 65 m.p.h. respectively; elsewhere maximum speed was permitted, except for slight reductions over curves through certain intermediate junctions and elsewhere.

In 1935 the German State Railways turned out two completely

streamlined 4-6-4 locomotives for working the morning and evening non-stop "FD" (extra fare) service between Berlin and Hamburg. Each of these notable engines had driving wheels no less than 7 ft. 6½ in. diameter, three cylinders 17¾ in. diameter by 26 in. stroke, 3,723 sq. ft. of combined heating surface, 50·6 sq. ft. of grate, 285 lb. pressure, and a weight in working order of 124¾ tons, of which 55½ tons ranked for adhesion. With a ten-wheel tender, holding 10 tons of coal and 8,140 gallons of water, the total weight in running order was 209 tons. The basis of the design was that the engine should be capable of working a 250-ton train on the level continuously at 150 km.p.h. (93 m.p.h.), and when necessary for the recovery of lost time should be able to raise this to 175 km.p.h. (109 m.p.h.). After careful experiments, it was calculated that the complete streamlining would reduce air resistance to the extent of a 20 per cent. reduction in the power output needed to move a 250-ton train at 93 m.p.h.

On a visit of the Institution of Locomotive Engineers in 1936 to Germany, at which I was present, No. 05·002 of this type was turned out to give the party a demonstration run from Berlin to Hamburg

TABLE 64

YEAR 1936
GERMAN STATE RAILWAYS 4-6-4 TYPE
Engine No. 05.002
Load: 135 tons tare, 141 tons gross

Dist.		Time	Speeds	
			Max. and Min.	†Av'ge
miles		min. sec.	m.p.h.	m.p.h.
0·0	NAUEN (sig. stop) ..	0 00	—	—
4·2	Berger Damm ..	5 38	—	49·3
8·5	Paulinenaue	8 26	99	90·6
13·5	Vietznitz	11 30	101	99·6
16·3	Friesack	13 15	97½	97·7
24·9	NEUSTADT	18 29	97	97·1
29·9	Zernitz	21 35	100½/93	97·4
35·3	Breddin	24 55	98	96·5
41·3	Glöwen	28 40	*88	95·5
48·1	Bad Wilsnack ..	33 07	—	92·1
52·6	Kuhblank	36 27	—	81·3
		sig. stop		
56·7 } 0·0	WITTENBERGE	{ 48 02 { 0 00	—	—
5·6	Dergenthin	6 39	82	51·0
11·0	Karstadt	10 18	97½	87·7
17·5	Wendisch	14 07	106½	102·5
25·0	Km. 167	18 09	118	111·6
27·4 } 0·0	LUDWIGSLUST ..	{ 20 58 { 0 00	—	—
6·2	Jasnitz	7 17	78	50·7
8·7	Strohkirchen ..	9 09	83	81·7
13·1	HAGENOW LAND ..	12 27	*71	80·2
19·8	Pritzier	17 10	97½/*82	85·4
25·3	Brahlstorf	20 51	95	90·1
29·5	Kuhlenfeld ..	23 22	101	99·2
33·7	Boizenburg	26 03	*85	93·0
38·4	Schwanheide ..	29 18	93	87·2
42·4	BUCHEN	31 46	98	96·6
48·8	Schwarzenbeck ..	35 48	93½	95·2
		p.w.s.	25	
55·2	Friedrichsruh ..	42 07	—	60·7
65·1	Mittlerer Land ..	50 40	—	69·8
		sig. stop		
72·0	HAMBURG	63 06	—	—

* Speed reduced for curves
† Average speed, station to station

and back. It is unfortunate, perhaps, that the load, including the dynamometer car, was no more than four coaches, weighing 135 tons tare and 141 tons gross, as it would have been particularly interesting to sample the maximum capacity of the engine with at least the 250 tons for which the design had been prepared. But the running certainly left no doubt that the engine could travel for indefinite distances at 100 m.p.h., and could attain considerably higher speeds if necessary. The runs are set out in Tables 64 and 65.

On the outward journey we had several signal checks in the suburbs of Berlin, and could not get going until after the signal stop at Nauen. From here we attained "even time" (8·45 miles in 8 minutes 26 seconds) in less than 8½ miles from the dead start, and 100 m.p.h. in about 13 miles. After Bad Wilsnack the engine was eased to avoid getting too much ahead of time; allowing for a signal stop, we ran the 56·7 miles from Nauen to Wittenberge in 41 minutes net, start to stop. For most of the journey a cut-off of 20 per cent. was used, with the regulator brought back to about the two-thirds position, sufficiently to give about 150 to 170 lb. pressure in the steam chest.

From Wittenberge the engine was "extended" rather more, and with 225 lb. in the chest out of the rated boiler pressure of 285 lb., we accelerated finally to 118 m.p.h. before stopping at Ludwigslust, having covered this 27·4 miles in 2 seconds under 21 minutes, start to stop. From the Wittenberge start the acceleration was so rapid that we were doing 62 m.p.h. in 1·8 miles, 79 m.p.h. in 4·5 miles, 87 m.p.h. in 6·8 miles, and 93 m.p.h. in 8·4 miles. On the run from Ludwigslust to Hamburg there were several slacks, as well as a stop for adverse signals; net time for the 72·0 miles was 56 minutes. Including the time taken in slowing down to and restarting from two intermediate stops, we had covered 156·1 miles in 118 minutes net.

TABLE 65

YEAR 1936
GERMAN STATE RAILWAYS 4-6-4 TYPE
Engine No. 05.002
Load: 135 tons tare, 141 tons gross

Dist.		Time	Speeds	
			Max. and Min.	Av'ge†
miles		min. sec.	m.p.h.	m.p.h.
0·0	HAMBURG ..	0 00	‡	—
16·8	Friedrichsruh ..	26 12	64	—
		p.w.s.	15	
23·2	Schwarzenbeck	33 44	—	—
29·6	BUCHEN ..	38 01	92	89·7
33·6	Schwanheide	40 29	100	96·6
38·3	Boizenburg ..	43 28	*86	94·9
42·5	Kuhlenfeld ..	46 22	—	86·1
46·7	Brahlstorf ..	49 01	98/*60	93·0
52·2	Pritzier ..	53 07	80½	80·6
58·9	HAGENOW LAND	58 45	*70	71·5
63·3	Strohkirchen ..	62 05	90½	79·4
65·8	Jasnitz ..	63 43	96½	93·3
72·0	LUDWIGSLUST	68 04	*70	84·8
76·6	Grabow ..	71 07	95½	91·7
81·9	Wendisch ..	74 20	100	97·4
88·4	Karstadt ..	78 25	96	98·3
91·2	Km. 140 ..	80 07	—	98·5
92·1 }	Km. 138·6 ..	{ 81 07	—	—
0·0 }		{ 0 00	—	—
1·7	Dergenthin ..	3 11	—	—
7·3 }	WITTENBERGE ..	{ 8 41	—	—
0·0 }		{ 0 00	—	—
4·1	Kuhblank ..	4 55	—	50·0
8·5	Bad Wilsnack ..	7 52	96	90·9
15·4	Glöwen ..	12 15	*80	94·2
21·4	Breddin ..	16 13	101	91·2
26·8	Zernitz ..	19 28	98½	98·6
31·8	NEUSTADT ..	22 32	100	98·4
40·4	Friesack ..	27 40	101	99·5
43·2	Vietnitz ..	29 22	103½	100·6
48·2	Paulinenaue ..	32 21	101	102·4
56·7	NAUEN ..	37 53	eased	91·6
62·0	Brieselang ..	41 31	—	88·2
65·9	Falkensee ..	44 06	—	90·8
70·1	Km. 13·9 (sig. stop)	48 32	—	—

* Speed reduced for curves
† Average speed, station to station
‡ Series of signal checks to Friedrichsruh

On the return journey (Table 65) a series of checks gave us a poor start out of Hamburg, but from Buchen onwards we got away well, with maximum speeds up to 100 m.p.h. at several points. Then came an entirely unrehearsed incident. Suddenly the flexible water feed connection between the engine and tender broke loose at the joint, and, dragging along the track, threw up showers of ballast against the underframes of the leading coaches. Immediately the driver was signalled to stop, and such was the efficiency of the brake equipment that with perfect smoothness we came down from a shade under 100 m.p.h. to a dead stand in precisely 60 seconds, covering no more than 1·4 km. (0·85-mile) from the first brake application to the stop. After the trouble had been located, we drew gently into Wittenberge, where temporary repairs were quickly effected, and then made a brilliant run over the 70·1 miles to a signal stop at a kilometre post 13·9 miles out of Berlin in 48 minutes 32 seconds, thus averaging no less than 86·7 m.p.h. from start to stop.

The start out of Wittenberge was amazing—the first 1·8 km. (1·1 miles) were run in 2 minutes 18 seconds; 60 m.p.h. was reached in $1\frac{1}{2}$ miles, 70 m.p.h. in $2\frac{3}{4}$ miles, and 80 m.p.h. in less than 4 miles of level track. Bad Wilsnack, 8·5 miles from the start, was cleared in 7 minutes 52 seconds, at 96 m.p.h., and after the 80 m.p.h. slowing through Glöwen, we ran for 26·8 miles right off at an average of 99·7 m.p.h., with a top speed of $103\frac{1}{2}$ m.p.h. It only remains to add that 250 miles of the day's round trip were covered at a mean speed of 91 m.p.h.

A couple of years later, Mr. W. A. Willox timed a run on the evening non-stop Berlin-Hamburg "FD" train, for which these engines were designed, on which 4-6-4 No. 05.001 had a six-coach load of about 260 tons tare and 275 tons gross. After taking 10 minutes 30 seconds over the speed-restricted 7·3 miles from the Lehrter station at Berlin out to Spandau, and 23 minutes 10 seconds to clear Nauen, 22·0 miles, the engine averaged 87·8 m.p.h. over the 24·9 miles to Neustadt, and 79·2 m.p.h. on to Wittenberge (a further 31·8 miles); then the Wittenberge-Ludwigslust length (27·4 miles) was run at 79·7 m.p.h., Ludwigslust-Hagenow Land (13·1 miles) at 89·0 m.p.h., and the 20·6 miles on to Boizenburg at 82·2 m.p.h.

From the Berlin start, Wittenberge, 78·7 miles, was passed in 64 minutes 20 seconds; the 132·5 miles from Spandau to Boizenburg were run off at an average of 80·9 m.p.h., speed rising twice to 93 m.p.h. —the maximum permitted normally with steam power over this route— for some miles consecutively at two different points. After Boizenburg there were many delays, so that the final 38·3 miles took 39 minutes 15 seconds; total time for the journey of 178·1 miles was exactly

148 minutes, though with a clear road this could have been cut easily to 144 minutes or less. At the time, the train was scheduled to take 149 minutes, though in 1936, when the load normally did not exceed 220 gross tons, the Berlin-Hamburg run was allowed 144 minutes only (74·2 m.p.h.), and in the reverse direction 145 minutes (73·7 m.p.h.).

That such tractive power was not confined to the 4-6-4 locomotives is clear from a run timed on the same express, in the reverse direction, by Mr. R. N. Clements, with an identical load of 275 tons, when the locomotive employed was one of the light Pacifics, No. 03.193, which had been streamlined to serve as a deputy for the larger engines when necessary. The "03" series of Pacifics are two-cylinder engines with $23\frac{1}{2} \times 26$ in. cylinders, 6 ft. $6\frac{1}{2}$ in. driving wheels, and 227 lb. pressure. A total of 149 minutes was needed for the run of 178·1 miles, but there were two permanent way and two signal checks, which between them were responsible for a loss of 10 minutes. The net time therefore was about 139 minutes, or a minute only in excess of the "Fliegende Hamburger" diesel-electric streamliner's schedule. The 39·1 miles from Zernitz to Falkensee were run at an average of 87 m.p.h., and at three different points on the journey speed reached 93 m.p.h.

For reasons already given, there is little information as to the performance of the larger German 4-6-2 and 2-8-2 classes in heavy load conditions; no evidence is available as to any "all out" feats of haulage comparable with those of the French rebuilds described earlier in this chapter. The best effort that I can trace in ordinary performance is one in which an "01" Pacific, on the Berlin-Königsberg main line, with 525 gross tons, ran the 100·0 miles from Schneidemühl to Küstrin Neustadt in $87\frac{1}{2}$ minutes net, at 68·8 m.p.h. start to stop, covering 32·5 miles at an average of 76·7 m.p.h. and reaching a top speed of 88 m.p.h., but this was little more than a routine run in which some lost time was regained.

Before the outbreak of the Second World War, the German State Railways put on the rails their first 4-8-4 express locomotives, built by Krupp at Essen. These completely streamlined engines were designed for working 650-ton trains at speeds up to 87 m.p.h., and were of a three-cylinder type, with $20\frac{1}{2}$ in. $\times$ 28 in. cylinders, 6 ft. $6\frac{3}{4}$ in. driving wheels, an evaporative heating surface of 3,109 sq. ft. and a superheating surface of 1,425 sq. ft., a grate area of 54·2 sq. ft., a working pressure of 284 lb. per sq. in. Weight in working order was $143\frac{1}{2}$ tons, and of the tender, fully charged, 82 tons, making a total of $225\frac{1}{2}$ tons. The general proportions thus closely resembled those of the French Chapelon 4-8-4, previously described, but no information is available as to the performances on the road of the two German locomotives.

18

PERFORMANCE—THE UNITED STATES
AND CANADA

IT is not too much to claim that the most spectacular locomotive performance in the world to-day is found in the Continent of North America. To American railway officers, as was remarked in a recent issue of the French periodical, *Chemins de Fer*, the railway locomotive is not merely an *"objet d'art"* designed to ornament a railway station, but is a tool required to deal with the greatest ton-mileage that it can handle. Moreover, the Americans have developed to a degree hitherto unknown elsewhere the efficiency of their maintenance methods, which play an essential part in the success of their locomotive power. There is little doubt also that the high level to which modern labour conditions in the United States have forced the cost of train operation has compelled the making up of both passenger and freight trains to maximum possible capacity, in order to reduce the number of separate train movements. It has also been necessary to increase locomotive power accordingly, and in doing so, North American railways have had the benefit of their ample loading gauge, permitting heights up to 15 ft. 6 in. from rail, and widths up to 10 ft. 9 in.

To British standards, American locomotive coal consumption is extremely high, on a coal per train-mile basis, but consumption must be viewed in relation to power output. The modern American passenger coach measures up to 85 ft. in length and 10 ft. 6 in. in width, as compared with the British 60 ft. and slightly over 9 ft. respectively. The latest streamline cars in the United States, with all their elaborate air-conditioning and other equipment, weigh 45 to 60 tons apiece, though weight reduction has been pursued to the maximum possible degree by the use of light aluminium alloys and stainless steel. The older standard vehicles, massively built in steel, weigh from 75 to 85 tons each. Fourteen or fifteen such vehicles easily can make up a passenger train of 1,000 tons; and this is by no means the limit.

Table 66 gives the leading dimensions of a few representative modern American steam locomotive designs. Some of these immense machines, as will be seen, turn the scale at from 200 to over 300 tons, or with their tenders at from 400 to over 500 tons. Tractive efforts rise to over 100,000 lb.; combined heating surfaces to more than 8,000 sq. ft., and in one case to over 10,000 sq. ft.; firegrate areas to well over 100 sq. ft.; and working pressures to 300 lb. per sq. in.

While many high speed records were claimed for American railways in earlier years, few if any of them have any reliable authentication. In most cases it is simply stated that a certain train ran a mile in so many seconds, or that so many miles were covered in so many minutes, without any supporting testimony; and some of these claims are so fantastic as to be incredible. But as to the feats of speed and haulage that are going on to-day in the United States there can be no dispute; passenger train loads of 1,000 tons and over, as just mentioned, and maximum speeds of 100 m.p.h., in the course of ordinary running, no longer excite comment on the other side of the Atlantic.

In the first decade of the present century, some of the fastest running in the United States was done on the then Philadelphia & Reading Railroad, between Camden, across the Delaware River from Philadelphia, and Atlantic City. The best train was allowed 50 minutes only for the 55½ miles—the fastest schedule in the world at that time—and time was frequently picked up, when the ferry had been delayed on the river crossing. On one occasion in May, 1905, an Atlantic locomotive worked a train of 280 tons over the course in 42 minutes 33 seconds, at an average speed of 78·3 m.p.h. from start to stop. In later years, however, when the load had grown to 650 tons and more, the booking was eased out to 55 minutes. Mr. R. E. Charlewood mentions a trip that he had in November, 1902, on the competing West Jersey & Seashore R.R., in which a 6 ft. 8 in. Atlantic, No. 67, covered the 58·3 miles from Camden to Atlantic City in 52 minutes 47 seconds, or 49¼ minutes net, with a 310-ton train. A distance of 49 miles was run in 40 minutes 6 seconds (73·3 m.p.h.) and the top speed was 87½ m.p.h.

For a short time, about the year 1932, the Canadian railways came into the speed limelight owing to the development of a strong competition for the traffic between Montreal and Toronto. In that year, the Canadian National Railways reduced the time by their 334-mile route to 6 hours, all intermediate stops included, and the Canadian Pacific to 6¼ hours, over a course longer by 6¼ miles and more than half single track. To maintain its overall times, the C.P.R. had to book its "Canadian" express over the 124 miles of double line from Montreal West to Smith's Falls in 109 minutes, and the "Royal York" over the same stretch in the reverse direction in 108 minutes, at 68·2 and 68·9 m.p.h. respectively. For a short period these were the fastest railway runs in the world, and compelled the Great Western Railway in England to accelerate its "Cheltenham Flyer" in 1932, in order to regain the "blue riband."

Two journeys over the C.P.R. line concerned, one on each train

TABLE 66

TYPICAL MODERN U.S.A. STEAM LOCOMOTIVES—LEADING DIMENSIONS

Wheel Arrangement	Railway and Class	Cylinders			Driving Wheels, Dia.	Heating Surface			Fire-grate Area	Working Pressure	Tractive Effort‖	Engine Wheel-base	Weight		Tender				Engine & Tender	
		No.	Dia.	Stroke		Evapor-ative	Super-heater	Total					Adhesion	Engine	No. of Axles	Coal	Water	Weight	Weight	Length Overall
			in.	in.	ft. in.	sq. ft.	sq. ft.	sq. ft.	sq. ft.	lb./sq. in.	lb.	ft. in.	tons	tons		tons	gallons	tons	tons	ft. in.
4-4-2	Chicago, Milwaukee, St. Paul & Pacific	2	19	28	7 0	3,245	1,029	4,274	69·0	300	30,685	37 7	62·5	125·5	10	¶4,000	13,000	110·5	236·0	78 11
4-6-2	Pennsylvania ("K4s")	2	27	28	6 8	4,058	962	5,020	70·0	205	44,400	—	89·8	141·0	8	15½	9,200	95·5	236·5	—
4-6-4	Chicago, Milwaukee, St. Paul & Pacific	2	23½	30	7 0	4,166	1,695	5,861	96·5	300	50,300	42 4	96·5	185·3	12	22¼	20,000	167·5	352·8	93 6
4-6-4	New York Central "Hudson" ("J3A")	2	22½	29	6 7	4,187	1,745	5,932	82·0	275	*43,440	40 4	87·5	160·7	12	26¾	14,000	139·4	300·1	83 8
4-8-2	Boston & Maine ("R1A")	2	28	31	6 1	4,544	1,924	6,468	79·0	240	67,000	44 2	120·0	185·1	12	18¾	20,000	164·9	350·0	92 8
4-8-2	New York Central ("Mohawk") ..	2	25½	30	5 9	4,676	2,103	6,779	75·3	255	§60,100	43 1	118·0	176·0	12	43	15,500	136·0	309·0	96 0
2-8-4	Detroit, Toledo & Ironton	2	25	30	5 3	4,493	1,795	6,288	88·3	250	63,250	39 3	110·9	183·0	12	19¾	22,000	151·0	334·0	86 1
4-8-4	New York Central "Niagara" ("S16")	2	25½	32	6 7	4,827	2,060	6,887	100·1	275	61,570	48 5	122·8	209·8	14	41	18,000	187·9	397·7	97 3
4-8-4	Southern Pacific ("Daylight").. ..	2	25½	32	6 8	4,887	2,086	6,973	90·4	300	†64,760	47 8	123·0	212·0	12	¶6,100	23,300	140·0	352·0	96 3
4-8-4	Union Pacific	2	25	32	6 8	4,470	1,900	6,370	100·2	300	63,800	50 11	120·5	215·6	14	22¼	23,500	181·5	397·1	103 10
4-4-4-4	Pennsylvania ("T1")	4	19¾	26	6 8	4,218	1,680	5,898	91·3	300	65,000	51 11	119·8	222·0	16	36½	19,500	193·2	415·2	107 0
2-10-4	Bessemer & Lake Eire ("H1C") ..	2	31	32	5 4	5,903	2,487	8,390	106·5	250	‡96,700	45 6	165·5	232·0	12	22¼	23,000	171·0	403·0	95 3
2-6-6-4	Pittsburgh & West Virginia	4	23	32	5 3	5,914	1,873	7,787	102·3	225	97,500	55 8	175·7	234·3	12	22¼	20,000	160·9	395·2	98 4
2-6-6-6	Chesapeake & Ohio ("H8")	4	22½	33	5 7	7,240	3,186	10,426	135·0	260	110,200	62 6	210·2	322·2	14	22¼	25,000	190·4	512·6	112 11
4-8-8-2	Southern Pacific ("AC7")	4	24	32	5 3½	6,468	2,601	9,069	139·0	250	123,000	67 3	229·8	285·0	12	¶5,880	22,000	174·2	459·2	111 9
4-8-8-4	Union Pacific ("Big Boy")	4	23¾	32	5 8	5,889	2,466	8,355	150·0	300	135,375	72 6	241·0	345·4	14	25	24,000	195·0	540·4	117 7

* Plus booster, 12,100 lb. † Plus booster, 13,000 lb. ‡ Plus booster, 13,100 lb. § Plus booster, 13,900 lb. ¶ Gallons of fuel oil ‖ 85 per cent. working pressure

mentioned, are set out in Table 67; the westbound run was timed by Mr. R. F. Legget and the eastbound by Mr. W. H. C. Kelland. On the westbound trip, 4-6-4 No. 2800 had a fairly substantial train of 600 tons, but succeeded in gaining over 3 minutes on schedule, thereby achieving a start-to-stop average of 70·3 m.p.h. There was some high speed in parts; three successive 10-mile stages between mileposts 67-77, 77-87, and 87-97, were run at 78·3, 79·1 and 75·0 m.p.h. respectively, and speed must have exceeded 80 m.p.h. at a number of different points.

TABLE 67

YEAR 1932
CANADIAN PACIFIC RAILWAY, "2800" CLASS (4-6-4)

Engine No. 2800 Load: 600 tons gross				Engine No. 2811 Load: 425 tons gross		
Schedule	Time	Distance		Distance	Time	Schedule
min.	min. sec.	miles		miles	min. sec.	min.
0	0 00	0·0	MONTREAL WEST	124·0	102 52	108
5	6 30	4·9	Dorval	119·1	98 38	103
—	9 05	7·9	Lakeside	116·1	96 28	—
—	12 30	12·2	Beaurepaire	111·8	93 24	98
14	15 20	15·7	STE. ANNE'S*	108·3	90 29	93
17	18 20	19·0	Vaudreuil	105·0	87 45	90
21	22 30	23·7	St. Lazare	100·3	83 55	86
26	27 45	29·7	St. Clet	94·3	79 07	81
31	32 40	35·5	De Beaujeu*	88·5	73 35	76
37	38 05	41·7	Dalhousie Mills	82·3	68 39	71
43	44 35	49·3	Green Valley	74·7	62 38	65
50	51 35	58·0	Apple Hill	66·0	55 21	58
55	56 15	63·4	Monklands*	60·6	50 28	53
—	59 10	67·0	Milepost 67	57·0	—	—
59	60 05	68·2	Avonmore	55·8	46 46	49
65	64 35	74·3	Finch*	49·7	41 25	43
—	66 50	77·0	Milepost 77	47·0	—	—
71	70 30	82·0	Chesterville	42·0	35 27	37
—	74 25	87·0	Milepost 87	37·0	—	—
76	75 10	87·9	Winchester	36·1	31 05	31
—	77 45	91·1	Inkerman	32·9	28 38	—
82	81 30	95·9	Mountain	28·1	25 02	25
—	82 25	97·0	Milepost 97	27·0	—	—
89	87 45	103·2	BEDELL*	20·8	18 52	19
—	91 00	106·9	Swan	17·1	16 05	—
—	94 25	111·1	Burritts	12·9	12 52	—
99	97 30	114·9	Merrickville	9·1	9 46	9
—	99 10	117·0	Milepost 117	7·0	—	—
—	101 30	119·9	Rosedale	4·1	5 40	—
—	103 10	122·0	Milepost 122	2·0	—	—
109	105 50	124·0	SMITH'S FALLS	0·0	0 00	0

* Service slacks (50-60 m.p.h.)

In the opposite direction, 4-6-4 No. 2811 had five cars instead of eight, with the gross load down to 425 tons, and did some lively travelling, cutting the 108-minute booking by more than 5 minutes. All but 14 miles from Mountain to Chesterville were run at 80·2 m.p.h., and the 9·6 miles from Beaurepaire to Lachine at 82·3, with a maximum of 90 m.p.h. The quickest running was from Apple Hill onwards, for the next 53·1 miles to Dorval took 42 minutes 37 seconds only, average 74·8 m.p.h. For the entire journey the start-to-stop average speed was 72·5 m.p.h.

Over the competing Canadian National line speeds also ruled high. On two typical runs with the eastbound "Inter-City-Limited," timed by Mr. Richard Hassall, 4-6-4 locomotives of the "5700" series, with 23 in. × 28 in. cylinders and 275 lb. pressure, were at the head of six-car formations weighing 480 tons. Between Danforth and Lachine, 320·7 miles, No. 5704 made an actual running time of 303½ minutes, including slowing down to and restarting from six intermediate stops and a number of speed restrictions; No. 5800 did even better with a time of 299 minutes. On the latter run, No. 5800, after starting from Cornwall, passed Lancaster, 13·7 miles, in 13¾ minutes, ran the 16·1 miles to Coteau at an average of 88 m.p.h., and the 46 miles from Lancaster to Lachine in 35¼ minutes (78·3 m.p.h.), making 49 minutes only for 59·7 miles from the dead start. The approach to Montreal is tortuous and slow; the time for the 67·7 miles from Cornwall was 63½ minutes. In the following year, rather unhappily, the two railways agreed to pool their traffic, for the sake of economy, and having thus extinguished all competition, they slowed down their services considerably. Recently, however, the Canadian National has returned to 6¼-hour timings between Montreal and Toronto with the principal trains.

We come now to present-day locomotive running in the United States. As previously indicated, the schedules of some well-known trains, even steam-hauled, are such as to demand speeds up to 100 m.p.h. in daily service, though diesel-electric power, as described in Chapter 20, is now taking over all the fastest duties. There are several routes, however, with steam haulage still predominating, over which the standard of speed prevailing is higher than anything yet developed in Great Britain, even in peacetime conditions. Of such the Pennsylvania New York-Chicago main line west of Fort Wayne is a notable example. The 1947 summer timetable showed 16 trains booked daily to cover the 141 miles between Englewood, outside Chicago, and Fort Wayne in from 120 to 135 minutes start to stop, in most cases with one or two intermediate halts. The majority of these workings were with heavy trains of from 750 to over 1,000 tons weight. In all cases, the logs now to be described were made in ordinary working conditions, and represent performance without any special attempt at high-speed records. The trainloads quoted are in British tons of 2,240 lb., and not the American tons of 2,000 lb.

The first American run to be described (Table 68) was the "Chicago Arrow," the westbound counterpart of the eastbound "Detroit Arrow," and the fastest train on the Pennsylvania-Wabash Chicago-Detroit service. It is of interest in that the locomotive was one of the now obsolescent "E6" Atlantic type, introduced in 1905, but until that date still regarded as adequate provided the load did not exceed six cars. On this run, recorded by Mr. Donald Steffee, five cars were in the formation, totalling 350 tons.

Up the 1 in 200 out of Fort Wayne, the 4-4-2 was slower in starting than a Pacific, and dropped 2 minutes to Warsaw, but this was easily regained, and with an average speed of 78·3 m.p.h. over the 119·4 miles from milepost 324 to Gary, and of no less than 85·3 m.p.h. over 52·7 miles from milepost 365 to Wanatah, the locomotive reached Englewood 2 minutes early. For the run the start-to-stop average speed was 74·3 m.p.h., and the maximum reached was 93 m.p.h.

The most recently-built Atlantic class in the U.S.A. has been the series of four fully streamlined locomotives introduced in 1935 by the Chicago, Milwaukee, St. Paul & Pacific Railroad for working the "Hiawatha" express between Chicago and the Twin Cities of St. Paul and Minneapolis. The schedule of this train demands maximum speeds up to 100 m.p.h. on practically every trip. Yet the run set out in Table 69 shows that these 125-ton locomotives (236 tons with tenders) had a substantial margin in hand on the booking, even with

TABLE 68

YEAR 1938
PENNSYLVANIA R.R. (U.S.A.) "E6" CLASS (4-4-2)
Engine No. 1649
Load: 335 tons tare, 350 tons gross

Dist.		Sched.	Actual		Speeds†
miles		min.	min.	sec.	m.p.h.
0·0	FORT WAYNE	0	0	00	—
3·6	*Milepost 324*	—	5	38	38·4
8·4	Arcola ..	—	9	20	77·9
14·1	Coesse ..	—	13	58	73·8
18·9	COLUMBIA CITY	—	17	50	74·5
26·6	Larwill ..	—	23	45	78·1
30·9	Pierceton	—	27	20	72·0
39·0	Warsaw..	32	34	05	72·0
45·8	Atwood..	—	39	28	75·8
53·5	Bourbon	—	44	40	88·8
64·1	PLYMOUTH	51	51	50	88·7
71·0	Donaldson	—	57	00	80·1
78·2	Hamlet ..	61	61	45	90·9
89·1	Hanna ..	—	70	20	76·2
95·3	Wanatah	75	74	20	93·0
104·4	VALPARAISO	82	81	08	80·9
114·7	Hobart ..	—	90	00	69·7
117·8	LIVERPOOL	93	92	50	65·6
123·0	GARY ..	98	97	10	72·0
140·9	ENGLEWOOD	115	113	05	67·5

† Average speed, station to station

trains of over 400 tons in weight. The fastest part of the schedule is between Tower A20 and Lake, on the Chicago-Milwaukee section, with an allowance of 38 minutes only for 57·6 miles, which demands an average speed of 90·9 m.p.h.

The times of the run tabulated were recorded by Baron G. Vuillet, already mentioned in connection with French locomotive work, who rode on the footplate. Notwithstanding three bad permanent-way checks to between 18 and 30 m.p.h. each, the loss between Chicago and Milwaukee was not more than 70 seconds, and the net time for the 85 miles was 67½ minutes (75·5 m.p.h. start-to-stop, including severely limited speed for the first 3 miles out of Chicago, and slow running over two drawbridges at the entry to Milwaukee). After Sturtevant, 4 miles were run consecutively at 103 to 106 m.p.h., and between posts 70 and 79 speed averaged 100·7 m.p.h. for 9 miles. At six different points on the journey speed exceeded 100 m.p.h.; also a speed of 68 m.p.h. was maintained up a 1 in 150 grade, and of 82½ m.p.h. up 1 in 300.

For the 92·9 miles from Milwaukee to Portage the net time was 75½ minutes; the actual time of 32 minutes 30 seconds for the 43·1 miles from Portage to New Lisbon gave a start-to-stop average of 79·6 m.p.h.; and the 59·8 miles from New Lisbon to La Crosse, with severe slowings at both ends of the short single-line section beyond Tunnel City, were run in a net time of 46 minutes (78·0 m.p.h. start to stop). In recovering time lost by out-of-course checks, the Atlantic gained 24½ minutes; for the entire 411·5 miles the engine maintained a running average of 72 m.p.h., including all regular speed restrictions. Among working details, Baron Vuillet noted that the 4-4-2 could run freely at 100 m.p.h. on the level with full regulator and 28 per cent. cut-off, the oil-firing keeping the boiler pressure steadily up to the 300 lb. mark, and steam-chest pressure at round about 285 lb. per sq. in. Water consumption was 42½ gallons per mile, and fuel oil was being burned at the rate of 49½ lb. per mile.

TABLE 69

YEAR 1937
CHICAGO, MILWAUKEE, ST. PAUL & PACIFIC
RAILROAD, "HIAWATHA" CLASS (4-4-2)
Engine No. 1
Load: 385 tons tare, 415 tons gross

Dist.		Sched.	Actual	Speeds
miles		min.	min. sec.	m.p.h.
0·0	CHICAGO ..	0	0 00	—
3·0	Western Avenue	—	6 25	*
5·6	Pacific Junction	9	9 40	61
9·0	Mayfair ..	—	12 50	70
			p.w.s.	
14·6	Morton Grove	—	18 10	—
24·4	Deerfield ..	—	24 30	—
28·2	West Lake Forest	—	27 10	96
32·4	RONDOUT ..	30	30 00	*80
43·1	Wadsworth	37	37 08	100
47·2	Russell..	—	39 55	94
			p.w.s.(2)	18
57·7	Somers ..	—	52 18	—
62·0	STURTEVANT	50	56 45	—
69·5	Caledonia	—	62 03	100/106
77·9	Lake ..	—	67 05	97/102
85·0	}MILWAUKEE..	75	76 10	—
0·0		0	0 00	—
5·4	Wauwatosa	—	8 20	*48
20·3	Pewaukee ..	—	21 25	90
24·9	Hartland ..	27	24 35	*70
29·8	Okauchee ..	—	28 20	—
32·8	Oconomowoc	33	30 12	100
			p.w.s.	
38·5	Ixonia ..	—	35 30	—
			sig. stop	
46·0	WATERTOWN	44	48 40	†
55·6	Reeseville	—	57 10	†
64·7	Columbus ..	—	63 30	†
74·1	Doylestown	—	70 25	†
83·9	Wyocena ..	—	78 00	—
92·9	}PORTAGE ..	84	85 18	—
0		0	0 00	—
6·9	Wisconsin Dells	—	14 30	93
25·5	Lyndon ..	—	20 45	102/90
36·1	Mauston ..	—	27 15	102/90
43·1	}NEW LISBON	36	32 30	—
0·0		0	0 00	—
6·0	Camp Douglas	—	6 45	—
12·3	Oakdale ..	—	11 37	90
18·8	Tomah..	—	15 45	96
22·2	TUNNEL CITY	18	18 35	*45
30·3	Camp McCoy..	—	25 10	—
35·2	Sparta ..	28	28 10	102
			p.w.s.	40
41·8	Rockland ..	—	33 40	—
45·4	Bangor ..	—	37 10	—
50·0	West Salem ..	—	40 35	93
59·8	LA CROSSE ..	51	49 35	—

* Service slack   † Four 70 m.p.h. slacks between Watertown and Portage; maximum speed 94 m.p.h.

As the weight of the "Hiawatha" grew to formations of 12 and 14 cars, and even more at times of pressure, and to permit the return of the engines overnight on heavy sleeeping-car trains, some semi-streamlined coal-fired 4-6-4 locomotives were introduced, of considerably larger dimensions, as set out in Table 66. One of these engines has covered 5 miles of undulating track at 120 m.p.h. On a demonstration run, another Milwaukee 4-6-4 was called upon to handle the combined "Olympian" and "Pioneer Limited" sleeping-car trains, made up to a total of 1,905 tons, and succeeded in accelerating this vast assemblage of stock from a dead start to a speed of 70 m.p.h. in no more than 12 miles of level track.

The French journal *Chemins de Fer* has recorded a run in 1942 with No. 101 of this class, hauling a 14-coach train of 680 tons, on which 47·8 miles were covered in 27 minutes 20 seconds, at an average of no less than 104·9 m.p.h., including a slight service slack to 90 m.p.h. In 1943 another engine of the same type, with 16 coaches (780 tons), did even more brilliantly, in view of the heavier load, covering 62 miles in 37 minutes, at 100·5 m.p.h. for the entire distance, with a top speed of 102½ m.p.h. On the first of these two runs the time from Milwaukee to Chicago, including the slow running enforced through the city limits of both cities, was cut to 65 minutes, and on the second to 63 minutes, in recovery of late starts.

On yet another run, with the eastbound "Morning Hiawatha," timed by Mr. Eric Crickmay, 4-6-4 No. 100, hauling a lighter nine-coach load of 465 tons, covered 148 individual miles of the journey from Minneapolis to Chicago at 90 m.p.h. or over, and 58 miles at between 100 and 106 m.p.h., including an average of 98·3 m.p.h. over 62 miles of the Milwaukee-Chicago section. The most exacting of the point-to-point timings was that of 58 minutes for the 78·3 miles from Sparta to Portage, at 81·0 m.p.h. from start to stop, and the only schedule in the world that has ever demanded a start-to-stop speed of over 80 m.p.h. from steam power.

On this section the 4-6-4 accelerated its load to 80-82 m.p.h. up a gradient ot 1 in 200, and despite having to climb 251 ft. in 9¾ miles, at 1 in 200 and 150, and to reduce speed twice to 40 m.p.h. at the entry and exit from a stretch of single line through a tunnel, Tunnel City, 13·0 miles from Sparta, was passed in 12 minutes 2 seconds from the dead start. Then followed three successive stages of 100 m.p.h. running, separated by slight service slacks—11 miles at 102·3 m.p.h., 14 miles at 100·4 m.p.h., and 9 miles at 100·6 m.p.h.—which made it possible to complete the 78·3-mile run in 57 minutes 14 seconds, but little better than schedule time. Last came the thrilling burst of speed

TABLE 70

YEAR 1940

CHICAGO, MILWAUKEE, ST. PAUL & PACIFIC

RAILROAD, "HIAWATHA" TYPE (4-6-4)

Engine No. 100

Load: 9 cars, 430 tons tare, 465 tons gross

Dist.			Sched.	Actual	Speeds†
miles			min.	min. sec.	m.p.h.
0·0	ST. PAUL	.. ..	0	0 00	—
				sigs.	
3·6	Oakland	.. ..	—	8 00	27·0
18·4	St Croix Tower	..	18	21 11	67·3
19·6	HASTINGS*	.. ..	20	22 40	48·5
32·5	Eggleston*	.. ..	—	34 00	68·3
40·6	}RED WING	.. {	39	41 54	61·5
0·0			0	0 00	—
15·9	Lake City	.. ..	—	15 27	61·8
29·4	Wabasha	.. ..	26	25 37	79·7
46·2	Minneiska	.. ..	—	37 58	81·6
56·3	Minnesota City	..	—	45 49	78·2
62·4	}WINONA	.. {	55	52 42	53·0
0·0			0	0 00	—
9·0	Lamoille	.. ..	—	8 42	62·1
17·6	Dakota	.. ..	—	15 37	74·6
24·7	Bridge Switch*	..	—	22 02	65·5
26·7	}LA CROSSE	.. {	30	26 08	28·3
0·0			0	0 00	—
9·8	West Salem	.. ..	—	9 48	60·0
14·4	Bangor	.. ..	—	12 53	89·5
18·0	Rockland	.. ..	—	15 15	91·2
24·6	}SPARTA	.. {	20	20 03	82·5
0·0			0	0 00	—
13·0	TUNNEL CITY*	..	12	12 02	59·8
16·4	Tomah	.. ..	—	15 49	73·3
22·9	Oakdale	.. ..	—	19 43	100·0
29·2	Camp Douglas	..	23	23 37	96·9
35·2	NEW LISBON	..	27	27 42	88·2
42·2	Mauston	.. ..	—	32 10	94·0
52·8	Lyndon	.. ..	—	38 36	98·9
61·4	Wisconsin Dells	..	44	44 32	87·5
78·3	}PORTAGE	.. {	58	57 14	79·8
0·0			0	0 00	—
9·0	Wyocena	.. ..	—	8 16	65·3
18·8	Doylestown	.. ..	—	15 44	78·8
24·6	Fall River	.. ..	—	19 41	88·1
28·2	}COLUMBUS	.. {	22	22 36	74·1
0·0			0	0 00	—
9·1	Reeseville	.. ..	—	8 20	65·5
18·7	WATERTOWN	..	17	15 53	76·3
31·9	Oconomowoc	..	—	25 50	79·6
39·8	Hartland	.. ..	—	31 13	88·0
50·5	Brookfield	.. ..	—	38 42	85·6
59·3	Wauwatosa*	..	—	46 24	68·6
64·7	}MILWAUKEE	.. {	60	55 59	33·8
0·0			0	0 00	—
7·1	Lake	.. ..	9	10 56	39·0
12·2	Oakwood	.. ..	—	14 49	78·8
16·9	Tower A 68	..	17	17 54	91·5
23·2	STURTEVANT	..	21	21 48	96·9
32·4	Truesdell	.. ..	—	27 12	98·6
42·1	Wadsworth	.. ..	34	33 02	99·8
52·7	RONDOUT	.. ..	41	39 37	96·6
61·1	Deerfield	.. ..	—	44 45	98·2
64·7	Tower A 20	..	49	46 56	99·0
70·7	Morton Grove	..	—	50 31	100·5
76·0	Mayfair*	.. ..	—	54 19	83·7
79·6	Tower A 5*	..	62	60 58	32·4
85·0	CHICAGO	.. ..	75	73 49	25·2

* Service slack, severe

† Average speed, station to station

from Milwaukee to Chicago, with the 68·9 miles from Lake to Mayfair reeled off in no more than 43 minutes 23 seconds, and this at the end of continuous steaming at such speeds for more than 400 miles. The details of this run are set out in Table 70.

Reverting now to the Pacific wheel arrangement, we come to the celebrated Pennsylvania "K4s" type, a simple and straightforward design which for many years has worked some of the fastest steam trains in the world. These are not exceptionally large engines by modern American standards; they have 27 in. × 28 in. cylinders, 6 ft. 8 in. driving wheels, 5,020 sq. ft. combined heating surface, 70 sq. ft. of firegrate, no more than 205 lb. pressure, and an engine weight of 141 tons. A sample "K4s" performance, also timed by Baron Vuillet from the footplate, appears in Table 71. This was with the famous "Broadway Limited," made up to eight cars, and weighing 630 tons gross, on the first stage of its Chicago-New York run; one of the special 24,000-gallon tenders was in use, weighing 174 tons instead of the normal 95½ tons.

From Englewood there is not much chance of getting into speed until the train has cleared Gary. The line undulates, with gradients for the most part not steeper than 1 in 330; over this the Pacific maintained an average speed of 77·1 m.p.h. for 90 miles, 84·5 m.p.h. for 22 miles, and 88 m.p.h. for 9 miles, reaching a top speed of 90 m.p.h. Water consumption averaged 78 gallons per mile, and coal consumption the high figure of 135 lb. per mile; pressure remained steady at 195 lb. per sq. in., and for most of the journey the regulator was partly open only, although it was opened to full for the 22 miles between posts 344 and 322, before slowing down to stop at Fort Wayne.

The single-headed limit for one of these locomotives is a train of 870 tare tons. Yet Mr. Eric Crickmay has recorded a run with the "Manhattan Limited" in which No. 3874, after having suffered checks earlier in the run, worked an 11-car train of 880 gross tons up to 85½ m.p.h., covering 24 miles at an average of 78·2 m.p.h., and ran the 123 miles from passing Gary at 15 m.p.h. to the stop at Fort Wayne in 113 minutes 58 seconds. Unhappily, a speed limit of 75 m.p.h. throughout from Crestline to Chicago was imposed by the Pennsylvania management late in 1947, so that, for the time being at least, very high speed running between Fort Wayne and Chicago is possible no longer.

TABLE 71

YEAR 1937
PENNSYLVANIA R.R. (U.S.A.) "K4S" CLASS (4-6-2)
Engine No. 5422
Load: 630 tons gross

Distance				Actual	Speeds†
miles				min. sec.	m.p.h.
0·0	ENGLEWOOD	..	..	0 00	—
5·5	South Chicago	..	..	6 50	—
12·9	Indiana Harbour	..	..	13 45	—
18·0	GARY	..	..	17 55	73·5
36·6	VALPARAISO	..	..	34 30	67·6
52·1	Hanna	..	..	46 45	76·0
62·5	Hamlet	..	..	55 00	75·7
69·9	Donaldson	..	..	60 35	80·0
76·8	PLYMOUTH	..	..	66 28	70·4
87·6	Bourbon	..	..	75 15	78·5
95·2	Atwood	..	..	82 05	66·0
101·7	Warsaw	..	..	87 30	71·0
132·6	Arcola	..	..	110 35	80·3
139·4	Milepost 322	..	..	115 30	83·0
141·0	FORT WAYNE	..	..	118 10	—

† Average speed, station to station

speed running between Fort Wayne and Chicago is possible no longer.

In 1941 No. 5399 of the "K4s" type was fitted with the Franklin system of steam distribution, including poppet-valves, and some astonishing performances were recorded after this transformation. The volume of the main steam-pipe was increased from 36½ to 73 per cent. of the cylinder volume, and four 6 in. diameter intake and four 7 in. diameter exhaust poppet-valves, each with a lift of 1 in., were fitted. As a result, No. 5399, under test with a train of 900 gross tons, maintained an average speed of 83 m.p.h. for 100 miles between Gary and Fort Wayne, touching 95 m.p.h., and barely falling below 80 on 1 in 330 uphill stretches. This was done on cut-offs between 28 and

50 per cent.; but the engine could do much of the work with normal loads on 17½ per cent. cut-off.

On another journey, with a train of 816 tons tare and 860 tons gross, No. 5399 passed Liverpool, 117·8 miles from Fort Wayne, in 91 minutes, the speed averaging 84·4 m.p.h. for 78·8 miles; also a train of no less than 1,025 tons has been worked over the 148 miles from Chicago to Fort Wayne in 133 minutes, and on over the 131·7 miles to Crestline in 120 minutes, the latter including the usual stop at the overhead coal stage beyond Fort Wayne to replenish the tender supply. In tests on the Altoona plant, No. 5399 several times exceeded an indicated horsepower of 4,000, with a maximum of 4,267 at 75 m.p.h. on 30 per cent. cut-off.

The success of these tests prompted the Pennsylvania Railroad to apply the Franklin system of steam distribution to its remarkable passenger locomotives of the later "T1" class. These have been introduced in order that the double-heading of trains exceeding 870 tons in weight, when the Pacifics were used, might be avoided. The "T1" locomotives have the 4-4-4-4 wheel arrangement, though they are not articulated; the four driving axles are held in a rigid frame. The purpose of the design is to obtain the tractive power of a 4-8-4 locomotive, but to reduce both the internal resistance and the weight of the moving parts by dividing the driving wheels and cylinders into two independent groups. Another aim was to introduce a class of locomotive which could work unchanged over the 713 miles from Harrisburg (where electric working from New York terminates) to Chicago.

The dimensions of this impressive machine are given in Table 66. Although the requirements on which the design was based did not demand more than the maintenance of 100 m.p.h. on level track with a load of 880 short tons (790 tons of 2,240 lb.), No. 6111, one of these locomotives, has hauled a 16-car test train of 1,120 tons (1,000 British tons) at an average speed of 102 m.p.h. for 69 miles continuously; No. 6110, with 1,025 tons (915 British tons), has covered half the 280 miles from Crestline to Chicago at a mean speed of 100 m.p.h. The loads quoted, moreover, do not include the 193-ton 16-wheel tender attached to these engines, which helps to bring the total weight to 415 tons. On the Altoona test plant a drawbar-horsepower figure of 6,100 has been attained, a record 46 per cent. higher than any previously measured at this testing-station. Unhappily, although the "T1" 4-4-4-4s have thus made records never previously attained with U.S.A. steam power, the all-conquering diesels already have ousted them from the principal Pennsylvania passenger workings.

SOFT COAL AND HARD WORK

109.   An impressive shot of an articulated 2-6-6-6 locomotive of the Chesapeake and Ohio Railroad, U.S.A., working a coal train of nearly 10,000 tons weight uphill.   (*Rail Photo Service, Boston, Mass., B. F. Cutler.*)

110. Semi-Streamlined 4-6-4 "Hiawatha" class, Chicago, Milwaukee, St. Paul and Pacific Railroad. (*Courtesy, American Locomotive Co.*)

111. General Purpose 4-8-2 "Mohawk" class, with 12-wheel tender, New York Central System. (*Courtesy, Lima-Hamilton Corporation.*)

112. Heavy Duty 4-8-4 "Niagara" class, with 14-wheel tender, New York Central System. (*Courtesy, American Locomotive Co.*)

113. Latest 4-4-4-4 "T1" class, non-articulated, with 16-wheel tender, Pennsylvania Railroad. (*Courtesy, Baldwin Locomotive Works.*)

RECENT AMERICAN PASSENGER LOCOMOTIVES

114. One of the celebrated Pennsylvania "K4s" type Pacifics, with 8-wheel tender. This class is now being scrapped. (*Courtesy, Pennsylvania Railroad.*)

115. A New York Central "Hudson" 4-6-4 of the "J3" class, with 12-wheel tender, specially styled for hauling the "Empire State Express." (*Courtesy, New York Central System.*)

116. Another of the enormous Pennsylvania "T1" class 4-4-4-4 locomotives, with running-plate raised to clear coupled wheels and cylinders. (*Courtesy, Pennsylvania Railroad.*)

DEVELOPMENT OF AMERICAN PASSENGER POWER

117.   The "Chippewa" of the Milwaukee Road at 80 m.p.h., headed by one of the stream-lined Atlantics specially built in 1935 for working the "Hiawatha."   (*Rail Photo Service, Boston, Mass., H. W. Pontin.*)

118.   One of the handsome semi-streamlined Milwaukee 4-6-4s, at full speed with the "Hiawatha," a train which requires 100 m.p.h. maximum speeds daily.   (*R. H. Kindig.*)

119.   The Southern Pacific "Daylight" leaving San Francisco for Los Angeles, with a specially styled "Daylight" 4-8-4.   To the right is a second section of the same express.   (*Rail Photo Service, Boston, Mass., C. N. Lippincott.*)

STYLING OF MODERN AMERICAN PASSENGER LOCOMOTIVES

120.   The largest and most powerful 4-8-4 type in the world—one of the latest Santa Fe 4-8-4s hauling the "Grand Canyon Limited" over the Cajon Pass, California.   (*Courtesy, Santa Fe Railway.*)

121.   The heaviest steam locomotives in the world, a 540-ton Union Pacific "Big Boy" 4-8-8-4 leading a freight train through Echo Canyon, Utah.   (*Courtesy, Union Pacific Railroad.*)

AMERICAN MOTIVE POWER RECORDS

122. In the heart of the Rockies—a Canadian Pacific 4-8-4, with 15-coach train, approaching Field, British Columbia. (*G. H. Soole*.)

123. A Canadian National 4-8-4 tackles a heavy freight train, near Welland. Note the feed-water heater across the top of the smokebox. (*Rail Photo Service, Boston, Mass., H. W. Pontin.*)

124. A Canadian Pacific "Selkirk" type 2-10-4 starting westwards from Calgary towards the Great Divide in zero weather.

MODERN CANADIAN LOCOMOTIVES

125. With 12,000-gallon tender for the journey across the waterless Nullarbor desert— a 4-6-0 of the Commonwealth Railways. (*Courtesy, Commonwealth Government Railways.*)

126. The "Overland Express" for Melbourne leaving Adelaide, South Australia, for the Victorian frontier with a 4-8-4 locomotive, on the 5 ft. 3 in. gauge. (*Courtesy, South Australian Government Railways.*)

127. One of the "C.38" class Pacifics, New South Wales Government Railways, specially styled for working the "Spirit of Progress" over the 4 ft. 8½ in. gauge to the Victorian frontier. (*Courtesy, New South Wales Government Railways.*)

SOME MODERN AUSTRALIAN LOCOMOTIVES

A MODERN AMERICAN MAMMOTH

128. Geared turbine locomotive No. 6200, 6-8-6 type, Pennsylvania Railroad; the forward turbine is seen above the third pair of coupled wheels. Weight, engine 259 tons, tender 184 tons, total 442 tons. Working pressure, 310 lb. per sq. in. Length overall 108 ft. (*Courtesy, Pennsylvania Railroad.*)

Reference has been made previously to the 4-6-4 wheel arrangement in connection with the Milwaukee "Hiawatha" train. But the railway which has developed to the maximum the use of the "Hudson" or 4-6-4 type is the New York Central System, on which it was first introduced in 1927 and remained the standard express passenger power for nearly 20 years. The first "Hudsons," of the "J1" type, had 12 per cent. more starting effort, 37 per cent. more power output at 70 m.p.h., and 28 per cent. more maximum drawbar-horsepower, than the previous "K5" Pacifics. When the final "J3" development appeared in 1937, the contrast with the "K5" Pacifics was even more startling.

While the engine weight had gone up by just under 30 per cent., from 124 to $160\frac{3}{4}$ tons, the maximum indicated horsepower on test had risen from 2,140 to 4,725, and whereas the former power output was realised at 54 m.p.h., the latter was at 75 m.p.h. Similarly, the maximum recorded drawbar-horsepower had grown from 1,750 at 40 m.p.h. to 3,880 at 65 m.p.h. The average driving axle loading had increased from 25 to 30 tons, but the adverse effect, from the track stress point of view, was largely nullified by a lightening of the motion parts, with improved design and the use of alloy steels and by improved balancing. As to fuel consumption, coal consumption per indicated horsepower-hour was shown to have dropped from 2·46 lb. in the "K5" Pacifics to the very economical figure of 2·03 lb. in the "J3" 4-6-4 engines. Such has been the progress in American locomotive design in no more than ten years.

As an example of the work of the "J3" class "Hudsons" on the road, a run on the well-known "Twentieth Century Limited" express, recorded from the footplate by Baron Vuillet, appears in Table 72.

TABLE 72

YEAR 1937
NEW YORK CENTRAL SYSTEM (U.S.A.) "JIE" CLASS (4-6-4)
Engine No. 5277
Load: 1,025 tons gross

Distance					Actual		Speeds†
miles					min.	sec.	m.p.h.
0·0	TOLEDO	..	..	..	0	00	—
11·0	Milepost 11	..	..	..	16	10	—
15·0	Milepost 15	..	..	..	20	10	60·0
53·6	Bryan	..	..	..	50	20	76·8
63·9	Edgerton	..	..	..	59	00	71·3
70·8	Butler	..	..	..	64	10	80·1
78·7	Waterloo	..	..	..	70	35	86·2
91·4	Kendallville	..	..	..	80	50	74·3
102·5	Wawaka	..	..	..	89	00	81·6
107·9	Ligonier	..	..	..	92	45	86·4
115·0	Millersburg	..	..	..	97	48	84·4
131·8	Milepost 131¼	..	..	..	110	20	80·3
					sigs.		
133·0		..	..	{	115	20	—
0·0	ELKHART				0	00	—
11·1	Mishawaka	..	..	..	14	20	—
15·1	South Bend	..	..	..	17	40	72·0
28·5	New Carlisle	..	..	..	28	45	72·5
41·8	La Porte	..	..	..	40	02	69·7
49·6	Milepost 51	..	..	..	46	02	78·0
59·5	Chesterton	..	..	..	53	00	85·2
74·4	GARY	..	..	..	63	50	81·8
81·2	Indiana Harbour	..	..	..	68	50	81·6
88·7	South Chicago	..	..	..	74	35	78·3
					sig.		
93·9	ENGLEWOOD	..	..	..	82	00	—

Net times: 113 and 81 minutes
† Average speed, station to station

parts, with improved design and the use of alloy steels and by improved balancing. As to fuel consumption, coal consumption per indicated horsepower-hour was shown to have dropped from 2·46 lb. in the "K5" Pacifics to the very economical figure of 2·03 lb. in the "J3" 4-6-4 engines. Such has been the progress in American locomotive design in no more than ten years.

As an example of the work of the "J3" class "Hudsons" on the road, a run on the well-known "Twentieth Century Limited" express, recorded from the footplate by Baron Vuillet, appears in Table 72.

With a 13-car train of 1,025 gross tons, the engine completed the 133·0 miles from Toledo to Elkhart in 112½ minutes net, and the succeeding 93·9 miles from Elkhart to Englewood in 82 minutes, or 79½ minutes net, at net start-to-stop averages of 70·9 m.p.h. in each case. On the former stretch, 116·8 miles were run at 77·8 m.p.h., and 40·4 miles at 82·2 m.p.h.; on the latter 85·3 m.p.h. was maintained for 31 miles continuously, with a maximum of 94 m.p.h. for 2 miles.

To equal such a performance as this, weight for weight, one of the L.M.S.R. "Duchess" Pacifics would require to be hauling a train of 705 tons, an "A4" streamlined Pacific of the L.N.E.R. 675 tons, and a Great Western "King" 585 tons. Baron Vuillet noted that New York Central 4-6-4 No. 5277 required to be opened out to 35 per cent. cut-off with this 1,025-ton train to reach 92½ m.p.h. down 1 in 400 and 85 m.p.h. down 1 in 1,000; 42 per cent. cut-off to maintain 75 m.p.h. up 1 in 1,000; and 57 per cent. for 65 m.p.h. up 1 in 330. Calculations showed that the locomotive was indicating horsepowers up to 3,650 at 80 m.p.h. and 4,000 at 65 m.p.h., on several stages of the run. Again, on the New York Central, diesel-electric locomotives now handle the "Twentieth Century Limited" and many other well-known trains.

A few notes on American locomotive performance in the mountainous areas of the Western States will provide a fitting conclusion to this chapter. Most of the main lines connecting Chicago with the Pacific coast have to traverse very difficult country in the final 1,000 miles or so of their westward course, including summit levels in the Rockies and parallel ranges which in several instances rise to from 6,000 to over 8,000 ft. above sea level. Of these, the Atchison, Topeka & Santa Fe main line to Los Angeles is one, as described in some detail in Chapter 20. Some of the uphill speeds maintained by the large Santa Fe 4-8-4 engines would seem almost unbelievable up corresponding inclinations in Great Britain. For example, Chemins de Fer quotes a couple of runs with the "Chief" express, on one of which No. 3777 took a 14-car train of 780 tons up the 31 miles from Needles to Goffs, surmounting a difference in level of 2,100 ft., with speed never once falling below 43½ m.p.h., even up continuous 1 in 67 inclines. On the other run No. 3784 had to handle a 15-coach train of 850 tons up the 20½ miles from Ash Fork to Supai, with a ruling gradient of 1 in 50 against the engine, and did so with no lower minimum than 26¾ m.p.h.

Another locomotive of the same type ran the second section of postal train No. 7 from Dalies to Gallup, 134·5 miles, in 124 minutes, with a load of 25 vehicles weighing 1,590 tons; the section has a ruling gradient of 1 in 220, beginning with 12 miles down, then 80 miles up, and finally 32½ miles down. On the long up-grade speed was kept up steadily at round the 59 m.p.h. mark, with the engine developing 5,500 horsepower continuously; downhill 90 m.p.h. was maintained. The latter is the nominal maximum speed permitted, though there is a tolerance to 100 m.p.h. over suitable sections of the line, when necessary for time recovery purposes. The maximum permitted load without assistance up 1 in 55 grades is 1,150 tons.

More detailed figures were given some years ago in *The Railway Magazine* of a run timed by Mr. M. A. Park on the "Chief," although in this case the load was a good deal lighter, consisting as it did of eight cars only of 590 tons weight. Westwards out of La Junta, 4-8-4 No. 3764 accelerated to 47 m.p.h. up 1 in 91, and later kept up 58 m.p.h. on the same inclination and 54 m.p.h. on 1 in 80. Touching 67 m.p.h. down a slight dip, the engine then maintained 63 m.p.h. up much of the 1 in 89 that follows. The 32·7 miles from Timpas to Simpson, almost unbrokenly up at 1 in 89, were completed at an average speed of 46 m.p.h., notwithstanding a permanent-way slowing in the middle of the climb. Later, an 8-mile stretch at the same inclination, begun at 68 m.p.h., was finished at 53 m.p.h. Thus the 81·8 miles from La Junta up to Trinidad, including a dead stop of 1¼ minutes to take on fuel, occupied no more than 106½ minutes; in this time a difference in level of 1,931 ft. was negotiated, but 47·4 m.p.h. was the average speed sustained over 79 miles of the climbing. Like the "Super-Chief" and "El Capitan" streamliners, the "Chief" also has now been turned over to diesel-electric power.

The Great Northern Railway of the U.S.A. prides itself on getting through the Rockies with no more than 55 miles of its main line above the 5,000 ft. level, and with a maximum altitude of 5,213 ft. in the Marias Pass. Over this section powerful 4-8-4 locomotives also are used, with 29 in. × 29 in. cylinders, 6 ft. 8 in. driving wheels, 7,045 sq. ft. heating surface, 98 sq. ft. of firegrate, 250 lb. pressure, and a weight of 188 tons, or 334 tons with tenders. Baron Vuillet rode on one of these locomotives, with a trailing load of 16 vehicles, whose gross weight of 1,240 tons would be equivalent to between 28 and 30 British bogie corridor coaches. Up a 1 in 200 ascent, with 60 per cent. cut-off, No. 2588 maintained 46 m.p.h. for 5 miles; up continuous 1 in 100 grades, with curves as sharp as 22 down to 14½ chains radius, a steady 27½ m.p.h. was kept up. In the reverse direction the same locomotive, with a much lighter train of 630 tons, mounted the 44·7 miles from Belton to the Marias Pass summit in 96 minutes 40 seconds; in this distance, the train was lifted all but 2,000 ft. up gradients as steep, over one section, as 1 in 56 for 10 miles, and with even sharper curvature, where the sustained speed was 22½ m.p.h.

Over the neighbouring Union Pacific Railroad there work the monster 4-8-8-4 locomotives of the "Big Boy" class, of which the 540 tons of weight, tender included, would equal that of a British 4-6-2 with tender *and* a 13-coach train. These Union Pacific engines work through the Wasatch Mountains, between Ogden and Green River, Utah, with continuous gradients up to 1 in 83 in steepness, and are allowed to take trains of as much as 3,175 tons in weight. On a typical westbound run with 70 bogie wagons, weighing 2,910 tons, No. 4015 ran from Ogden to Evanston, 76 miles, in 3 hours 55 minutes, lifting its train through 2,450 ft. altitude in the process; indeed, the average gradient for the entire distance is 1 in 164 against the train. During this run a stop of 23 minutes was made to take water and coal. After a 20-minute stop at Evanston, the run of 41 miles to Carter, including one 12-mile climb at 1 in 120, was made in 76 minutes. At Carter, 11 minutes were spent, and then came the 59-mile run to Green River, completed in 73 minutes; as this also includes a 5-mile ascent at 1 in 120, over a considerable length of level track this vast locomotive and train, 3,450 tons in all, were travelling at 59 to 62 m.p.h.

In conclusion it may be said that, so far as the United States is concerned, the coupling of four axles appears to offer little resistance to the attainment and maintenance of very high speeds. On test, one of the Union Pacific standard 4-8-4 locomotives, with 25 in. × 32 in. cylinders and 6 ft. 8 in. driving wheels, has maintained 89 m.p.h. with a 16-coach train of 912 tons up a slight gradient of 1 in 770, and has been worked up to $102\frac{1}{2}$ m.p.h. on the level. One of the famous "Daylight" 4-8-4s of the Southern Pacific, also with 6 ft. 8 in. wheels and in this case with $25\frac{1}{2}$ in. × 32 in. cylinders, has got up to $105\frac{1}{2}$ m.p.h. in a similar test, and has maintained $54\frac{1}{2}$ m.p.h. up a 1 in 100 incline with a 925-ton train. Most astonishing of all, one of the highly efficient "J" class 4-8-4s of the Norfolk & Western, with eight-coupled drivers of no more than 5 ft. 10 in. diameter, has travelled at 110 m.p.h. on straight, level track, with a 15-car train of 915 tons behind the tender. This is a tribute, both to the value of roller bearings for axles and motion parts, and also to the advance that has been made in front-end design and in the freedom of exhaust at high speeds. From the foregoing it is clear that American railways have nothing to learn from Europe in the matter of high speed with steam.

19

THE RIVALS OF STEAM—ELECTRIC TRACTION

IT was in 1879 that the first practical demonstration was given of the possibilities of electric traction on railways. Werner von Siemens, who had built a small electric locomotive for use in a coal mine, with power supplied from a dynamo, installed it in an exhibition at Berlin, where it hauled three passenger cars round a circular track. Current was picked up from an insulated third rail in the centre of the track, and was returned through the running rails. The same locomotive was demonstrated in the Crystal Palace, London, in 1881. In 1883, electric working was begun on a tramway from Portrush to the Giant's Causeway, in Northern Ireland, with current generated in a small hydro-electric station; and in the same year Magnus Volk installed his small electric line along the beach at Brighton.

The first serious introduction of electric traction for passenger service in Great Britain, however, was not until 1890, when the City & South London tube was brought into operation with independent electric locomotives, followed by the Liverpool Overhead Railway, with multiple-unit trains, in 1893, the Waterloo & City Railway, also with multiple-unit trains, in 1898, and the Central London Railway, at first with independent locomotives, in 1900. By 1900, the total route mileage of electrified lines in Great Britain was 22 only; to-day it totals 958 miles of routes, and 2,392 miles of single track. In the world as a whole, the total electrified route mileage is just over 25,000; Italy takes the lead with 4,400 miles, followed by Sweden with 3,421 miles, the United States with 3,091 miles, Switzerland with 2,793 miles, and France with 2,194 miles. So far as her railways are concerned, Switzerland with little doubt is the most completely electrified country in the world.

To the "man in the street" the advantages of electric traction on railways seem so obvious that he wonders why electrification does not proceed more rapidly than it has done until now. But the problem is not so simple as it may appear. As with so many other desirable improvements, the ruling consideration is finance. Electrification is so costly a business that certain well-defined conditions must obtain before the savings in operation made possible by changing from steam to electric power can pay interest on the capital cost of carrying out the electrification itself. Moreover, the problem is complicated in these days by the attraction of the self-contained mobile power-station, as embodied in the diesel-electric locomotives described in Chapter 20, which give the advantages of electric traction without any of the cost of line equipment required for an electric railway.

One of the conditions justifying electrification is a cheap source of power. In mountainous countries, and more particularly those whose summits thrust upwards beyond the permanent snow line, Nature herself offers, in abundant measure, the power needed. Water deposited from the clouds, and melted from the snow and ice, rushes down the steep mountain gorges to find lower levels. In the Alps, for example, there are illimitable resources of water power. Water is collected at the high levels in great lakes or reservoirs, produced by damming up the narrow valleys, in order to provide ample storage capacity, both during hard winters and dry summers; from these lakes the water is brought by steeply-inclined pipelines down to the power stations in the valleys. Here it is used to drive large water-turbines, which are coupled to generators for the production of electric power.

Up to the time of the First World War the Swiss railways had relied, for the haulage of their trains, on steam produced by the use of coal imported from France and Germany. During the war this supply of coal by degrees was cut off; wood-firing had to be used as a substitute, and rail transport was seriously affected. As a result, the management of the Swiss Federal Railways realised, as never before, both the urgent necessity to electrify and the vast natural resources of their country for the supply of power. Before the war had ended, the first stages of the conversion from steam to electricity were well under way; and since then the progress has been so rapid that to-day, with a few very minor exceptions, the whole of the Swiss railways, both nationally and privately owned, are electrically operated; the actual figures are 93 per cent. of the total route mileage electrified, and 98 per cent. of the traffic in Switzerland hauled by electric power.

It must not be supposed, however, that the costs entailed even in the use of water power are negligible. Some of the barrage schemes carried out high up in the mountains, have, indeed, been extremely costly. For example, the great Barberine Dam, built by the Swiss Federal Railways near the southern frontier of Switzerland in the Valaisian Alps, is 935 ft. long, and, at its maximum, 256 ft. high and 192 ft. thick at the base; it contains in all 269,000 cubic yards of masonry and concrete, and cost £800,000 to construct. The dam impounds 51,000,000 cubic yards of water, at an altitude of 6,200 ft. above sea level.

From the dam the pipeline has a fall in altitude of 2,300 ft. into the power-station at Châtelard, where five groups of turbo-alternators are installed, each consisting of one Pelton turbine of 16,400 horse-power, directly coupled to a 10,000-kVA generator producing current at 15,000 volts. The latter is transformed to current at 66,000 volts for transmission to railways all over the south of Switzerland. On this power-station alone, with its dam and associated works, a total of £2,000,000 was spent, and it is but one of the six required to assure the Swiss Federal Railways the average of more than a million kilowatt-hours of current required for each day's operation, rising to a peak load at any given moment of over 75,000 kilowatts.

Even where abundant water-power is available for the generation of current, therefore, heavy outlay is needed for damming up the valleys to ensure a constant flow of water; lengthy pipelines must be laid down; and power-stations require to be built, equipped and maintained. Arrangements must then be made for the distribution of the power throughout the length of the electrified tracks, with all necessary sub-stations, transformers, and line equipment. Electric locomotives have to be built, displacing a large number of steam loco-motives for which no further use can be found, though it may be possible to sell some of them to railways or countries still using steam. In Switzerland also considerable use is still made of small steam tank locomotives for shunting purposes, in order to avoid the cost of equipping lengthy mileages of siding tracks with electric conductors. On the other hand, at a time of shortage of both coal and steel during the Second World War, some of the Swiss steam shunters were fitted with pantographs, to collect current from the overhead conductors, and this is used for steam generation in their boilers by means of immersion heaters!

In a country like Switzerland another advantage of electrification is the unlimited power made available for working trains up the steep gradients which are inevitable in a so mountainous a *terrain*. For example, the Gotthard Railway, which climbs 2,080 ft. from Erstfeld, just south of the Lake of Lucerne, to Göschenen, at the mouth of the Gotthard tunnel, has an average inclination of 1 in $45\frac{1}{2}$ for 18 miles continuously, including $7\frac{1}{2}$ miles at 1 in $38\frac{1}{2}$, $3\frac{3}{4}$ miles at 1 in 40, and 2 miles at 1 in $41\frac{1}{2}$. The Lötschberg line is even steeper, with long stretches at 1 in 37 continuously. Whereas in steam days two or even three locomotives were needed to haul the heaviest trains, with electric power locomotives have been developed up to 6,000 h.p. for single units, and 12,000 h.p. for articulated twin units manned by single crews, which can draw from the line conductors all the electric power they need to make those horsepower ratings effective.

On heavily-graded routes, therefore, electrification makes for economy in working, and these high-power locomotive outputs also make it possible considerably to speed up the train services. For engine-crews and passengers alike there has been the considerable asset of doing away with the steam locomotive exhaust which in former years made a nightmare of the running through the many tunnels on these mountain lines. The same benefits have been realised in all the other European countries which have electrified on a considerable scale. Most major electrification projects on the mainland of Europe have been carried out in areas which either are mountainous or are bordered by high mountain ranges, and so have at their command abundant hydro-electric power; and an additional attraction, in countries like Italy, Sweden and Switzerland, is that they now supply from their own resources power for the production of which in steam days they needed to import coal.

One interesting economy made possible by electrical working of long and steep inclines is concerned with the descending rather than the ascending grades. By reversing the function of the traction motors so that they act as generators, strong resistance is opposed to the motion of a train, so that the need for continuous braking of the wheels on falling gradients is greatly reduced, and at the same time the wear-and-tear of the brake-gear. Moreover, the current generated by the reversal of the motors, if so desired, can be fed back into the conductors, with the result that the descending train itself is supplying current, rather than drawing on the current supply. This principle is known as regenerative or rheostatic braking.

On the mainland of Europe there are the longest continuously electrified railway routes in the world. It is possible, for example, to start a journey at Narvik, the Atlantic port in the extreme north of Norway, to cross the Swedish frontier 28 miles later at Riksgränsen, and continue through the Kiruna ore-mining region and then down the whole length of Sweden through Stockholm and Malmo to Trälleborg, on the Baltic, with electric haulage throughout. The distance of 1,393 miles from Narvik to Trälleborg is the world's record for continuous railway electrification.

This is closely rivalled by the route, partly over the German and partly over the Italian State Railways, which begins at Saalfeld, in the Thuringian forest region of Germany, and continues through Nuremberg, Munich and Innsbrück to the Brenner Pass; from here the Italian main lines concerned are electrified all the way through Verona, Bologna and Florence to Rome, Naples and Reggio di Calabria, on the Straits of Messina. From Saalfeld to Reggio is 1,268 miles. Before the war, by the combined Scandinavian and the Germano-Italian electrified routes, one could travel for just over 3,000 miles, from the extreme north to the extreme south of Europe, behind electric locomotives for the entire distance, save only for the gap of about 425 miles between Trälleborg and Saalfeld. Other lengthy stretches of continuously electified line are in France from Paris to Hendaye and Port Bou, on the Spanish frontier, 605 miles, and from Geneva in Switzerland to Salzburg in Austria, 529 miles.

An English railway in the same "mountain" category, now being electrified, but without the advantage of hydro-electric power, is the Sheffield-Manchester main line of the late L.N.E.R. The summit level of the line, at the east end of Woodhead Tunnel, is 966 ft. above the sea, and it is approached from both directions by long and toilsome gradients over which a heavy coal and general freight traffic is worked. Woodhead Tunnel itself, 3 miles in length, has been a considerable handicap, for with steam locomotives heavy freight trains in the east-bound direction, which is on a continuous up grade, have taken anything from 10 to 15 minutes to clear the section. Electrification should halve the transit time and thus in effect double the line capacity.

A further reason justifying electrification is dense traffic, and especially dense suburban traffic. Here the characteristics of suitable traction motors make possible more rapid acceleration than is reasonably possible with steam power. Because the trains can get away more rapidly from the closely-spaced stops in suburban areas, they may be crowded on to the lines in more rapid succession, and the passenger therefore gets the double advantage of more speedy and more frequent service. One has only to note the lively growth of building estates round suburban lines which have been electrified recently to realise the attraction offered by a fast and frequent electric train service.

From the railway operating point of view, also, the possibility of putting more trains on to existing lines as a result of electrification is of value as this may make it possible to avoid the even more expensive business of laying additional tracks. For this reason electrification has been applied to busy main lines in areas in which neither heavy gradients nor water power have offered any inducement to electrify. Of this the most notable example is the Pennsylvania main-line electrification in the United States. Between New York and Philadelphia the Pennsylvania has one of the busiest routes in the world, carrying an endless procession of expresses from New York to Baltimore, Washington and the southern and eastern states, and to Pittsburgh, Chicago, St. Louis and the Middle West.

The electrification is now continuous over the 225 miles between New York and Washington, and on the Chicago main line as far as

Harrisburg, 189 miles.   Also the Pennsylvania has put its electric power to the maximum use, for with the help of extremely powerful 2-C+C-2 electric locomotives (two groups of three motor-driven axles each, and leading and trailing bogies), it works the world's fastest main-line electric service.   Every day, on the Pennsylvania electric lines, there are nearly 400 runs, with a total mileage of over 17,800, timed from start to stop at 60 m.p.h. or more; in view of the relatively short average length of these runs, they require not only rapid acceleration from stops, but running speeds between stops up to and at times exceeding 80 m.p.h.   Moreover, these speeds are maintained with trains of the very weighty rolling stock in common use in the United States, in some cases exceeding 1,000 gross tons per train.

As examples of the everyday performance of the Pennsylvania 2-C+C-2 electric locomotives of the "GG1" class, three runs timed by Mr. E. L. Thompson on the New York-Washington service are worth quoting.   Two were made on the northbound "Advance Congressional," a train which was run for some years during and after the Second World War to relieve the pressure on the "Congressional" proper.   Its run of 214·6 miles from Washington to Newark, outside New York, was the longest regular non-stop journey then made in any part of the world with electric power, though now exceeded in length by certain daily runs on the French electrified main lines.   The load was usually 14 cars of the heaviest all-steel standard stock, of about 1,050 gross tons weight.   Lengthy speed restrictions are enforced to 15 m.p.h. through Baltimore, 45 over Havre de Grace viaduct, 45 at Wilmington, 40 all through Philadelphia, and 50 at Trenton.

On one run the journey was completed in 186 minutes (9 minutes inside schedule), inclusive of three additional slacks to take cross-over roads; 161 miles were covered at an average of 80·5 m.p.h. and 32·3 miles at an average of 90·1 m.p.h.   On an even faster second trip, Princeton Junction, 176·2 miles from Washington, was cleared in 157¾ minutes, and but for a series of signal checks later, the 214·6 miles to Newark would have been run easily in 3 hours, again with a load of 1,050 tons, at an average of 71·5 m.p.h. throughout, inclusive of all checks.

In the reverse direction, another of these locomotives, hauling the "President," made up to a 15-car train of 1,150 tons gross weight, was delayed to such an extent as to leave Trenton, 58·1 miles out of New York, 18 minutes late.   Some very fast running followed.   The 27·9 miles from Trenton to North Philadelphia were run in 22½ minutes start to stop (78·4 m.p.h.), and the 25·7 miles from 30th Street, Philadelphia, to Wilmington in 22 minutes (70·1 m.p.h.).   Next, the 64·8 miles from Wilmington to passing Bayview were reeled off in 50¼ minutes, and with the usual slow approach Baltimore, 68·4 miles, was reached in 57¼ minutes (71·8 m.p.h. start to stop). Inclusive of the even slower approach to Union Station, Washington, the last 40·1 miles from Baltimore were run in 36¼ minutes.

Of the whole journey, a total of 128 miles was covered at an average of 80·5 m.p.h.; the fastest stretch was from Odenton to Landover, 15·2 miles at 93·5 m.p.h. Although 3½ minutes overtime had been spent at the Baltimore stop, the "President" was no more than 1½ minutes late in arriving, the driver having gained 20 minutes in running from Trenton onwards. This run is set out in detail in Table 73.

At present the only comparable main-line electrification in Great Britain is that which was carried out by the late Southern Railway, between London and the popular resorts of the South Coast. With all allowance for the most praiseworthy enterprise of the late S.R. management in electrifying on this scale, conditions have been more than usually propitious for the work. The areas of Surrey, Sussex, Hampshire and Kent tapped by the electrified lines, together with the Sussex coastline, contain what is probably the most attractive of all the country so closely adjacent to the capital, and the new long-distance residential traffic so developed has more than amply justified the cost of the electrification. Apart from this long-distance network, the Southern Railway, in its suburban electric lines round south-west, south and south-east London, developed a more extensive electrified suburban system than any other single railway in the world.

The Southern Region main-line electric trains are capable of speeds up to 80 m.p.h., though in ordinary service 75 m.p.h. is seldom exceeded. The general practice is to maintain high uphill speeds—as, for example,

TABLE 73

YEAR 1944
PENNSYLVANIA RAILROAD
2-C-C-2 ELECTRIC LOCOMOTIVE No. 4808
15 all-steel cars, 1,150 tons gross

Dist.		Sched.	Actual	‡Speeds
miles		min.	min. sec.	m.p.h.
0·0	NEW YORK	0	0 00	—
			sigs.	
58·1	TRENTON..	60	77 30	44·9
1·5	Morris	—	2 45	32·7
8·5	Greene	9	8 00	80·0
20·2	Holmes	20	16 00	87·7
25·0	Shore	—	19 30	82·2
27·9	NORTH PHILADELPHIA	27	22 30	58·0
4·4	30TH STREET	8	7 30	35·2
3·2	Brill	7	5 30	34·9
10·7	Baldwin	14	11 15	78·2
21·1	Bellevue	23	18 30	86·0
25·7	WILMINGTON	28	22 00	78·8
11·8	Davis	11	10 30	67·4
18·1	Elkton	16	15 00	84·0
32·3	Perryville	28	25 15	83·1
38·3	Aberdeen*	—	30 45	65·4
48·0	Edgewood	42	38 00	80·2
56·3	Bengies	48	43 45	86·6
64·8	Bayview	55	50 15	78·5
68·4	BALTIMORE	62	57 15	30·8
3·5	Gwynns Run	7	6 45	31·1
17·8	Oderton	19	17 15	81·7
33·0	Landover	32	27 00	93·5
38·6	Tower F†	—	31 00	84·0
40·1	WASHINGTON	42	36 15	17·1

* Long service slack, Havre de Grace viaduct
† Severe speed restriction, Tower F into Union Station
‡ Average speeds, station to station

60 m.p.h. up the long 1 in 264 gradients of the Victoria-Brighton main line—so that excessive speeds downhill are unnecessary for timekeeping.

Last of the advantages of electrification, as compared with operation by steam, is that the electric locomotive is always ready for use. It requires no hours spent in "lighting up" and raising steam, before its work can begin; it is using no fuel while standing; it can work continuously for 24 hours a day if necessary; it can be cleaned in less than half the time needed by a steam locomotive; the lengthy training of a steam locomotive driver, to get the best out of his engine by making the most scientific and efficient use of his steam, has no counterpart in the simpler manipulation of electric controls; and in suburban working, at least, the driver and fireman of a steam locomotive can be replaced by a single motorman, which means a considerable economy in running expenses.

In main-line working with independent electric locomotives, it is possible to couple two or more locomotives together, provided they are fitted with suitable control connections and apparatus, and to work them with a single crew. The same principle applies to multiple-unit suburban stock. Against these economies, of course, there must be set the maintenance and operation of the costly power-station and transmission equipment which supplies the electric current, as well as the loss of energy in the transmission itself.

It is by generating in large power-stations all the power required for the movement of the trains, whether the current be produced by steam or hydro-electric means, that the efficiency of electric working is largely obtained. As we have already seen, the steam locomotive is a self-contained power plant, rigidly restricted in its development by the limitations of the loading gauge and maximum permissible axle-loads, which compel the use of steam in a manner that thermally is of low efficiency. The fixed steam power-station, on the other hand, is unrestricted either in size or weight, and has water-tube boilers of large dimensions, mechanical firing, high-speed turbines, and condensing plants which reduce the back pressure of the steam to a figure even less than atmospheric pressure. These conditions should ensure that a considerably larger proportion of the energy of the steam is converted into useful work than is possible in steam locomotive working, but with recent improvements in the overall thermal efficiency of modern steam locomotives, the economic advantage of electric working to a large extent has been whittled away.

In a generating-station, the turbines, whether driven by steam or water, are coupled to dynamos which supply high voltage alternating current; this is transmitted by overhead or lineside cables to the sub-stations which feed the current, at points equally distributed (in relation to power demands rather than distance), to the line conductors. In direct-current electrification, the high-pressure alternating current is converted to low-pressure direct current by large rotary converters, which need skilled attendance and control, or, in the latest systems, by mercury-arc rectifiers, which are considerably the more economical method, as they can be installed in unattended sub-stations.

In alternating current systems, the sub-stations may contain voltage transformers only; and although such transformers may be of large size, and require oil-cooling, the attention they require is less than with rotary converters, and the sub-station equipment in general is smaller and simpler than that required with direct current. Incidentally, the need for sub-stations arises from the fact that if attempts were made to pass current at high voltage direct to the line conductors, insulation to prevent short circuits would be extremely difficult, and quite impracticable in the motors themselves.

Brief reference is now necessary to the methods of railway electrification in use in different parts of the world. In general, these are three in number—direct current, single-phase alternating current, and three-phase alternating current. In the d.c. installations, up to a pressure of 600 to 650 volts, current is supplied either through a third rail or through overhead conductors; with pressures higher than 650 volts d.c., and in all a.c. electrification, overhead conductors are used exclusively for current supply. Three-phase a.c. requires three conductors, two "live" (overhead) and one "neutral" (the rails), and the expense so entailed, and the complicated wiring, especially at junctions, have confined this method to 1,100 route miles of line in Northern Italy. In their later conversions, however, in Central and Southern Italy, the Italian State Railways have changed to d.c. electrification. For the latter the limit of voltage is about 3,000; but in a.c. electrification the customary voltages range from 11,000 to 16,000, at $16\frac{2}{3}$ cycles. Details of the world's principal a.c. and d.c. railway electrifications appear in Tables 74 and 75 respectively.

Whereas in d.c. installations the current has been transformed before it reaches the locomotive, the locomotive using a.c. requires to carry its own transformer, and is considerably increased in size and weight in consequence. This is one of the reasons why d.c. electrification is preferred for suburban working with multiple-unit trains, for the control of equipment can be housed in a small compartment at the end of a motor-coach, so taking but little from the seating space, or, as in the latest London tube stock, can be carried in the very limited space between the coach-floors and the track, with no curtailment of seating accommodation at all.

As the term "multiple-unit" indicates, electric trains in this category are made up into units of two, three, four, or six passenger vehicles, each provided with one or two motor-coaches and driving cabs at both ends; either one or both bogies of each motor-coach are motor-driven. When the traffic demand increases, as at the morning and evening rush hours of residential electric services round a city, two or perhaps three units are coupled together, and by multiple-unit control all the motors are brought under the control of the one motorman at the head end. Coaches other than the motor-coaches are trailers, with the electrical connections and controls carried through them; and at rush hours two

TABLE 74

THE WORLD'S PRINCIPAL RAILWAY ELECTRIFICATION SYSTEMS
Alternating Current

Country	Railway	Total Route Mileage	Voltage	Phase	Cycles	Conduction
Sweden	State	2,887	16,000	Single	16⅔	Overhead
,,	Private (various)	323	,,	,,	16⅔	,,
,,	State (Riksgränsen-Lulea) ..	273	,,	,,	15	,,
Switzerland	Federal	1,592	15,000	,,	16⅔	,,
,,	(Private various)	396	,,	,,	16⅔	,,
Germany	State	1,163	,,	,,	16⅔	,,
,,	,, (Höllental)	35	,,	,,	50	,,
Austria	Federal	575	,,	,,	16⅔	,,
,,	,, (St. Polten-Gusswerk) ..	57	,,	,,	25	,,
Norway	State	325	,,	,,	16⅔	,,
Hungary	,, ...	117	,,	,,	50	,,
U.S.A.	Great Northern	73	11,500	,,	25	,,
,,	Pennsylvania..	688	11,000	,,	25	,,
,,	New York, New Haven & Hartford	142	,,	,,	25	,,
,,	Virginia	134	,,	,,	25	,,
,,	Reading	84	,,	,,	25	,,
,,	Norfolk & Western	77	,,	,,	25	,,
Switzerland	Rhaetian & Furka-Oberalp.. ..	303	,,	,,	16⅔	,,
Italy	State (Northern Lines) ..	1,229	3,700	Three	16⅔	,,

such trailers are sometimes coupled between two motor-coach units. The advantage of such methods in suburban working needs no stress; on arrival at terminals no "running-round" of the locomotive is needed, but the motorman merely needs to walk from one end of the train to the other. Moreover, by the multiple-unit principle the tractive power available is proportioned automatically to the load.

For most main line working, however, the independent type of locomotive is needed, so that stock of any description, passenger or freight, may be hauled. A limited amount of multiple-unit suburban working is done with a.c. electrification—as, for example, on the Pennsylvania and Reading Railroads of the United States, round New York and Philadelphia—but this is unusual. There are many single motor-coaches, also, on a.c. electrified lines, and in Switzerland a.c. locomotives are combined with brakevans on some of the light-weight streamline trains, but beyond these, the independent locomotive is the universal practice.

There is no doubt that for train services of maximum frequency, such as those in suburban areas, where the greatest reliability is essential, and time and cost of maintenance must be kept down to a minimum, d.c. is superior to a.c. electrification. As already mentioned, up to a pressure of about 650 volts, the current conductor usually is a third rail, rolled from so-called "conductivity steel" (actually the nearest prac-ticable approach to pure iron, which is a better conductor than normal carbon steel), and laid on insulators between the running rails. In

TABLE 75

THE WORLD'S PRINCIPAL RAILWAY ELECTRIFICATION SYSTEMS
Direct Current

Country	Railway	Total Route Mileage	Voltage	Conductor
Italy	State (Central & Southern)	2,117	3,000	Overhead
U.S.S.R.	Main Lines	828	,,	,,
U.S.A.	Chicago, Milwaukee, St. Paul & Pacific	659	,,	,,
Morocco	Various	474	,,	,,
Brazil	Paulista, Central, Sorocabana	310	,,	,,
Chile	State & Transandine	165	,,	,,
France	National	2,040	1,500	,,
South Africa	Government	545	,,	,,
U.S.S.R.	Moscow, Leningrad, Caucasus	433	,,	,,
Japan	Government	381	,,	,,
India	G.I.P.R., B.B. & C.I.R.	240	,,	,,
Great Britain	Manchester, South Junction & Altrincham	9	,,	,,
,,	*L.N.E.R. Sheffield-Manchester (under conversion) ..	43	,,	,,
,,	*L.M.S.R. Manchester-Bury	14	1,200	Third-rail
Germany	State, Berlin Suburban	158	800	,,
Great Britain	Southern	698	650	,,
,,	*L.M.S.R. (Wirral)	10	,,	,,
U.S.A.	Illinois Terminal	431	,,	Overhead
,,	Long Island	141	,,	Third-rail
Great Britain	L.M.S.R., London Suburban	40	630	Fourth-rail
,,	*London Transport	187	600	,,
,,	*L.N.E.R., Tyneside	43	,,	Third-rail

* Railways which carried out electrification; now a part of British Railways

third-rail systems the current is returned through the running rails, but on most of the lines carrying the densest traffic, such as those of London Transport and the London Midland Region lines in the London area, a fourth rail is used for current return. The latter method both economises in current by reducing the resistance and also makes it possible to work with a lower maximum voltage, with less risk of disturbance to Post Office and other electric circuits. The Southern Region, however, is content with third-rail electrification throughout.

One of the main items of expenditure in third-rail and fourth-rail d.c. electrification is the cost of the sub-station equipment and of the conductor rails, which on the busiest lines may be even heavier than the running rails themselves, for every increase in cross-section reduces the resistance to the flow of the current. A further disadvantage, as compared with overhead electrification, is that breaks are necessary in the continuity of the conductors through switch and crossing work. Also icing of the rails in winter (ice being a non-conductor) is far more troublesome with conductor rails than with overhead conductor wires, and calls for special preventive measures. On the other hand, the use of conductor rails avoids any necessity for altering overhead structures, such as bridges and tunnels, in order to leave sufficient clearance for the overhead equipment.

It is of interest to recall that the original London, Brighton & South Coast Railway electrification of its London suburban area was at 6,600 volts a.c., with overhead conductors. Some years after the formation of the Southern Railway, all this was changed to third-rail electrification at 650 volts d.c., in order to be uniform with the London & South Western and South Eastern & Chatham systems, and so to permit interchangeability of stock and through working of trains between the different suburban areas.

Since then there has been no other a.c. railway electrification in Great Britain, with the exception of a short experimental length, also with 6,600 volts a.c., 25 cycles, between Lancaster, Morecambe and Heysham, electrified in 1909 by the one-time Midland Railway and now part of the London Midland Region. But overhead electrification, in this case at 1,500 volts d.c., reappeared in this country with the electrification of the Manchester South Junction & Altrincham Railway (jointly by the late L.M.S. and L.N.E. Railways) in 1931; it is also to be the standard for the Sheffield and Manchester main line electrification of the late L.N.E.R., and for the Eastern Region London suburban electrification from Liverpool Street to Shenfield, now in course of equipment.

There are many different types of electric motor. Those used in railway work must be capable of a high turning moment, or "torque," at the moment of starting, and should be of the type in which the speed of rotation decreases as the current demand increases. But for this characteristic, the motors would attempt to work their trains up adverse gradients at full speed, and thus would become overloaded and so badly overheated as eventually, in all probability, to burn out. Electric locomotives have what is known as a continuous power rating, and also a maximum rating which nominally is limited in duration to, say, one hour, in order to safeguard the motor from damage through overload. It should be added that the heating of motors in service is largely kept in check by forced-draught ventilation. The motors are geared to the driving axles, and the gear is designed according to the class of work for which the locomotive is intended; this is an advantage of electrification, for by variation of gears the same motor or locomotive can be adapted to a wide variety of duties.

In motor design the chief problem is to obtain maximum output with minimum weight. Whereas the earliest locomotive motors were totally enclosed, the modern methods of ventilation just referred to, with air supplied from fans, have made higher power outputs possible, though at the expense of increased maintenance, because of moisture, dirt and brake dust drawn into the motor with the air. Often the fans are mounted on the armature itself, and draw the ventilating air in through pipes supplied from louvres high up on the coach-body sides, so tending to minimise the dirt and dust trouble. Such has been the improvement in the design of d.c. traction motors, that whereas certain totally-enclosed motors fitted to British electric stock in 1919, and developing 123 h.p. at 700 r.p.m., weighed 7,000 lb. apiece, some of the latest self-ventilating motors, fitted from 1939 onwards, develop a continuous horsepower of 188 at 1,600 r.p.m., and yet weigh 4,100 lb. only. The weight of the motor per horsepower thus has been decreased from 57·0 to 21·8 lb.—a notable achievement.

On the latest standard London Transport tube stock (600 volts d.c.), the traction motors are rated at 240 h.p. each; the Southern Region (650 volts d.c.) uses 275 h.p. motors on its suburban stock, with both axles of one bogie only on each motor-coach motor-driven. On the six-car sets of coaches for express train working, all four axles of each motor-coach are driven with 225 h.p. motors, making a total of 900 h.p., or 1,800 for the complete unit.

For the 1,500-volt d.c. Eastern Region Sheffield-Manchester electrification, seventy 1,800 h.p. locomotives for mixed traffic and eight 2,100 h.p. locomotives for express passenger traffic are being built, each carried on two four-wheel bogies with all four axles motor-driven. In this connection it should be mentioned that the notation of such locomotives, is B_o-B_o, "B" to indicate a group of two axles both motor-driven, and the small "o" suffix that these axles are not coupled together. By comparison, the large streamlined electric loco-motives of the Pennsylvania Railroad, previously mentioned, are of the 2-C_o-C_o-2 type, having two groups of three motor-driven axles each, with uncoupled wheels, and leading and trailing bogies. As individual axle drives and uncoupled wheels are becoming the general practice, rather than the use of larger motors driving two or more axles by means of yokes or connecting-rods, the small suffix "o" is often now omitted.

So far as Great Britain is concerned the vast majority of motors on electric stock are "nose-suspended"; that is to say, the motor is carried on the axle by suspension bearings, and on the opposite side, by means of a lug on the motor frame, the motor is bolted to a transom on the bogie, with some form of resilient suspension interposed. Roughly half the motor weight is thus carried by the axle and the other half by the sprung bogie frame. The motors themselves are of the plain series interpole type, and drive the axles through single-reduction gearing. Roller bearings are largely used both for armatures and also for the axle bearings of electric stock, and some progress has been made in their application to the motor axle suspensions.

The control system has for its first function the regulation of the power supply to the traction motors, and in this connection the acceleration of the train is the main problem. The control equipment is used also to reverse the train; it should provide protection against overloading of the motors or faults in the electrical system; also, if any kind of electrical braking is in use, whether regenerative or of the eddy-current type, the control is concerned with deceleration as well as acceleration. In general, two types of control are in use—electromagnetic and electro-pneumatic (sub-divided into contactor and camshaft types) and in recent years these have been supplemented by an entirely new type of control known as the Metadyne, which has been fitted by London Transport to certain of its trains.

As each multiple-unit of three coaches or more usually includes at least four motors, advantage may be taken of this fact to arrange the motors for series-parallel control. On starting, all four motors are in series, so that each motor receives one-quarter of the line voltage, while at first resistances are inserted in series with each motor. As the train accelerates, these resistances are cut out one by one by means of contactors; then the motors are changed over, first from series to series-parallel working, in two pairs, and then to parallel working, with the voltage increasing to one-half and finally to full. With each transition all the resistances are reinserted, after which the process of cutting out step by step is gone through again until the full running position is reached. More steps, or notches, are needed with an independent electric locomotive than with multiple-unit working, in order to ensure smooth starts with trains of widely varying weights.

In the electric locomotives of the Southern Region, British Railways, the three motors on each bogie are all in series with a motor-driven generator. The output of this generator is regulated in pressure and direction by adjustment of its field, so that this output either assists or opposes the ordinary traction voltage. In this way as many as 35 notches are provided on the controller, and no resistances are needed.

Some new electric locomotives of the 1-D$_o$-1 type have just been completed for the Netherlands Railways, in which the controllers have no fewer than 60 notches. This control is obtained by having a series connection with all eight motors in series, a series-parallel connection with two parallel groups each of four motors in series, a parallel connection with four parallel groups each of two motors in series, with sixteen resistance and four weak-field notches available with each grouping, and full parallel. In these 100-ton locomotives, with a maximum one-hour rating of 4,480 h.p., every possible variation in power demand thus is provided for.

Electro-magnetic control is the older method, and has been applied very widely on British 600-volt d.c. electrified lines. The contactors are operated magnetically by current taken direct from the 600-volt supply, and all interlocks and control circuits work at this voltage. British applications have all been of the contactor type; electro-magnetic camshaft control is confined to d.c. electrifications abroad at 1,500 volts and upwards. With the electro-pneumatic contactor method, the contacts are worked by air cylinders, which are controlled by small magnet valves operating on a current supply at low voltage; a small motor-generator set is used to supply the low-voltage control current, at about 50 volts. This type has the advantage that control is not dependent on the line current voltage, and it also increases the force available for closing the contactors; the air valves of the pneumatic equipment, on the other hand, add to the costs of maintenance.

A modern example of electro-pneumatic contactor control is that of the London Midland Wirral electric trains; the four motors of each motor-coach are in two pairs, connected permanently in parallel, with the two motors of each pair in series. The control is arranged in 17 steps, and gives an acceleration, on straight and level track, of 1·5 m.p.h. per second. With all such systems, the control works automatically, the arrangement being that as the motor current drops to a predetermined value, the next contactor operates automatically; apart from any retardation by the driver, therefore, the rate of acceleration is unvarying, and it is this feature which makes possible such precise timing and regularity of working of electric services.

In electro-pneumatic camshaft control, the unit contactors are operated by a camshaft, which is rotated by compressed air under electric control and gives the required resistance connections; as the camshaft provides mechanical locking, no sequence interlocks are necessary. The latest type, as installed on the 1938 tube stock of London Transport, is known as P.C.M. control. It is ingeniously arranged. While 18 steps of control are provided for, the camshaft actually has nine steps only, for after working in the nine steps up to full series, the camshaft then reverses and takes the nine steps in the reverse order up to full parallel. The equipment is arranged under the car in two sections—a control unit and a main resistance unit, mounted in line—and its simplicity of wiring, accessibility, and ease of replacement give it many advantages. With this method of control, a seven-car train (five motor-coaches and two trailers) also has an acceleration of 1·5 m.p.h. per second.

The Metadyne control system requires a d.c. converting unit consisting of one large and two small machines coupled together. The unit takes current at line voltage, and gives out to the motors a supply which during acceleration is varied automatically in such a way as to give a smooth acceleration to the maximum output, while subsequently reducing the current to give the even running speed required. Main resistances are dispensed with. In decelerating to a stop, the motors are used to regenerate current. Although the Metadyne equipment is heavier and more costly than the methods previously described, its use can be fully justified on routes with numerous stops, which need rapid acceleration and retardation.

As already mentioned, the world's principal main-line electrifications all use alternating current, with overhead conductors; and with a few exceptions in suburban areas round large cities, independent locomotives provide the motive power. These locomotives are divided into three groups—those carried on two power bogies; those with articulated frames in two parts; and those with fixed plate frames, and leading or trailing bogie or pony trucks which are not power-driven.

In the first group are such locomotives as the Southern Region C-C type, each carried on on two six-wheel bogies with all axles motor driven (though in this particular case using d.c. supply). In the second group the Pennsylvania 2-C+C-2 locomotives of the "GG-1" series provide a notable example, with twin-armature motors driving two articulated groups of three axles apiece, and leading and trailing bogies; these locomotives weigh 205 tons each, can handle trains of 1,000 tons weight and over, and can travel at speeds up to 100 m.p.h. Many different types are included in the third group, such as the widely used 2-D-1 type of the Swiss Federal Railways, the 1-D-1 type now standard in Germany, Sweden and elsewhere, and others.

In the third group also are the most powerful electric locomotives in the world, of the Swiss "Ae 8/14" class. These consist of two units coupled together, each of the 1-B_o-1-B_o-1 type. Three examples have been built, in 1931, 1932 and 1939, of progressively increasing power; the first was of 7,500 h.p., the second of 8,800 h.p., and the third of no less than 11,400 h.p.—hourly rating in each case—though the weight of each complete locomotive has diminished from the 243 tons of the original No. 11801 to the 233 tons of the third, No. 11852.

Since then a more efficient type has been developed, in the series "Ae 4/6" numbered from 10801 to 10812. These machines are of the 1-D_o-1 wheel arrangement, and pack 5,540 h.p. into a total weight of $104\frac{1}{2}$ tons, or 11,080 h.p. into a pair of 209 tons, if worked multiple-unit. A single unit is rated as capable of working a train of 785 tons on the level at 59 m.p.h., of 740 tons up 1 in 100 at 40 m.p.h., and of 360 tons up 1 in 38—the ruling gradient of the Gotthard line, on which this class is mainly employed—at 37 m.p.h.

The Berne-Lötschberg-Simplon Railway of Switzerland is another railway in the designs of whose locomotives remarkable reductions in weight in relation to power developed have been achieved. Main-line locomotives of the 1-C_o-C_o-1 type introduced in 1926 for the Berne-Spiez-Brigue main line, with its lengthy 1 in 37 gradients, had a weight of 142 tons each, of which 118 tons was adhesion weight; their six traction motors gave a rating of 5,280 h.p., and they were geared for maximum speeds up to 56 m.p.h. The latest Lötschberg locomotives, of the B_o-B_o type, while exerting a maximum horsepower of 4,000 and geared for speeds up to $77\frac{1}{2}$ m.p.h., weigh no more than 79 tons each. So a tractive capacity of 36·2 h.p. per ton of locomotive weight has increased to 49·3 h.p. per ton.

Even greater progress in the same direction has been made with the outstanding "Re 4/4" class which has been built by the Swiss Federal Railways (Nos. 401 to 426) for the working of its inter-city lightweight high-speed trains. In length and weight no more than 48 ft. 3 in. in overall and $55\frac{1}{4}$ tons respectively, locomotives of this class have an hourly rating of 2,240 h.p., and can haul trains of up to ten coaches of the new lightweight streamline stock, weighing 300 tons, at a speed of 78 m.p.h. on level track. Actually, as the following records show, these diminutive B_o-B_o machines perform their assigned tasks without the slightest difficulty. The runs were timed by myself in course of a journey from Berne to Geneva and back in the summer of 1948.

Table 76 gives detailed logs of the running over the fairly level course between Lausanne and Geneva. Westbound, with six light-weight coaches (180 tons) we ran the 37·4 miles in 34 minutes 17 seconds, start to stop, or $32\frac{1}{2}$ minutes net; the 18·2 miles from Renens to Gland were covered at an average of 75·7 m.p.h., and between several slight easings for curves speed rose at various points to between 80 and 82 m.p.h. Similarly on the return journey, though this time with nine coaches of a total weight of 270 tons, No. 406 ran from Gland to Renens at 75·6 m.p.h., and from Geneva to Lausanne in 35 minutes 32 seconds, or 33¾ minutes net, with maximum speeds again up to 80-82 m.p.h.

Over the very heavy gradients between Lausanne and Berne equally notable work was done. With the six-coach load of 180 tons, 1 in 100 gradients were climbed steadily at 60 m.p.h., while a seven-coach train of 210 tons was lifted up the 10-mile incline from Lausanne to Corbéron —through a difference in level of 775 ft. and at an inclination for the most part of 1 in 53½-55—at 50 m.p.h. or slightly over. The distance of 60·4 miles from Berne to Lausanne, including the climb of 675 ft.

TABLE 76

YEAR 1948
SWISS FEDERAL RAILWAYS
Lightweight electric locomotives, Series "Re 4/4," Type Bo-Bo

Locomotive No.				413			406		
Load, coaches				6			9		
Load, tons tare/full				166/180			253/270		
Distance				Times		Speeds	Distance	Times		Speeds
miles				min.	sec.	m.p.h.	miles	min.	sec.	m.p.h.
0·0	LAUSANNE	..	..	0	00	—	37·4	35	32	43·7
2·8	RENENS†	..	..	3	29	48·2	34·6	31	41	71·4
5·2	Denges†	..	..	5	29	72·0	32·2	29	40	76·7
7·8	MORGES†	..	..	7	33	75·5	29·6	27	38	77·1
10·5	St. Prex	..	..	9	44	74·2	26·9	25	32	80·3
13·4	Allaman	..	..	11	56	79·1	24·0	23	22	72·0
15·2	Perroy	..	..	13	24	73·6	22·2	21	52	72·0
16·5	Rolle	..	..	14	31	69·6	20·9	20	47	77·7
18·4	Gilly	..	..	15	59	77·7	19·0	19	19	73·7
21·0	Gland	..	..	17	55	80·7	16·4	17	12	60·0
23·0	Prangins	..	..	19	39	69·2	14·4	15	12	41·0
				p.w.s.*						
23·9	NYON	..	..	21	25	31·2	13·5	13	32	49·2
								*p.w.s.		
26·0	Crans	..	..	23	41	55·6	11·4	11	13	77·8
29·2	Coppet	..	..	26	09	77·8	8·2	8	45	74·0
30·7	Mies†	..	..	27	20	76·1	6·7	7	32	68·4
32·2	Versoix†	..	..	28	50	60·0	5·2	6	13	60·4
34·6	Les Tuileries	..	..	30	56	68·6	2·8	3	50	66·7
36·1	Pregny	..	..	32	13	70·2	1·3	2	29	31·4
37·4	GENEVA	..	..	34	17	37·8	0·0	0	00	—

† Slight service slacks—between Renens and Denges, 69 m.p.h.; through Morges (westbound), 68 m.p.h. between Mies and Versoix, 60 m.p.h.   * 20 m.p.h.

between Flamatt and Vauderens, a slack through Fribourg, 16 miles of single track from there to Romont, and numerous restrictions over curves which in places are as sharp as 17 chains' radius, were covered in 63 minutes 21 seconds start to stop; the reverse run, with seven coaches in place of six, and two out-of-course checks costing 3 minutes, occupied 67 minutes 53 seconds.

Even up the mountain lines of Switzerland, such as the Brünig, the Furka-Oberalp, and the Visp-Zermatt, the latest B_o-B_o rack-and-pinion locomotives, weighing no more than 46 tons, are maintaining speeds up to 18 m.p.h. on inclinations as steep as 1 in 10 and even 1 in 9, with four or five coaches of very light bogie stock.   The Visp-Zermatt Railway works trailing loads of 100 tons up 1 in 8 gradients at slightly lower speeds.

On locomotives intended for high-speed work the coupling of axles has now been abandoned completely in favour of individual axle drives with various types of equipment to ensure flexibility of drive.   One popular method is the "quill" type, in which the axle is surrounded, at an appropriate clearance, with a hollow sleeve or quill; the two ends of the quill, in the plane of the locomotive wheels, are flanged, and to these flanges there are attached driving members which fit into the spaces between the driving-wheel spokes.   The pressure on the spokes is exerted through the medium of some type of springing, such as coil or leaf springs, or rubber cushions, giving the necessary flexibility, and, incidentally, reducing to a minimum any tendency of the driving wheels to slip.   With this type of drive, the locomotive frames must be outside the wheels.

A drive which originated in Switzerland, and has been largely used in that country, is the Büchli, and is used with inside locomotive frames; the drive members, quadrant-shaped, are housed inside the gear wheel, which is concentric with and outside the driving wheel. Frequently the drive is provided on one side of the locomotive only, instead of on both sides, as with quill drive.

As the transformer is carried on the locomotive in all a.c. electrification systems, control of a.c. motors in general is simpler than that of d.c. motors.   Control can be effected gradually by switching in successive sections of the secondary winding of the transformer, and thus varying the voltage.   It is customary to use contactors, but their arrangement and winding is simpler than that in d.c. locomotives.   The simplest of all a.c. control systems, used on large electric locomotives in conjunction with Déri brush-shifting motors, is that in which the applied voltage is varied by moving through various angles a set of adjustable brushes.

In multiple-unit trains, the shoes for current collection are provided on all motor-coaches throughout the train's length, so that if the train is brought to a stand in the middle of switch and crossing work, where there may be gaps in the line conductors, some of the shoes at least are in contact with the conductors.   With independent locomotives of d.c. types working over third-rail equipped track, however, there is risk that the collecting shoes may not be sufficiently far apart to bridge the biggest gaps in the conductor rails.   This difficulty can be met by fitting the locomotives with heavy flywheels between the generators and the traction motors; the kinetic energy stored in the flywheel, which continues to drive the generator for an appreciable time even when the locomotive is standing, ensures that sufficient current, supplemented by the battery supply, is still available to re-start the locomotive in such conditions. This principle is adopted in the electric locomotives of the Southern Region, British Railways.

A necessary detail of control equipment on all electric locomotives or motor-coaches which are manned by a driver only (without a helper) is some provision for cutting off the current supply to the motors in the event of the driver's illness or sudden death. The usual form adopted is the "dead-man's handle." This is a light spring device in the handle of the master controller, which without effort on the driver's part is kept depressed by the palm of his hand. If the pressure is relaxed, current is cut off automatically and a brake application is made. In some cases, a predetermined delay of several seconds is provided for before the cut-off and braking action becomes effective.

20

THE RIVALS OF STEAM—DIESEL-ELECTRIC
TRACTION

DURING recent years a second most formidable competitor has arisen to challenge the supremacy of steam on the railways. It has become so potent a rival, indeed, that in 1946, twelve years only after the introduction of the first passenger motive power units of this kind in the United States, it was estimated that the displacement of locomotive coal consumption by this new mode of propulsion on railways had reached the enormous total of 21,000,000 tons in a single year. That is to say, the new competitor had already become responsible for one-eighth of the ton-mileage of freight moved on the railways of the U.S.A., one-quarter of the passenger-car mileage, and one-third of the shunting and marshalling. It is the diesel-electric locomotive. In 1947, United States railways ordered from the builders 2,501 diesel-electric units, as compared with 79 steam locomotives only.

It was inevitable that the success of the internal-combustion engine on the roads and in the air should prompt the idea of applying it successfully to railway transport also. The first rail experiments were with engines using petrol and other special fuels, and most of the high-speed railcars used in France up to the time of the Second World War, such as the Bugatti and Micheline types, have had petrol engines. But it was soon realised that the diesel engine, using a far less costly type of oil-fuel, would be a more reliable and economical unit for the purpose.

Some of the earlier diesel-engined shunters, of relatively small power, had mechanical transmissions. But as the wider possibilities of diesel propulsion opened up, and greater tractive efforts were called for, it became progressively more difficult to design mechanical transmissions adequate to meet these increasingly severe demands. Much greater flexibility of operation would be possible if the actual propulsion were turned over from diesel to electric power. It is on these lines, therefore, that the railway use of diesel engines has developed. The modern diesel locomotive is a complicated mobile power-station; the engines drive generators, producing electric current, which is used, through traction motors, for the actual movement of locomotive and train.

The first use of diesel-electric power for passenger service was probably that of the Canadian National Railways in 1925. In that year eight railcars were put into service, seven of them single cars and the eighth a twin unit of two cars articulated together; each car was driven by an eight-cylinder modified diesel engine, of a type then being built by the Scottish firm of Beardmore. These engines were of the solid-injection four-stroke cycle type, developing 340 horsepower at 650 revolutions per minute; and by the careful selection of high tensile steels and special alloys in the engine construction, the weight of the engine was kept down to 16 lb. per horsepower—a very low figure. The eight cylinders drove a crankshaft coupled direct to the engine generator.

At the time it was remarked that the Canadian National Railways might be inaugurating a new era in motive power for railways, and so it has proved. A test to which one of the cars was put was to run it across Canada from Montreal to Vancouver, a total distance of 2,930 miles, without once stopping the diesel engine, though the car itself made a number of halts during this transcontinental run of 67 hours. Thus the experimental run foreshadowed, in a striking way, what would be the greatest asset of diesel power on railways—continuous availability over long periods.

Three years later the Canadian National Railways built a far larger and more powerful twin-unit diesel-electric locomotive, of the 2-D-2 + 2-D-2 type, weighing 290 tons. Beardmore-diesel engines again were incorporated in the design; each unit had a 12-cylinder engine block, of the solid injection type, and the combined power of the two units was 2,660 horsepower at 800 r.p.m. The locomotive was rated as being capable of developing a tractive effort of 100,000 lb. while accelerating, and 42,000 lb. continuously while at speed. After so promising a beginning, which gave a lead to the world, it is curious that the Canadian National since has made such limited use of diesels.

Before long the advantage of continuous operation began to make a new appeal to railway authorities in connection with shunting. A diesel or diesel-electric locomotive, if required, can spend nearly 100 per cent. of its day actually at work, instead of needing spells between its turns of duty, as does the steam locomotive, for attention to cleaning the fire, taking water, and other locomotive needs. While expensive in first cost, it can be operated very cheaply. From about 1930 onwards, therefore, the diesel locomotive began to make definite headway. For the most part units of small power were built, for shunting or branch-line work, and many of them with simple mechanical transmission rather than the more complicated electric generators and traction motors.

Then came the year 1932, in which the German State Railway first demonstrated to the world the possibilities of high-speed railway transport with diesel-electric power.   After much experimenting, in the spring of that year there appeared an articulated twin unit, streamlined from end to end, and 137 ft. 6 in. in length.   At both ends of the train there were engine compartments containing 12-cylinder Maybach-diesel engines of the airless-injection V-type using heavy oil.   These were directly coupled to generators, and gave a total horsepower of 820 to drive this 77-ton train.   Inside the train there was comfortable seating for 102 passengers; and a refreshment buffet, lavatories and luggage space also were provided.

Before the end of 1932 the new diesel train had run the 178 miles from Berlin to Hamburg in 142 minutes, at 75 m.p.h.   From the beginning of March, 1933, the train went into regular service on this route as the famous *"Fliegende Hamburger"*—the "Flying Hamburger" —scheduled daily to run the distance between the two cities in 138 minutes, at 77·4 m.p.h. average speed, and to return in 140 minutes. Allowing for reduced speed in the Berlin suburban area, out to Spandau, and for some distance also into Hamburg, as well as for the slowing to 37 m.p.h. over the curve through Wittenberge, this schedule, for the first time in railway history, called for regular running speeds up to 100 m.p.h.   To make travel safe at such speeds, a double system of braking was used—the Knorr air-brake, applied to the wheels, for ordinary use, and an electro-magnetic rail-brake in reserve for emergencies.

The "Flying Hamburger" marked the beginning of an epoch in transport on rails, and its influence was felt in many parts of the world. High-speed diesel-electric streamline services spread by degrees all over Germany.   By the time the Second World War broke out, a network of services of this description crossed Germany in all directions.   Three of them ran in each direction daily between Berlin and Hamburg; others worked into the capital from all the principal cities in the Reich.   From Munich, Nuremberg, Stuttgart, Frankfort, Cologne, Bremen, and Beuthen (on the Polish frontier), it was possible to start early in the morning, to be in Berlin by midday or shortly after, to have the afternoon for business or other appointments, and then, starting back between 5 and 7 p.m., to arrive back in one's home city by or before midnight.   This was being done over distances as great as that between Glasgow and London.

Very high speeds were run.   The *"Fliegende Kölner,"* for example, was booked nightly to run the 157·8 miles from the Zoological Gardens station in Berlin to Hanover in 114 minutes, and the 109·7 miles to Hamm, in Westphalia, in 80 minutes, involving start-to-stop speeds of

83·1 and 82·3 m.p.h. in succession. There were eight runs at over 80 m.p.h., and no fewer than 33, totalling in length 3,558 miles, made daily at over 75 m.p.h. by these trains. The streamlined diesel-electric sets grew to three-car units, and some of these were run in pairs, making six-car trains, with multiple-unit control. Among these was the "*Fliegende Kölner*," which ran in two independent sections between Hamm and Cologne, serving different routes through the industrial area of the Ruhr.

As a typical example of the speeds of one of these German diesel-electric streamliners, a log is given in Table 77 of a run that I made in 1936 on the "*Fliegende Münchener*",when the authorities permitted me to travel with the driver and his helper from Leipzig to Berlin. The experience was unforgettable. To be at the extreme front end, without the length of a steam loco-motive boiler along which to look, but with the track dis-appearing directly under one's feet at speeds up to a hundred miles an hour, is thrilling beyond description, and no less the overhauling of trains travelling at speed on the adjacent track, almost as though they were standing still. Other im-pressions included the light-ning rapidity of the accelerations—to 90 m.p.h. in 7 miles from the start, and also after the slacks through Delitzsch, Bitterfeld and Wittenberg. Speed twice reached the three-figure level, but was not allowed to pass it; the fastest stretch was from Zahna to Grossbeeren, 40·7 miles at an average of 95·8 m.p.h. The run of 102·2 miles was completed in 77 minutes 11 seconds, and even including the Wittenberg permanent-way slowing and the two service slacks, we had run 92·2 miles continuously at a mean speed of 85·7 m.p.h.

It was not long after the introduction of the first German diesel-electric streamliners that similar activity began to break out in the

TABLE 77

YEAR 1936
GERMAN STATE RAILWAYS
Two twin diesel-electric units coupled, 4 cars
181 tons tare; 190 tons gross

Dist.		Times	Speeds Max. & Min.	Average†
miles		min. sec.	m.p.h.	m.p.h.
0·0	LEIPZIG	0 00	—	—
4·2	Neuwied	5 55	—	42·6
7·0	Rachwitz	7 55	90	84·0
10·0	Zachortau	9 48	98½	93·9
13·0	Delitzsch	11 57	75*	83·7
16·8	Grube Ludwig	14 28	92½	90·6
20·3	BITTERFELD	17 27	50*	70·4
23·5	Muldenstein	20 30	—	63·0
26·6	Burgkemnitz	22 49	92½	80·3
32·7	Radis	26 40	—	95·1
37·3	Bergwitz	29 29	100	98·0
41·0	Pratau	31 59	—	88·8
		p.w.s.	30	
43·2	WITTENBERG	35 12	—	41·0
50·0	Zahna	40 38	90	75·1
55·4	Blonsdorf	44 05	—	93·9
63·0	JÜTERBOG	48 45	100	97·7
71·1	Luckenwalde	53 45	—	97·2
80·7	Trebbin	59 43	—	96·5
86·8	Ludwigsfelde	63 30	98	96·7
90·7	Grossbeeren	66 08	—	88·8
		eased	—	—
96·4	Lichterfelde Ost	70 27	—	79·2
102·2	BERLIN (ANHALT)	77 11	—	—

* Service slack   † Station to station

United States.   The attraction in North America was the greater in that most of the coal deposits are in the Eastern and Southern States, whereas on the Pacific Coast and in Oklahoma and Texas there are considerable natural resources of oil.   It was west of Chicago, therefore, that most of the earlier diesel passenger development took place; since then, as indicated in the opening paragraph of this chapter, diesel building in the United States has gone ahead by such leaps and bounds that by the end of 1947 nearly 6,000 diesel-electric locomotives were at work, on high-speed streamlined and ordinary express passenger trains, long-distance freight services, and in shunting and marshalling yards as well as transfer work between them.

By 1948, all the principal passenger services on the Baltimore & Ohio, Chicago, Burlington & Quincy, Atchison, Topeka & Santa Fe, Atlantic Coast Line, Seaboard Air Line, Southern, Alton, and several other large railways, were being operated by diesel-electric locomotives; and heavy freight working on most of the heavily-graded main lines through the mountainous areas in the west of the United States had been turned over largely to diesel-electric power, and over some routes to diesels exclusively.   Some railways of considerable size, such as the Missouri-Kansas-Texas (familiarly known as the "Katy Lines"), the amalgamated Gulf, Mobile & Ohio and Alton Railroads, and the Chicago, Indianapolis & St. Louis, are now in course of complete "dieselisation" of their systems, and of doing away entirely with steam locomotives; this has taken place already on one or two of the smaller lines, such as the Susquehanna and the New York, Ontario & Western Railroad. Most significant of all is the fact that the New York Central and Pennsylvania Railroads, which have always prided themselves on the efficiency of their steam power, at last have yielded to the new competitor and are running their most famous expresses with diesel locomotives, as mentioned already in Chapter 18.

As in Germany, the first of the diesel-operated passenger trains in the United States were self-contained units of lightweight stock, from three to five cars, with the power housed in the first car; but from then onwards the building has been almost entirely of independent locomotives, which can be used with any description of stock.   While many of the diesel-hauled passenger trains are lightweight streamliners of the latest type, the diesels are used also to a large extent in hauling trains of the heavy standard cars of earlier types.

Diesel-electric locomotives in the United States are divided into three types—"switchers," as the Americans call them, for shunting, marshalling, and inter-yard transfer work; freight locomotives; and passenger locomotives; to a certain extent the two last-named types are designed to be interchangeable. A more recent development is that of combined freight and shunting diesels of 1,000 and 1,500 b.h.p.

Shunters are in units of 380, 660, and 1,000 b.h.p., of which the 1,000 h.p. type is in by far the most extensive use. These locomotives are mounted on two four-wheel power bogies, with all axles motor-driven. A typical locomotive in the 1,000 h.p. range is 45 ft. in length, and weighs just over 100 tons; it can traverse a curve with a minimum radius of 50 ft., and so is useful in yards where there is much sharp curvature. The cab is at one end, and the six-cylinder supercharged diesel engine and main generator are housed under a long narrow hood which extends to the front end of the locomotive. With its 40-in. driving wheels, the shunter is capable, if necessary, of a maximum speed of 63 m.p.h.; it has a starting tractive effort of all but 70,000 lb. There is a fuel oil capacity of about 650 gallons, which permits continuous operation for long periods without re-fuelling, and the lubricating oil capacity is 80 gallons.

These diesel shunters are deservedly popular, for a variety of reasons. One is their nearly 100 per cent. availability, day in and day out; with systematised maintenance procedure, daily inspections can be cut down to half-an-hour or less, so that practically continuous working is possible. On some railways they are used for long-distance freight work on subsidiary routes up to 500 miles in length. They can handle loads up to 2,000 tons or so, and if necessary, provided they are fitted for multiple-unit working, two can be coupled together and worked by a single crew as a 2,000 h.p. locomotive. Their ready manoeuvrability is a second advantage, and a third is the noiseless and smokeless way in which they set about their work—a special advantage in freight yards situated in the heart of a city, where much of the noise of shunting can be suppressed in this way, and where, also, city ordinances limiting the emission of smoke are becoming increasingly severe. For branch and intermediate main-line service, new 1,500 horsepower diesels are now being introduced.

In the passenger realm, the United States development has been almost entirely in units of 2,000 b.h.p., carried on six-wheel bogies of which the outer axles in each case are motor-driven. Where more tractive power is needed, these are coupled in pairs or triplets of 4,000 or 6,000 b.h.p. respectively; and occasionally quadruple units of 8,000 b.h.p. are used on the most arduous duties. All the diesel engines, electric generators, and motors are under the control of the one "engineer," or driver, at the front end. He is provided with a "fireman," or helper, corresponding to the fireman on a steam locomotive. The latter has no fire to which to attend, of course, but the engine room is in his immediate charge, and as far as possible he joins the driver to assist in the observation of signals. The most powerful single-unit diesels in the United States are some 3,000 b.h.p. articulated locomotives of a recent Baldwin design, with the 2-D-D-2 wheel arrangement (two groups of four motor-driven axles each, and leading and trailing bogies). Each of these monsters is 91 ft. 6 in. long and weighs 258 tons.

In the triple-unit and quadruple-unit locomotives the power plant is so large that on some main lines, such as the Santa Fe, a third man is needed to look after it. He is known as a "travelling maintainer"; he spends all his time in the engine-rooms, and is capable of making minor repairs, if necessary, *en route*. Also he relieves the maintenance depot to which the locomotive is attached by doing a certain amount of the regular inspection work while normal running is in progress. This is all the easier in a multiple-unit locomotive, because it is possible to shut down one or more of the engines completely when the train is running on the level or on the easier downhill grades. The "fireman" then can spend most of his time with the driver, devoting himself largely to track and signal observation—a matter of increasing importance in view of the high speeds at which many of these diesels have to travel. Indeed, on many main lines it is compulsory for the "fireman" to be at the head end all the time a diesel-hauled passenger train is in motion.

In passenger working the advantage of continuous availability is seen in the exceptional distances over which some of these diesels are used without change. Between Chicago and the Pacific Coast cities of Los Angeles, San Francisco, and Portland, for example, on the joint "City" streamline trains of the Chicago & North Western, Union Pacific and Southern Pacific Railroads, and on the "Super-Chief" and "El Capitan" streamliners of the Atchison, Topeka & Santa Fe, the same locomotives are used throughout for journeys ranging from 2,226 to 2,301 miles. Locomotive crews are changed at all the divisional points, roughly 200 miles apart, but the locomotives themselves continue for the entire $39\frac{3}{4}$ hours. A round trip of from 4,452 to 4,602 miles is completed in six days, and all the necessary locomotive maintenance is done in the terminal turn-around times, ranging from 7 to 9 hours.

According to their weight, these flyers are worked by twins or triplets of 4,000 or 6,000 b.h.p., and the tasks that they are set are arduous indeed, seeing that their loads may range from 9 to 13 or 14 luxurious cars, weighing from 500 to 800 tons, and that at least one-half of each route is through exceedingly mountainous country. On the 2,226-mile main line of the Santa Fe between Chicago and Los

Angeles, to which reference was made in Chapter 18, the "Super-Chief" and the "El Capitan" have to be lifted to the 7,622-ft. altitude of the Raton Tunnel, and then to pass in succession over altitudes of 7,437 ft., 4,963 ft. (Albuquerque), 7,248 ft., 4,856 ft. (Winslow), 6,896 ft., 483 ft. at the crossing of the Colorado River at Needles, 2,585 ft., 789 ft., and, finally, 3,822 ft. on the Cajon Pass—a colossal switchback indeed. From Cajon Summit down to San Bernardino the lines drop 2,744 ft. in 26 miles, with maximum grades of 1 in 30 westbound and 1 in 45 eastbound. On some of these workings steam locomotives come to the assistance of the diesels in surmounting the worst inclinations. The Union Pacific main line, over which the well-known "City" streamliners work, rises to the even greater altitude of 8,013 ft. on Sherman Hill.

To compensate for loss of speed and increased time through the mountains, in order to maintain their overall averages of between 56 and 58 m.p.h., these streamline trains must run at extremely high speeds over the thousand miles or so of prairie territory between Chicago and the mountain foothills. Here the schedules call for start-to-stop average speeds of 75 m.p.h. and more, and running speeds of 80 to 100 m.p.h. over long distances. In this connection it is of interest that by the end of 1947 the American timetables contained no fewer than 187 daily runs, ranging in length from 15 to 288 miles, timed from start to stop at speeds of from 70 to 86·2 m.p.h., and all but 22 of them worked by diesel-electric locomotives.

Among remarkable American diesel achievements are those of the Burlington "Denver Zephyr" and the joint North Western and Union Pacific "City of Denver" between Chicago and Denver, the capital of Colorado. The two routes are 1,037 and 1,049 miles in length respectively, and the times allowed are 16 hours westbound and 15 hours 35 minutes eastbound, all stops included. This means inclusive speeds of 64·8 and 65·6 m.p.h. from Chicago up to Denver, which is precisely one mile above sea level, and 66·5 and 67·3 m.p.h. in the opposite direction, with some of the start-to-stop runs timed at over 80 m.p.h. It is a remarkable tribute to the reliability of the locomotives used that from going into service in October, 1936, the two Burlington twin-unit 4,000 h.p. diesels used on the "Denver Zephyr" covered 1,084,101 miles and 1,239,970 miles respectively between their first and second visits to the shops for general overhaul, notwithstanding the fact that each was running 7,259 miles weekly, seven days a week, at these tremendous speeds, with roughly 8 hours between each trip for routine maintenance. Some of the American passenger diesels have worked for periods of two to three years, on runs of 700 to 800 miles,

129.   Six-car unit used on the Southern Region multiple-unit workings between London and the South Coast—Victoria-Eastbourne express near Quarry Tunnel.   (*O. J. Morris.*)

130.   Three-car light articulated set used on the Swiss "Flèche Rouge" high speed services. It is on the viaduct at La Conversion, above Lausanne, en route to Berne.   (*Courtesy, Swiss Federal Railways.*)

SELF-CONTAINED ELECTRIC UNITS

131. I-B-B-I locomotive (two groups of four-coupled wheels) piloting 2-Do-I locomotive (four axles independently driven) on the Gotthard line at Göschenen, Swiss Federal Railways. (*Cecil J. Allen.*)

132. A locomotive of the I-E-I type on the Lötschberg Railway, with twin motors driving five coupled axles by the yoke arrangement seen above centre axle. (*Courtesy, Bern-Lötschberg-Simplon.*)

133. A later Lötschberg locomotive of the I-Co-Co-I type, with six independent motor-driven axles; 5,280 h.p., weight 144 tons. (*Courtesy, Bern-Lötschberg-Simplon.*)

TYPES OF ELECTRIC LOCOMOTIVE

134. For the Manchester-Sheffield electrification at 1,500 volts D.C., Eastern Region—a Bo-Bo locomotive weighing 88 tons, with maximum one-hour rating of 1,870 h.p. (*Courtesy, British Railways.*)

135. One of the latest Bo-Bo locomotives for high speed passenger work, 15,000 volts A.C. Weight 79 tons, 4,000 h.p., maximum speed 78 m.p.h. (*Courtesy, Bern-Lötschberg-Simplon.*)

136. A Pennsylvania Class "GG-1" streamlined locomotive, type 2-Co-Co-2, 11,000 volts A.C. Weight 205 tons, 4,620 h.p., maximum speed 100 m.p.h. (*Courtesy, Pennsylvania Railroad.*)

MODERN ELECTRIC LOCOMOTIVE POWER

137. At the regulator of an American 4-8-4 on the "Empire Builder" westbound, Great Northern Railway, U.S.A. The needle of the speed indicator is at 70 m.p.h. (*Rail Photo Service, Boston, Mass., W. J. Pontin.*)

138. What the driver sees—a view from the footplate of a rebuilt "Royal Scot" 4-6-0, London Midland Region, taken near Skipton on the Leeds-Carlisle run. (*Canon E. Treacy.*)

ON THE LOCOMOTIVE FOOTPLATE

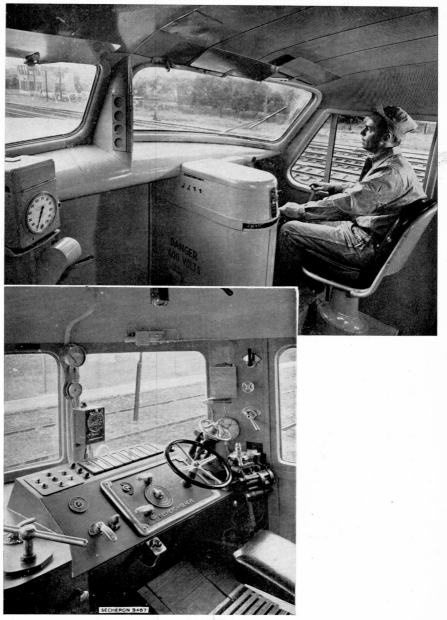

139. Driving cab of "Alco" quadruple-unit 6,000 b.h.p. diesel-electric locomotive. (*Courtesy, American Locomotive Company.*)

140. Driving cab of the latest Lötschberg 2-Co-Co-2 high speed electric locomotive. (*Courtesy, Bern-Lötschberg-Simplon.*)

ELECTRIC AND DIESEL-ELECTRIC CONTROLS

141. The original "Fliegende Hamburger" two-car unit of the German State Railways, 820 b.h.p., at 100 m.p.h. near Friedrichsruh. (*Courtesy, German State Railways.*)

142. The first British diesel-electric passenger locomotive, No. 10000 of the London Midland Region, 1,600 b.h.p., near Elstree at the head of an express from St. Pancras to Derby. (*P. T. Handford.*)

143. Twin-unit "Electro-Motive" 4,000 b.h.p. locomotive leaving Chicago for Minneapolis with the "Twin Cities 400" streamliner. (*Courtesy, Chicago and North Western Railway.*)

THE DEVELOPMENT OF DIESEL-ELECTRIC POWER

144. High speed streamline service—the "City of Denver," one of the fastest trains in the world, approaching Denver with triple-unit diesel of 6,000 b.h.p., after running 1,048 miles in 16 hours. (*R. H. Kindig.*)

145. Long-distance freight working—a quadruple-unit diesel of 6,000 b.h.p. pulling up to Sherman Summit, Union Pacific Railroad, 8,013 ft. above sea level, with a train of 51 bogie wagons. (*R. H. Kindig.*)

146. One of the popular 1,000 b.h.p. shunters, used also for transfers from yard to yard and short-distance road service. (*Rail Photo Service, Boston, Mass., James D. Bennett.*)

TYPES OF DIESEL-ELECTRIC LOCOMOTIVE SERVICE

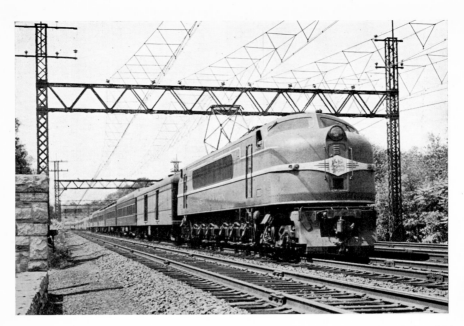

147. One of the hourly expresses between New York and Boston, New York, New Haven and Hartford Railroad, hauled by 2-Co-Co-2 electric locomotive. Between New Haven and Boston the train will be taken over by a twin-unit 4,000 b.h.p. diesel. (*Courtesy, New Haven Railroad.*)

148. The "City of Los Angeles," Chicago and North Western and Union Pacific Railroads, with triple-unit 6,000 b.h.p. diesel-electric locomotive working through unchanged over the 2,301 miles between Chicago and Los Angeles in 39¾ hours. (*Courtesy, Union Pacific Railroad.*)

MOTIVE POWER RIVALS TO-DAY

seven days a week, without missing a single trip—a reliability record which also it would be difficult to parallel with steam.

Before the "Denver Zephyr" went into regular service, a demonstration run was made from Chicago to Denver, with one 4,000 b.h.p. locomotive hauling eight passenger cars, in which the 1,017 miles of the shortest Burlington route between these two cities was covered without a single intermediate stop in 12 hours 12½ minutes, at an average speed of 83·3 m.p.h. throughout.

Another striking diesel performance is that of the two daily "Twin Cities Zephyrs" of the Burlington, maintaining streamline service daily between Chicago and the cities of St. Paul and Minneapolis. The westbound "Morning Zephyr," which leaves Chicago at 8.15 a.m., covers the 431 miles from Chicago to St. Paul, with eight intermediate stops, in 6¼ hours, at 69 m.p.h. inclusive. After some slow running over the 10 miles between St. Paul and Minneapolis, it reaches the latter city at 3.0 p.m. In no more than 30 minutes the train is emptied, cleaned, turned, revictualled, and refilled with passengers, and at 3.30 p.m. is starting back as the "Afternoon Zephyr," with a 6¼-hour run over the 431 miles from St. Paul to Chicago.

During the day, in 14 hours overall, the trains travel 882 miles, of which 862 miles, including 16 stops, are completed at an average speed of 69·0 m.p.h. On the westbound journey they make one of the fastest scheduled railway runs in the world, covering the 54·6 miles from East Dubuque to Prairie du Chien in 38 minutes, at 86·2 m.p.h. from start to stop. Included in this schedule is the point-to-point timing of 13 minutes for a fraction under 24 miles from Cassville to Crawford, at no less than 102·6 m.p.h. This is probably the first actual 100 m.p.h. booking that has appeared in a railway timetable.

As an example of the speeds which must be maintained by a train of this description, the log of a run with one of the eastbound "Twin Cities Zephyrs," timed by Mr. E. L. Thompson, is given in Table 78. The train left St. Paul 12 minutes late, and by delays through St. Paul yard was 20 minutes late past St. Croix Tower. As is customary in North America, regaining the lost time began at once, although overtime spent at stations resulted in the streamliner still being 18¼ minutes behind time on leaving East Dubuque. On section after section of the run, as will be seen, speed rose to well over 90 m.p.h. for considerable distances; one stretch of 8·2 miles, from Alma to Cochrane, was covered at 103·6 m.p.h., and another of 23·5 miles, from Glenhaven to Potosi, at an average of 99·0 m.p.h.

Eventually the whole of the arrears were regained, and the "Zephyr" ran into Chicago 2¾ minutes early. The actual running time from

St. Paul Yard to Chicago, a distance of 426·4 miles, including slowing down to and restarting from eight intermediate stops and all speed restrictions, had been 5 hours 44½ minutes, entailing an average speed of 74·3 m.p.h. for the entire distance. Between St. Croix Tower and Chicago, on one of the fastest schedules in the world, no less than 31 minutes had been regained, and as evidence of the efficiency of traffic operation in the U.S.A., it may be noted that, apart from the final 37·8 miles from Aurora, the entire route is single track.

A companion run on the westbound "Hiawatha" of the Chicago, Milwaukee, St. Paul & Pacific Railroad (Table 79), also timed by Mr. Thompson, furnishes an interesting comparison with the steam-hauled runs on the same train in Chapter 18 (Tables 69 and 70). In this case a twin-unit 4,000 b.h.p. diesel was hauling a substantial train of 14 cars, 730 tons all told, but without difficulty gained 15 minutes on schedule. Over the level line between Chicago and Milwaukee, 63·6 miles from Morton Grove to Lake were covered at 90·3 m.p.h., and speed rose to a maximum of 102·0 m.p.h. With the train on time, running was fairly normal after Milwaukee until a permanent-way check between Portage and New Lisbon gave the driver an excuse for regaining the lost time between New Lisbon and La Crosse. After

TABLE 78

YEAR 1943
CHICAGO, BURLINGTON & QUINCY R.R.
"TWIN CITIES ZEPHYR" STREAMLINE TRAIN
Twin-unit 4,000 b.h.p. diesel-electric locomotive
Load: 10 cars, 540 tons gross

Dist.		Sched.	Actual	Speeds†
miles		min.	min. sec.	m.p.h.
0·0	ST. PAUL	0	0 00	—
			sigs.	
0·5	St. Paul Yard	—	9 30	—
13·4	Langdon	—	22 45	58·4
18·5	St. Croix Tower*	20	28 00	58·3
21·4	Prescott*	—	32 15	40·9
50·3	Maiden Rock	—	54 00	79·7
62·9	Pepin	—	63 45	77·5
77·7	ALMA	—	74 15	84·6
85·9	Cochrane	74	79 00	103·6
95·2	Fountain City	—	85 00	93·0
100·8	WINONA JUNCTION	86	89 15	78·1
2·5	East Winona	—	4 15	35·3
10·7	Trempeauleau	—	10 30	78·7
24·5	Onalaska	—	19 30	92·0
26·9	NORTH LA CROSSE	21	23 00	41·1
2·6	LA CROSSE	5	5 15	29·7
10·7	Stoddard	—	9 45	65·8
23·5	Victory	—	18 00	93·1
35·2	Ferryville	25	25 15	96·8
50·0	Charme	—	35 15	88·8
57·7	PRAIRIE DU CHIEN	42	40 45	84·0
2·7	Crawford Tower	4	4 30	36·0
7·7	Wyalusing	—	9 15	63·2
16·9	Glenhaven	—	15 45	84·9
26·7	Cassville	25	21 45	98·0
40·4	Potosi	34	30 00	99·6
54·6	EAST DUBUQUE	44	40 15	83·1
12·7	Portage*	—	12 45	59·8
13·5	Galena Junction*	16	14 00	38·4
31·4	Proving Ground	—	27 15	82·9
39·4	SAVANNA	42	33 00	83·5
16·2	Chadwick	18	16 45	58·0
33·7	Polo	33	31 45	70·0
46·7	OREGON	45	44 00	63·7
6·0	Chana	5	7 00	51·4
15·1	Rochelle	13	14 45	70·5
31·2	Shabbona	28	27 45	74·3
43·2	Hinckley	—	35 45	90·0
53·6	Sugar Grove	47	42 45	89·1
60·4	AURORA	53	48 45	68·0
9·3	Napierville	—	10 00	55·8
24·0	La Grange	—	19 30	92·8
29·3	Clyde	—	23 00	90·9
34·0	Western Avenue	—	26 30	80·6
37·8	CHICAGO	42	32 45	36·5

* Severe service slack
† Average speeds, station to station

making the prescribed 40 m.p.h. slacks at both ends of the single-line section from Tunnel City to Raymore, he covered the 19·6 miles from Camp McCoy to West Salem at 98.0 m.p.h., with speed mounting once again to over 100 m.p.h. for some miles. Neither of the runs just quoted would be regarded as exceptional in present-day United States operating practice.

The equipment of the modern American high-speed streamline locomotives and trains is very complete. Above the usual American electric headlight there is an additional headlight of the "Mars" type; this is rotated by a small motor and throws a moving beam of light high up into the sky. The purpose is to warn motorists and others at level crossings, especially in the open country where the crossings have no protection, that a streamliner is approaching—a necessary precaution, seeing that it may be travelling more or less noiselessly at from 90 to 100 m.p.h. The latest type of "Mars" headlight can exhibit either a white or a red beam, and by a valve working directly off the air line of the air-brakes, in the event of an emergency brake application being made, the change from white

TABLE 79

YEAR 1943
CHICAGO, MILWAUKEE, ST. PAUL & PACIFIC R.R.
"HIAWATHA" STREAMLINE TRAIN
Twin-unit 4,000 b.h.p. diesel-electric locomotive
Load: 14 cars, 730 tons gross

Dist.				Sched.	Actual		Speeds†
miles				Min.	min.	sec.	m.p.h.
0·0	CHICAGO	..	..	0	0	00	—
2·9	Tower A2	..	..	—	6	45	25·8
6·4	Healy	..	..	—	10	45	52·5
14·3	Morton Grove..	..	—	17	15	72·9
20·2	Techny ..	..	..	21	21	30	83·3
32·3	Rondout	..	..	29	30	00	85·4
42·9	Wadsworth	..	..	36	37	15	87·7
51·6	Ranney ..	..	..	42	42	45	94·9
61·8	STURTEVANT..	..	49	49	15	94·2
68·1	Tower A68	..	..	53	53	30	88·9
72·8	Oakwood	..	..	—	56	30	94·0
77·9	Lake	..	..	59	59	30	102·0
85·0	MILWAUKEE ..	..	70	69	00	44·8
9·9	Elm Grove	..	..	—	14	15	41·7
14·2	Brookfield	..	..	17	18	45	63·8
24·9	Hartland	..	..	—	27	00	77·8
32·8	Oconomowoc ..	..	—	32	45	82·4
38·5	Ixonia ..	..	..	—	36	15	97·7
46·0	WATERTOWN*	..	42	41	30	85·7
64·7	COLUMBUS ..	..	—	58	15	66·9
74·1	Doylestown	..	..	—	65	45	75·2
83·9	Wyocena	..	..	—	73	15	78·4
92·9	PORTAGE	..	..	81	80	15	77·1
16·9	Wisconsin Dells	..	—	16	15	62·4
					p.w.s.		
25·5	Lyndon ..	..	..	—	27	15	46·9
36·1	Mauston	..	..	—	36	00	72·7
43·1	NEW LISBON..	..	38	41	45	73·0
6·0	Camp Douglas ..	..	—	8	00	45·0
18·8	Tomah ..	..	..	—	17	45	78·8
22·2	Tunnel City* ..	..	—	20	45	68·0
30·4	Camp McCoy ..	..	25	27	00	78·7
35·2	SPARTA	..	..	—	30	00	96·0
41·8	Rockland	..	..	—	34	00	99·0
45·4	Bangor ..	..	..	—	36	15	96·0
50·0	West Salem	..	..	—	39	00	100·4
59·0	LA CROSSE ..	..	52	47	15	71·3

* Severe service slack
† Average speeds, station to station

to red is automatic, as a warning to other trains that something may be wrong. A similar rotating red tail-light comes into operation on the rear of the train in the event of a breakdown.

Every axlebox on each train contains a thermo-couple, sensitive to heat; and if any single box should "run hot," the thermo-couple closes a circuit, lights up a red warning light in the driver's cab, and rings an alarm bell. This is known as a "journal alarm." The brakes throughout the train are equipped with a form of electro-magnetic control, which, if any wheel should skid through an emergency brake application having been made, releases the brake and re-applies it. It is a most valuable piece of equipment to ensure efficient and rapid stopping of trains from high speeds when emergency stops are necessary. In addition, automatic sanding comes into operation before each wheel after an emergency brake application; and an automatic water-spray helps to keep the flanges cool on the long and steep inclines on mountain routes over which speed must be continuously restricted because of curvature.

Where there is an over-riding speed restriction over a considerable distance, a governor on the diesel engines sees to it that the speed is not exceeded. All the bogies on the locomotives and coaches are fitted with derailment flanges; the purpose of these is to engage with the heads of the rails, should a streamliner become derailed, and so to keep the bogies from slewing round to an angular position. In this way, as has been proved in more than one accident, the coaches of derailed trains are held in line, and can be prevented from spreading themselves all over the track, which would greatly increase the risk of severe damage and destruction.

On all the diesel locomotives used for long-distance work, over-heating of any part of the diesel engines, or of the lubricating oil, or any failure of the lubricating oil circuit, automatically shuts down the engines, to protect them from damage, and rings an alarm in the driving cabin. Thus every possible precaution is taken to ensure freedom from breakdown on these complicated power-stations, and the cost of installing and maintaining such safeguards is well justified in view of the fact that the capital cost of a diesel-electric locomotive is nearly double that of a steam locomotive of comparable power. One triple-unit or quadruple-unit diesel of 6,000 b.h.p., for example, to-day is worth well over $600,000.

Passenger and freight diesels alike have rounded noses, with the sloping front windows of the driving cab set well back, and the engine-room casings from end to end conforming to the ordinary coach external lines. The railway "insignia" are carried in front of the nose, together with the headlight or headlights; and the whole is painted in brilliant colours, varying according to the practice of the owning railway. In the case of passenger diesels used with streamline train sets, horizontal bands and lining of contrasting colours are often carried from the locomotive along the length of the train, making a most spectacular appeal to the public eye; indeed, it is not too much to say that the diesel streamline trains, with the additional advantage of their modernised interiors, have done more to boost the attraction of railway travel in the United States, against the strong competition of air transport, than any other development for many years past.

In American freight service the preference is for 1,350 or 1,500 b.h.p. units, chiefly assembled in quadruplets of 5,400 or 6,000 b.h.p. A complete locomotive of this type, consisting of two "A" units, each with a driving cab at the outer end, and two "B" or trailer units marshalled between them and without driving controls, is about 195 ft. in length and weighs over 400 tons. At any time, of course, to meet traffic requirements, it can be split into two independent locomotives of 2,700 or 3,000 b.h.p., each consisting of one "A" driving and one "B" trailer unit. The principal difference between the passenger and the freight diesels is that the former are geared for higher speeds, at the expense of tractive effort. Here also, as with straight electric locomotives, is an advantage of diesel-electric traction, for one single design can be adapted for either duty merely by an appropriate change in the gear ratio used.

Where the freight diesels have to work over long and continuous gradients in mountain country, considerable wear-and-tear of brake gear is involved in holding the trains on the falling gradients; it may be necessary, indeed, to schedule lengthy stops to allow overheated tyres and brake-shoes to cool off. But the direct-current traction motors of diesel-electric locomotives make it possible to utilise the regenerative principle, already described in the chapter on electric traction, to reverse the action of the motors so that they act as generators, and the magnetic influence thus created causes a "drag" or resistance which is equivalent to strong braking action at the head of the train.

With the diesels it is calculated that by this means 10 per cent. only of the normal braking is required when the dynamic braking is in use. The braking effect increases with speed, and diminishes as speed is reduced; it is not very effective at speeds below 10 m.p.h., and the air-brakes must be brought into use to stop the train. As distinct from dynamic braking on electrically-operated routes, it is not possible to feed the current so generated back into electric conductors, and it is therefore dissipated in the form of heat through heavy resistors, or grids, in the engine-room roofs.

The modern diesel-electric locomotive is of great complexity, and it would be impossible in the limited space available to go fully into its design and construction. Briefly, in the diesel engine cylinder a charge of air is compressed to a high pressure, and this has the effect at the same time of raising the temperature to such a degree that when the fuel oil is sprayed into the highly heated compressed air, combustion takes place immediately. Because the fuel is thus burned in the engine cylinders, a larger proportion of the heat units produced by combustion is available for useful work than in other types of internal combustion engine; in this respect, of course, the overall thermal efficiency of the diesel engine is far greater than that of a steam locomotive.

On the other hand, whereas a steam locomotive is able to start directly the steam is admitted to the cylinders, this is not the case with a diesel. The diesel engine has first to be started up by some external agency, ranging from manual starting, with a small engine, to compressed air or, in the large locomotives, electric battery power. Further, the diesel engine must run at a certain minimum speed—revolutions per minute—before it is able to produce useful work. This is why, as indicated in the opening paragraphs of this chapter, some intermediary is desirable, between the diesel engine and the driving wheels, so that the diesel engine revolutions may be maintained independent of the speed of the locomotive as a whole.

Direct mechanical transmission through change-speed gearing is applicable only to small-powered locomotives, and is not of much use in shunting because of the frequency of the gear changes needed. Hydraulic transmission has the advantage of smooth working; the principle is that of supplying oil under pressure, which can be varied by the driver to meet every running condition, from an engine-driven pump to hydraulic motors coupled to the driving wheels. But electrical transmission, though it adds considerably to the cost of building the locomotive, is by far the most flexible and popular method.

In a four-stroke diesel engine, the first or compression stroke compresses the air to a pressure of, perhaps, 500 lb. per sq. in.; just before the end of this stroke the oil fuel is injected in the form of a fine spray, and with the compressed air at a temperature of 1,500 to 1,800° F. ignites immediately. Burning with the oxygen from the air, the violent combustion causes the pressure in the cylinder to increase to between 700 and 800 lb. per sq. in., and forces the piston outwards. The next return stroke of the piston is used for "scavenging," or driving the spent gases out through the exhaust port. At the top of the stroke, the exhaust port closes and the inlet valve opens, admitting air in readiness for compression at the beginning of the next cycle.

Supercharging is applied to most modern diesel engines used in locomotives. This is an increase in the pressure of the air supplied to the cylinders for combustion purposes, and is obtained by various means. In the latest and most efficient system, known as turbo-supercharging, the exhaust gases from the engine are used to work a gas turbine, which in turn drives an air-compressor, and raises the atmosphere pressure by 17 to 22 lb. per sq. in. at the inlet manifold. The compressed air thus introduced into the cylinders provides for increased fuel consumption, and in this way the output of a diesel engine can be boosted by as much as 50 per cent.

Valves, worked off the main crankshaft, attend to the opening and closing of each port at exactly the right moment in the four-stroke cycle of compression, combustion, exhaust or scavenging, and air admission. Most of the sets of engines in a diesel railway unit have six to twelve cylinders, with the angles of their cranks so disposed along the main crankshaft as to divide up the circle into a corresponding number of parts, and thus to give an even torque.

There are also two-stroke diesel engines in railway use; one stroke provides for compression, and the other for combustion and expansion. Near the bottom of the latter stroke, the piston uncovers an exhaust port or ports in the cylinder wall, and so releases the spent gases. At a lower level still the piston uncovers the air inlet port or ports, and allows a charge of air to be forced into the cylinder under pressure. In its upward movement, the piston covers both air inlet and exhaust ports, and then compresses the air charge to the same degree as in the four-stroke cycle engine. Near the top of the stroke fuel injection takes place, followed by the usual combustion and expansion. In this type of engine, an air compressor is used to force the required air into the cylinder; this is done in greater quantity than is needed to fill the cylinder, so that the surplus may be used to assist in forcing the spent gases through the exhaust port before the latter is covered by the rising piston.

This method also helps to keep the cylinder temperatures within reasonable limits, for combustion is taking place on every return stroke, instead of on every second return stroke as in the four-stroke engine. To counteract the tendency of the cylinder walls to over-heat it is necessary to provide a water-cooling system, in which the water itself is cooled by means of air drawn in from the outside atmosphere. On the large modern diesels used in main-line service, the air supply for cooling is controlled by fans and movable shutters according to the degree of cooling required. Another elaborate cooling circuit is needed for the lubricating oil, and others for the air ventilation of generators and traction motors. Filters are needed both for the air, the fuel, and the lubricating oil, to prevent unnecessary wear of cylinder liners and pistons.

While the power strokes of a two-stroke diesel engine double those of a four-stroke engine, the power developed in the cylinders does not increase in the same proportion, for the former is less efficient in action. For this reason some manufacturers have developed double-acting diesel engines, both two-stroke and four-stroke, in which event the cylinders require covers both at the top and bottom, and the same combustion cycle is gone through both above and below the piston.

A further development of the same idea is the opposed-piston diesel engine. In this type, each cylinder is double the normal length and contains two pistons, working outwards from the centre of the cylinder; two crankshafts are needed, above and below the engine block, geared together to move in unison, or some yoke arrangement connecting each pair of pistons. Fuel injection takes place between the pistons, when they are at the inner end of their stroke, and the combustion drives both outwards; near the end of its stroke one of the pistons first uncovers the exhaust port, allowing the burnt gases to escape, and the other then uncovers the air inlet port. Scavenging action takes place until the former piston moves up and closes the exhaust port again, and after the second piston has closed the air inlet port compression follows as the two pistons move towards one another. The opposed-piston system, which has been largely used in marine work, is now being applied by the American firm of Fairbanks-Morse to diesel-electric locomotives.

Until now, the use of diesel power on British railways has been on a limited scale only, and with units of low power. The only serious passenger application until 1947 was in the railcars of the late Great Western Railway, all of the diesel-mechanical type. These cars have single-acting four-stroke six-cylinder diesel engines, with pre-selector gear-boxes and fluid flywheel transmissions. There are also two twin-car units for express passenger work, with a combined horse-power of 420 and capable of maximum speeds up to 75 m.p.h.

Shunting diesels in Great Britain began with diesel-mechanical types, but those now being built are all diesel-electric locomotives, of about 350 b.h.p. each, and with the 0-6-0 wheel arrangement. In the earlier examples, a single traction motor drove a jack-shaft which worked the end pair of coupled wheels by means of a diagonal con-necting-rod; but in the later locomotives, each of the end axles has its own axle-hung traction motor. Again the diesel engines are of the four-stroke single-acting type, with six cylinders. By far the most extensive building in Great Britain of diesel shunters has been by the late L.M.S.R., which has built over 80 of these locomotives. Each of the latest Western Region shunting diesels weighs 54 tons and has a tractive effort of 33,500 lb., sufficient to move a maximum of 90 loaded four-wheel wagons.

Hitherto, main line diesel development in Great Britain has not been favoured, because of the determination of British railways to use British coal, rather than imported fuel, as the basis of their motive power. During and since the Second World War, however, the diminishing quantity and declining quality of British coal, as well as its very considerable increase in price, have compelled a change of attitude. Before being merged into the national system, the Southern Railway was seriously considering a complete change-over from steam to diesel-electric locomotives on those sections of its line not electrically worked, as is now happening on certain of the American lines already mentioned. In December, 1947, the L.M.S.R. introduced its first diesel-electric express passenger unit of 1,600 b.h.p., and shortly afterwards the second appeared, making possible the experimental use of a twin-unit locomotive of 3,200 b.h.p. on the heavy express trains between Euston and Glasgow. But any large-scale change-over in this country inevitably must be gradual.

It may be noted here that the highest rail speed on record, 143 m.p.h., was achieved in 1931 by a coach powered by an internal combustion engine. The German Krückenburg car concerned was a freak vehicle, 95 ft. in length, carried on two axles 65 ft. 7 in. apart, and equipped with steering gear for the sharper curves. It was driven by a 12-cylinder petrol engine developing 600 b.h.p. at 1,600 revolutions per minute, and propelled by a two-bladed airscrew of 9 ft. 2 in. diameter. The weight of the car was $17\frac{1}{4}$ tons only, and it could accelerate to 62 m.p.h. in $\frac{5}{8}$-mile from a dead start. The 143 m.p.h. speed was reached on level track and maintained for $6\frac{1}{4}$ miles. Later the airscrew propulsion was abandoned, and the petrol engine replaced by a diesel engine, with hydraulic transmission, increasing the car weight to 28 tons.

In 1935 a three-car articulated unit was built on the same Krückenberg principle, again with Maybach diesel engines (of 1,200 b.h.p. in all) and hydraulic transmisssion; it contained seats for 100 passengers, lavatories and a small kitchen within the compass of a total length of 229 ft. 8 in. and a weight of $123\frac{1}{2}$ tons. With this unit a maximum speed of $133\frac{1}{2}$ m.p.h. was reached, and a rate of 125 m.p.h. was maintained for some distance on the level, though no details are available as to the running times. So far as authentic records are available, these maxima of 143 and $133\frac{1}{2}$ m.p.h. are the highest that have yet been reached on rails, with any description of motive power.

Reverting to the comparisons previously made between the efficiency of diesel-electric and steam propulsion, in defence of the steam loco-motive it must be admitted that a large part of the economy shown by diesel operation, even allowing for the higher initial cost of diesel power, has been due to the specialised methods of maintenance enjoyed by the diesels. In the United States, also, special duties have been selected for the latter which have enabled their capacity for continuous running to be put to the best advantage; special depots have been built and laid out for diesel maintenance, on the most modern and approved lines; and the systematic replacement of parts, after so many miles of running or so many round trips have been completed, whether the parts removed for reconditioning are badly worn or not, also has been a major factor in assuring the continuous availability which is the principal diesel asset. As yet the steam locomotive has never enjoyed all these advantages.

Moreover, with steam power, it has been necessary to have locomotives ready to hand for all duties, including both the duties which need continuous steaming and those which involve a good deal of stand-by time; also, as wholesale scrapping of the older locomotives on financial grounds would be impossible, steam power up to 30 or 40 years of age is still in service, whereas most of the diesels have been built within the last 10 or 15 years. It will be very interesting to compare overall costs, as between steam and diesel-electric, when the lines which are making a complete change from steam to diesel power have had, say, 10 years' experience of the new conditions. But by then, of course, it is quite possible that some new prime mover, such as the gas turbine, will have been perfected sufficiently to challenge the supremacy of the diesel-electric, the electric, and the steam locomotives alike.

21

SPEED—THE ART OF TRAIN TIMING

SINCE the present century began, a considerable amount of interest has developed in the performance of locomotives on the road. In earlier years occasional articles on the subject, giving details of the times and speeds which had been noted by competent observers on specific runs behind various locomotives, had appeared in *The Engineer* and other journals, but it was not until September, 1901, that regular attention became concentrated on the subject by a monthly article in *The Railway Magazine* entitled "British Locomotive Practice and Performance." This was conducted at first by the late Charles Rous-Marten, later by Mr. R. E. Charlewood and others, and from August, 1909, it has been continued without a break by the present writer, who passed his 400th "milepost" in the May, 1945, issue.

During these years there has come into being a *coterie* of amateurs well qualified to compile detailed "logs" of locomotive running, and to compare the work of different locomotives, types of engine and engine-crews, over various routes. The effects of modifications of design, embodied in new and rebuilt classes, may be traced in improvements in the quality of their work, at times quite revolutionary in character. It must be confessed that to the experienced observer few moments are more exciting than those in which all his previous records over a given route are going by the board in some outstanding locomotive performance with an enterprising engine-crew on the footplate. On the other hand, most locomotive classes have their "black sheep," which for some reason or reasons often unexplained resolutely refuse to steam as they should. Temperamental differences between drivers, resulting in differences in the way in which they handle their engines, also become apparent as the work of their charges is set on record.

The observer in the train, it is true, can never be fully conversant with all that is happening on the footplate. It is easy to attribute poor times and speeds to unenterprising driving, when actually bad coal may be the cause of the trouble. Or the engine itself may be running in a defective condition, with leaky or dirty tubes that hamper steaming, or a fallen brick arch, or some other handicap. But the observant amateur who has fairly frequent opportunities for travel will find ceaseless interest in the recording and tabulation of locomotive performance. As indicated in the last paragraph but one, it is in the breaking of records that the greatest thrills are experienced; and these include occasions on which, as described in Chapters 11 and 13, the earlier and smaller locomotives display prodigies of hauling power or speed never even suspected in their heyday. Should the observer add to his opportunities an enjoyment of the coveted and jealously-guarded privilege of travelling with the engine-crew on the footplate, then a world of additional interest is added to his record, by first-hand observation of the way in which the engine is handled.

For an intelligent study of locomotive performance the recorder needs certain equipment. This should include a reliable watch, preferably a pocket-watch, because of its larger dial, with a second-hand, for reading starting, stopping and passing times; and also a stop-watch, reading to one-fifths of a second, for the accurate record of maximum and minimum speeds. The latter should be provided with fly-back action, so that its long second-hand may be reset to zero directly a reading has been taken. The main watch and the stop-watch may be combined, of course, in a chronograph watch, in which a stop-watch second-hand, with independent starting, stopping and fly-back action, and its own minute recorder, are incorporated.

A better though more expensive stop-watch investment is a split-second stop-watch, which has two long second-hands. When the watch is started, the two hands move in unison; by a control separate from the usual pressure on the winding-head of the watch one of the two hands can be stopped at will, while the other continues to rotate. By a second pressure on the independent control, after the reading has been taken, the former hand flies round to catch up the rotating hand, and continues with it. A second pressure on the winding-head stops both hands, and an additional press causes both to fly back to zero. The advantage of such a watch is that it can be started at the moment the train starts from rest, and a continuous series of readings can be taken—as, for example, up or down a long incline—to fifths of a second if desired, without stopping the watch.

For myself, I normally carry a Venner type "C34" split-second stop-watch and a Swiss "Omega" chronograph, which has been in continuous use for more than 40 years and has travelled not far short of 2,000,000 miles—a notable tribute to Swiss watchmaking. At the beginning of the run I start the Venner, checking the exact time from the hour, minute and small second-hand of the Omega. Passing-times at stations and elsewhere are then all read from the large dial and the minute-recorder of the Venner.

If continuous recording of speeds is desirable, as, for example, up a long and severe incline, I do this by splitting off the additional second-hand of the Venner at, say, every half-mile, or, in special cases, every quarter-mile.   All the isolated readings of maximum and minimum speeds, however, are made with the help of the long stop-watch second-hand of the Omega.   At the moment of coming to rest at the end of the run, both hands of the Venner are stopped by means of the winding-head, and the overall reading is compared with the time in hours, minutes and seconds of the main Omega watch, so that in this way the two are used to check one another.

In addition, I have a Venner "F.60" stop-watch with fly-back action and a larger dial reading to one-tenths of a second, but this actually proves to have a finer measure of accuracy than that of the eye in picking up the mileposts; in general, one-fifth of a second readings are sufficiently accurate for all practical purposes.   It is of interest that the Venner watches also are of Swiss manufacture.   I might add that recently I have acquired a Swiss Longines wrist-watch, which has a particularly clear dial of $1\frac{1}{8}$ in. diameter and a long second-hand; this is more convenient to use than the large Omega, and, I think, is likely to prove as accurate.

When recording speeds, several alternative methods can be used. Every British railway is marked out throughout its length with mileposts, or distance-posts, as perhaps they should be called, for they include the quarter-, half-, and three-quarter miles as well as the full miles.   The design of the mileposts and their position relatively to the track varies considerably according to the practice of the individual railway companies before they were grouped together in 1923, and in general the old types of post, and their location on the up or down sides of the track, have remained unaltered.   The location of mileposts over the principal British main lines, with the zero points from which they are measured, is shown in Table 80 (p. 254).   On the mainland of Europe railway distances are marked out with even greater profuseness by distance-posts in kilometres and tenths.

The difficulty of picking up mileposts for speed estimation purposes varies with their position relatively to the train.   On some routes the posts are small in size and are set fairly near to the track, which makes it by no means easy to catch them when they are on the same side of the line as the recorder's coach, and the train is travelling fast.   On the other hand, it may be necessary to "clock" the posts across the full width of four tracks, in which event any variation in the angle of the recorder's vision may have a considerable influence on the accuracy of his readings.   At a speed of, say, 90 m.p.h., an error of no more than two-fifths of a second in a reading over a quarter of a mile will raise or depress the speed by as much as $3\frac{1}{2}$ m.p.h.   In all milepost reading from a train, the edge of a window-frame should be used as the basis of the observation, and the eye should read at as unvarying an angle as possible.

In the crowded conditions of modern travel, however, it is often the case that the observer cannot command a seat on the milepost side of the train, and has no desire to stand continuously in the corridor if the posts are on the corridor side. In such circumstances there is a ready method of acoustic speed reading, with the help of the rails over which the train is travelling. The most characteristic accompaniment of every railway journey is the rhythmic sound made by the wheels in passing over the rail-joints. Steel rails are cut to very exact lengths,

TABLE 80

LOCATION OF MILEPOSTS

Region		Division or Section	Side of Line	Zero Point	Notes
London Midland	..	Western Division	Down	Euston	A
" ..	..	Midland Division ..	Up	St. Pancras	—
Eastern ..	..	Great Northern Section	Down	King's Cross	—
" ..	..	Great Central Section ..	Up	Manchester London Road ..	B
" ..	..	Great Eastern Section ..	Down	Liverpool Street	—
North Eastern ..	..	Doncaster-York	"	King's Cross	—
" ..	..	York-Newcastle ..	"	York	—
" ..	..	Newcastle-Berwick ..	"	Newcastle	—
Scottish ..	..	Berwick-Edinburgh ..	Up	Edinburgh Waverley ..	C
" ..	..	Edinburgh-Dundee-Montrose ..	Down	" " ..	—
" ..	..	Carlisle-Edinburgh ..	Up	" " ..	C
" ..	..	Carlisle-Glasgow-Aberdeen ..	Down	Carlisle	—
Western ..	..	All main lines	Up	Paddington	D
Southern ..	..	Western Section.. ..	Down	Waterloo	E
" ..	..	Central Section	"	London Bridge	—
" ..	..	Eastern Section (ex-S.E. & C.) ..	"	Charing Cross..	—
" ..	..	" " (ex-L.C. & D.) ..	"	Victoria..	—

Notes: **A**—North of Warrington, on the Euston-Carlisle main line, new series of mileposts begin at Golborne Junction, Preston and Lancaster respectively, as shown on gradient profiles, pp. 265-266. **B**—From Harrow to Quinton Road Junction, down side, from zero at Baker Street; from Northolt Junction to Ashendon Junction, up side, from zero at Northolt Junction. **C**—Up side relatively to London. **D**—From Paddington to Penzance the mileposts are routed *via* Bristol, and are carried into and out of Plymouth Millbay Station. On the Westbury line, from Westbury to Castle Cary the mileposts are routed from Paddington *via* Swindon and Trowbridge. On the South Wales main line, from Severn Tunnel Junction onwards the mileposts are routed from Paddington *via* Gloucester. On the Birmingham main line a new series of mileposts begins from zero at Northolt Junction, and another from zero at Ashendon Junction; from Aynho Junction the routing is from zero at Paddington *via* Oxford. **E**—Due to inaccuracy in the original chainages, on the Waterloo-Plymouth main line the mileposts west of Salisbury are uniformly ¼-mile short of the actual distance from Waterloo.

and where these lengths are the normal British standard of 60 ft., a total of 22 lengths makes exactly one-quarter of a mile. If the stop-watch be started with the "click" of any rail-joint of 60 ft. track, there-fore, and stopped 22 rail-joints later, a timing has been obtained over a quarter of a mile precisely. In using this method, the recorder must be careful to begin his count of the 22 joints at zero and not at 1.

Unfortunately not all lines are laid with 60 ft. rails, and observers who use the rail-joint method of timing must learn to distinguish between rails of 60 ft., 45 ft. (29 lengths to the quarter-mile), 39 ft. (the standard American rail-length, of which 140,000 tons were supplied to Great Britain during the Second World War), 78 ft. and 117 ft. (into which many of the American rails have been welded), and other variations dating from earlier years. Acuteness of hearing is needed, especially in well-built modern rolling stock riding over well-maintained track.

There are further complications in passing through stations and junctions, over the variety of rail-lengths laid in switch and crossing work. Coaches of varied lengths, and with varying lengths of wheel-base, also can be deceptive in their rhythms to all but the most seasoned travellers. As in so many other realms, practice alone can make perfect; but when the science of rail-joint timing has been mastered, it is as accurate a method of speed estimation as could be devised, and the great majority of my own speed readings are made in this way. Incidentally, the use of telegraph posts for speed-recording purposes cannot be relied on for accuracy, and should be avoided.

The next matter of importance is to obtain accurate mileages of the stations and other important timing points along the routes over which the recorder is travelling. This is not an easy matter. Distances in miles and chains have been given in the working timetables of the late London & North Eastern, Great Western and Southern Railways, but these staff compilations are not issued to the public; occasionally it is possible to pick up used copies which give the desired information, even if the train-times in them be out of date. Accurate mileages also have been given in the Railway Clearing House maps, but these are expensive productions.

During the years 1929 and 1930 *The Railway Magazine* printed a series of gradient profiles of all the British main and subsidiary lines over which express trains normally work, with complete sets of distances in miles and tenths compiled by the present writer; but although the profiles were reprinted in book form as *The Railway Magazine Gradients of British Main Line Railways*, the mileage tables were not. Many of the distances appear in the tables of runs which are set out in Chapters 11 to 16 inclusive, and others can be collected from time to time from the logs of locomotive performances over different routes printed in my "British Locomotive Practice and Performance" articles in *The Railway Magazine*. Or the traveller over any given route, by careful calculation from mileposts and rail-lengths, can compile his own mileages, though this is a laborious method of acquiring the desired information. *Bradshaw's Guide* and the regional public timebooks, which are printed by the same publisher, give distances along each route in miles and quarters, though the accuracy of these figures at times leaves something to be desired.

It may be added that some meticulously careful recorders prefer to confine their passing-times to mileposts exclusively, using for this purpose the post which is nearest to the centre of each station at which passing times are taken. But this method requires a minutely particular knowledge of the location of the posts, which in large stations and yards may be planted in unlikely spots, and therefore difficult to discover. Moreover, after dark such a method of recording is out of the question, save to the most expert. For myself, I prefer to time as nearly as possible to the centre of stations, and to use mileages to the nearest one-tenth of a mile; to my mind, this method is one of all reasonable accuracy, and in conjunction with rail-joint speed estimation, provides for train timing both by day and by night.

There is next the matter of gradients. As previously mentioned, so far as Great Britain is concerned, a collection of these has been published in book form, or those with access to a bound file of *The Railway Magazine* can find the same series running through the years 1929 and 1930. On pp. 264-294 profiles are included of all routes over which the runs described in Chapters 11 to 16 inclusive were made. It would be almost impossible for the amateur to obtain the official profiles of the various railways, which are large-scale compilations, in most cases covering a very large number of sheets. However, as with the distance-posts, so the railways provide gradient posts which mark the beginning and end of each variation in the gradient; and intelligent observation of gradient-posts affords a considerable amount of information. Indeed, after a number of trips have been made over a route on which the changes of gradient are not too frequent, it is a simple matter to compile one's own profile with a fair measure of accuracy.

The importance of the gradients, of course, is that in large measure they govern the speeds attained on any given run. Minimum speeds at the summit of every rising gradient, and maxima at the foot of all descents, are essential to every complete log; the speed of beginning a rising gradient should be noted, and also, if the rate of fall flattens out to a sustained speed on the upper part of a bank, what the latter speed is, as from the maintained speed on an evenly rising gradient it is possible to calculate with fair accuracy the horsepower that is developed by the locomotive in climbing. The keen observer can usually detect the point on a long rise at which the driver lengthens the cut-off of his engine, or opens his regulator wider; a sudden fall in speed near the summit of an incline may indicate that the driver has "notched up" a little prematurely. Speeds on level track also need to be noted; here again the figures obtained provide a means for fairly accurate calculation of the horsepower developed.

A formula which is in common use for the calculation of the resistance of a passenger train to motion on a level track is that evolved some years ago by Dr. F. H. Johansen. In this formula, resistance in lb. per ton of train weight equals:—

$$4+0.025V+0.00166V^2$$

where V is the velocity of the train in miles per hour. The result, multiplied by the weight of the train in tons and divided by 2,240, gives the resistance in tons, which should equal the pull of the locomotive on the tender drawbar, granted reasonably straight track and an absence of any severe cross-wind.

To translate the pull into terms of horsepower, which is a rate of doing work (550 ft.-lb. per second), we need to use the formula:—

$$\frac{P \times 2240 \times S}{550}$$

where P is the pull in tons, and S the speed in feet per second. In order to assist the reader to avoid the lengthy calculations so involved. I have prepared the curve reproduced in Fig. 7 (p. 258). All that is necessary is to scale off the vertical ordinate at the appropriate speed of the train on the level, and to multiply the figure so obtained by the weight of the train (coaches, passengers and luggage) in tons, to secure the approximate *drawbar* horsepower.

If the train is travelling uphill, the locomotive must also overcome the pull of gravity. The added pull in tons due to the gravity component is simply the weight of the train in tons divided by the gradient—"100" for 1 in 100, "200" for 1 in 200, and so on. To transform this into horsepower requires the same formula as before:—

$$\frac{P \times 2240 \times S}{550}$$

In this case it is not possible to draw a curve comparable to the curve of resistance on the level, as there are three variables instead of two—inclination, speed and train weight.

A graph has been included on Fig. 7, however, of speed in terms of feet per second, multiplied by 2,240 and divided by 550; if the reader scales off this at the uphill speed of his train, multiplies by the train weight in tons (this time including engine and tender) and divides by the gradient, he will obtain the horsepower exerted in overcoming the pull of gravity. This must be added to the horsepower exerted in overcoming running resistance to obtain the total drawbar-horsepower put out by the locomotive. It should be emphasised that the speed must be steadily maintained on the gradient for these calculations to be

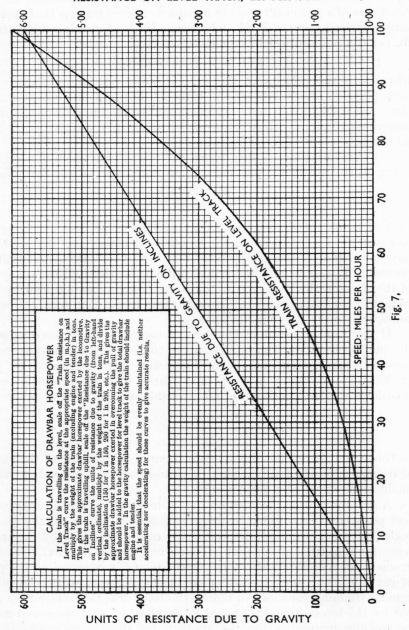

RESISTANCE ON LEVEL TRACK, LB. PER TON

TRAIN RESISTANCE ON LEVEL TRACK

RESISTANCE DUE TO GRAVITY ON INCLINES

SPEED: MILES PER HOUR

Fig. 7,

UNITS OF RESISTANCE DUE TO GRAVITY

CALCULATION OF DRAWBAR HORSEPOWER

If the train is travelling on the level, scale off the "Train Resistance on Level Track" curve the resistance at the appropriate speed (in m.p.h.) and multiply by the weight of the train (excluding engine and tender) in tons. This gives the approximate drawbar horsepower exerted by the locomotive.

If the train is travelling uphill, scale off the "Resistance due to Gravity on Inclines" curve the units of resistance due to gravity (from left-hand vertical ordinate), multiply by the weight of the train in tons, and divide by the inclination (150 for 1 in 150, 200 for 1 in 200, etc.). This gives the approximate drawbar horsepower exerted in overcoming the pull of gravity and should be added to the horsepower for level track to give the total drawbar horsepower. In the gravity calculation the weight of the train should include engine and tender.

It is essential that the speed should be evenly maintained (i.e. neither accelerating nor decelerating) for these curves to give accurate results.

even approximately correct; if a speed is used which is still falling when the top of the bank is reached, the horsepower calculated from it will be too high.

The calculation of the approximate *indicated* horsepower—the total power output of the locomotive—is less easy, because the internal resistance of the locomotive itself cannot be assessed accurately by formula, although the resistance due to gravity can be calculated in exactly the same way for the locomotive as for the train.

In connection with the gradients, many of the "key" points on a route, from the locomotive performance point of view, are at locations remote from stations. For example, Stoke summit, the highest point on the Eastern Region main line between London and York, is marked only by a signal-box 100·1 miles from King's Cross. Sharnbrook summit, on the Midland main line of the London Midland Region between St. Pancras and Leicester, though dignified with passing times for all express trains, is neither a station nor a box, but merely "Milepost 59¾." Shap and Beattock summits on the late L.M.S.R. main line from Euston to Glasgow, timetable passing points for all trains in each direction, also are signal-boxes and not stations, and should on no account be missed when trains are being timed. Indeed, the passing times at such summits are often of greater importance topographically than those at the nearest stations.

Preparation for the compilation of a log of locomotive performance therefore begins with setting down, in a vertical column, a list of the stations on the route, and of other important points—junctions which are not also stations, signal-boxes dividing up lengthy mileages between stations, mileposts or signal-boxes marking summits, and so on—at which it is intended to take times. To the left of the station column should be the mileages, and to the right of it the schedule of the train which is to be timed. In this matter, of course, access to the working timetables, if this is possible, is of the greatest value, not only because the times to which trains actually are worked may differ from those advertised to the general public, but also because the working books, in addition to giving all arrival and departure times, show passing times at certain junctions, stations, and summits at which trains are not booked to stop.

Two more columns are required on the right-hand side of the record, one for the actual times and the other for the maximum and minimum speed readings. Timings can be made in the rough, if desired, and then transferred later to a more permanent record, by those who have the time available. My own method has been to use notebooks in which one list of stations, on the left of the left-hand page, has served for a number of successive runs in parallel columns, and (by cutting off the margins of the pages) over a number of pages in succession, if the route has been one that I have been using frequently.

At some point on the run, either before starting, or at an intermediate stop at which sufficient time is available, or after arrival, it is necessary to obtain the weight of the train. At the end of every coach, on the left-hand side, generally near the waist-line at a convenient reading height, there is a small cast-iron plate on which the empty weight of the coach is shown in tons. Some railways give additional information, such as the length of the coach and the number of seats in each class; the late G.W.R. has given the weight only, but with two large figures in relief which are particularly easy to read. Addition of these weights gives the total empty or "tare" weight of the train. Any

TABLE 81

PRINCIPAL MAXIMUM SPEED RAILWAY RECORDS

Speed	Country	Railway	Propulsion	No. of Cars	Date	Notes
m.p.h.						
143	Germany	State	Petrol-airscrew	*1	June 21, 1931	Krückenburg experimental car
133½	,,	,,	Diesel-hydraulic	*3	June 23, 1939	,, ,, train
130	,,	,,	Electric	*1	1903	Siemens & Halske experimental car
126	Great Britain	L.N.E.R.	Steam 4-6-2	7	July 3, 1938	"Coronation" streamline train
126	Italy	State	Electric	*3	June 29, 1939	"Rapido" streamline set
125	,,	,,	,,	*3	July 27, 1938	,, ,, ,,
124½	Germany	,,	Steam 4-6-4	—	1935	
122	U.S.A.	Burlington	Diesel-electric	*3	1935	"Mark Twain Zephyr" train
120	,,	Milwaukee	Steam 4-6-4	—	1938	
120	,,	Union Pacific	Diesel-electric	*5	Oct. 25, 1934	"City of Portland" train
118	Germany	State	Steam 4-6-4	4	May 30, 1936	Inst. Loco. Engineers' Special
114	Great Britain	L.M.S.R.	,, 4-6-2	8	June 29, 1937	"Coronation Scot" streamline train
113	,,	L.N.E.R.	,, 4-6-2	8	August 7, 1936	"Silver Jubilee" ,, ,,
112½	,,	,,	,, 4-6-2	7	Sept. 27, 1935	,, ,, ,, ,,

* Power incorporated in train; no independent locomotive

variation of the train weight *en route,* by the addition or removal of coaches, or (on the Western Region) by reduction due to the slipping of coaches at speed, should be duly noted.

To the tare weight it is necessary to add the weight of passengers and luggage in order to arrive at the full or "gross" weight behind the engine tender. This is a matter of estimation, and needs a good deal of practice. During the war, when restaurant cars had been withdrawn, and both the seating and corridors of many trains were filled to capacity, the addition required for passengers and luggage was frequently as much as 12 to 15 per cent. of the tare weight of the stock, and occasionally even more. In normal conditions, however, it may be taken that a train with restaurant cars and normal luggage space, if practically all seats are occupied, has a gross weight about 10 per cent. more than the tare weight. For a moderately-filled corridor train an addition of

$7\frac{1}{2}$ per cent. should be sufficient, and for a lightly-loaded train 5 per cent. The customary calculation is based on an average estimate of 16 passengers to the ton, with a small addition for the weight of their luggage. With non-corridor stock seating five or six passengers a-side, the percentage addition for a full train may be 20 per cent. or even more.

With the train weight there must be entered the number and class of the locomotive; the name, if any, may be a useful entry also. The names of the driver and fireman, if these can be obtained, make possible interesting comparisons between the methods of working favoured by different men; and the name of the shed to which they are attached may prove a key to the driving traditions of one shed as

TABLE 82

PRINCIPAL SUSTAINED SPEED RAILWAY RECORDS

Average Speed	Distance	Between	Conditions	Country	Railway	Propulsion	Date
m.p.h.	miles						
107·5	25·0	Mileposts 30-55	pass-pass	Great Britain	L.N.E.R.	Steam 4-6-2	Sep. 27, 1935
104·9	47·8	‡Chicago-Milwaukee	pass-pass	U.S.A.	Milwaukee	„ 4-6-4	1942
102·6	24·0	Cassville-Crawford		„	Burlington	Diesel-electric	Daily schedule
102·0	195·8	Florence-Milan	start-stop	Italy	State	Electric	July 20, 1939
96·1	132·9	Rome-Naples	„	„	„	„	July 27, 1938
95·7	159·8	†Berlin-Hamburg	„	Germany	„	Petrol-airscrew	June 21, 1931
91·8	70·0	Wood Green-Fletton Junc.	pass-pass	Great Britain	L.N.E.R.	Steam 4-6-2	Sept. 27, 1935
91·6	444·8	Crete-Barr	„	U.S.A.	Burlington	Diesel-electric	Oct. 23, 1936
90·9	57·6	Tower A20-Lake	„	„	Milwaukee	Diesel and steam	Daily schedule
89·0	72·3	Welton-Kilburn	„	Great Britain	L.M.S.R.	Steam 4-6-2	June 29, 1937
87·5	70·0	Mileposts 72--2	„	„	G.W.R.	„ 4-6-0	June 6, 1932
86·7	70·1	Wittenberge-Spandau	start-stop	Germany	State	„ 4-6-4	May 30, 1936
85·3	27·0	Hitchin-Huntingdon	pass-pass	Great Britain	L.N.E.R.	„ 4-6-2	Daily schedule
84·0	54·6	E. Dubuque—Prairie du C.	start-stop	U.S.A.	Burlington	Diesel-electric	
83·3	*1,017·2	Chicago-Denver	„	„	„	„	Oct. 23, 1936
81·7	77·3	Swindon-Paddington	„	Great Britain	G.W.R.	Steam 4-6-0	June 6, 1932
79·7	158·1	Crewe-Euston	„	„	L.M.S.R.	„ 4-6-2	June 29, 1937

* Without intermediate stop   † Started and stopped outside city limits   ‡ Outside city limits

compared with another. It is better, however, that the observer should refrain from interviewing an engine-crew until the end of the run, as by such restraint he is likely to obtain the record of a performance uninfluenced by the spur of possible publicity or any other special incentive.

In the course of a run, reductions of speed are made for various reasons. Some are in conformity with permanent speed restrictions, imposed on account of curves, colliery subsidences, or at other locations where high speed is inadvisable. Others are temporary speed orders, due to the fact that the track or underline bridges are under repair, or because other works are in progress affecting track stability. Permanent-way checks should be noted as such, also signal checks and any other abnormal causes of lost time. It is customary to allow for these losses in order to arrive at a "net time" for the run, based on the probable times that would have been made had the run continued unchecked over the affected length. These allowances for checks should be made conservatively, as it is easy to exaggerate the possibilities of a run that has suffered from checks. Nevertheless the net times arrived at by an experienced recorder do accurately measure the power output of a locomotive, which has needed to develop additional power in recovering from the reduced speed called for by a speed restriction or compelled by adverse signals.

In Chapters 11 to 16 inclusive descriptions have been given of the most historic locomotive performances of the Twentieth Century, many of them compiled by myself. The "logs" reproduced show the practical application of the principles of recording locomotive performance that have been laid down in this chapter. Those who as yet have never set out in this way to study locomotive "form" will find this a most fascinating occupation on their journeys, as well as an instructive commentary on locomotive design and practice. Chapters 17 and 18 show that similar study of locomotive work is now well established both on the mainland of Europe and in the United States and Canada.

Tables 81 and 82 provide what may be regarded as a fitting conclusion to this book. Though I cannot claim that they provide an absolutely complete list, they summarise some of the most outstanding feats of speed that have been achieved on the world's railways up to the spring of 1947. They reveal, moreover, that there is but little difference between the highest speeds attainable with different kinds of motive power—133 m.p.h. with diesel-electric propulsion, and 126 m.p.h. with both electricity and steam—and rolling stock of normal design; that is to say, air resistance rather than motive power is the final limiting factor. When it comes to speed sustained over very long distances, however, diesel-electric propulsion has a substantial lead. Nevertheless all those who treasure in their hearts a genuine affection for the steam locomotive—and I am among their number—are glad that it is still able to put up so gallant a fight against its newer and more efficient competitors. Long may it continue so to do !

GRADIENT PROFILES

The gradient profiles in the succeeding pages are reproduced by courtesy of the Proprietors of *The Railway Magazine* from their book "Gradients of the British Main Line Railways." The routes selected are those referred to in Chapters 11 to 16 inclusive of this book. For gradients of other main lines, or of the branches indicated on the profiles by their respective sheet numbers, readers should consult the volume mentioned above.

INDEX OF PROFILES

For key to speed restriction signs, *see* p. 274.
For location of mileposts, *see* Table 80, p. 254.

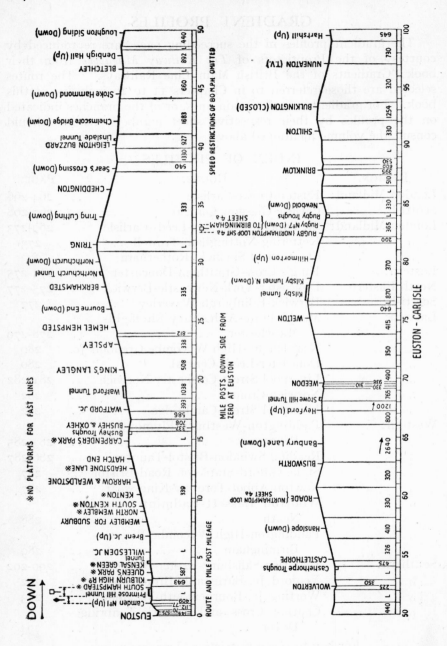

GRADIENT PROFILES

EUSTON - CARLISLE

SPEED RESTRICTIONS OF 80 M.P.H. OMITTED

MILE POSTS DOWN SIDE FROM ZERO AT EUSTON

ROUTE AND MILE POST MILEAGE

*NO PLATFORMS FOR FAST LINES

DOWN

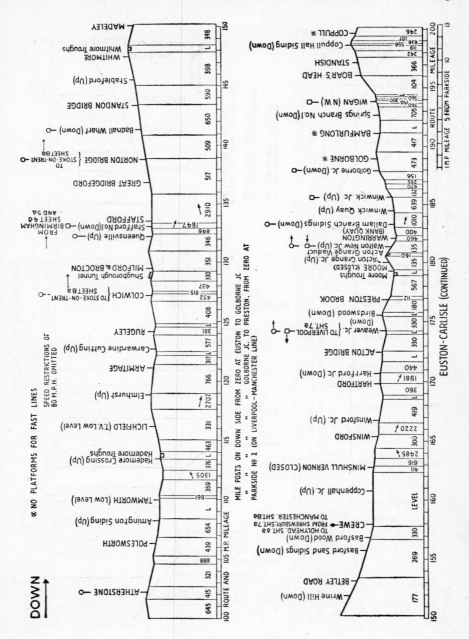

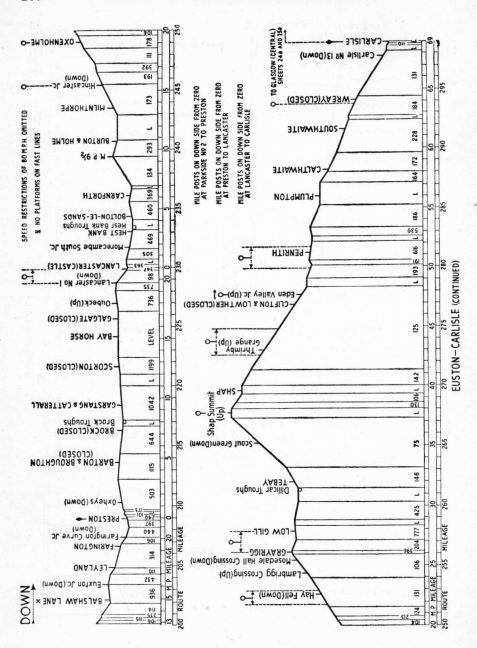

EUSTON—CARLISLE (CONTINUED)

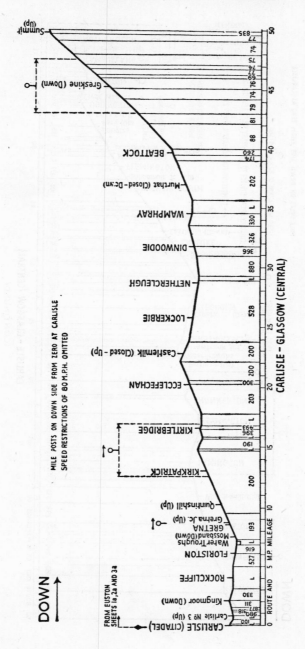

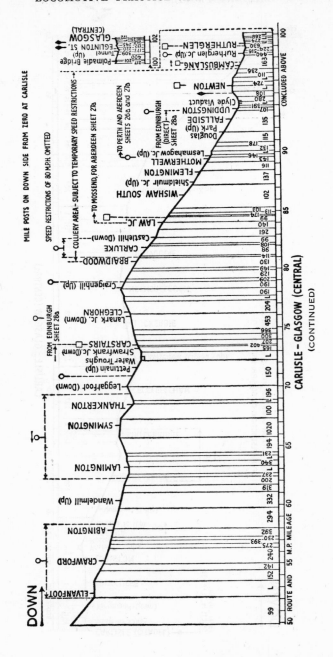

MILE POSTS ON DOWN SIDE FROM ZERO AT CARLISLE

SPEED RESTRICTIONS OF 80 M.P.H. OMITTED

COLLIERY AREA - SUBJECT TO TEMPORARY SPEED RESTRICTIONS

FOR ABERDEEN SHEET 27a

TO PERTH AND ABERDEEN SHEETS 26 and 27

FROM EDINBURGH SHEET 26a

FROM EDINBURGH SHEET 28a

CARLISLE - GLASGOW (CENTRAL)
(CONTINUED)

DOWN

ELVANFOOT

CRAWFORD

ABINGTON

Wandelmill (Up)

LAMINGTON

SYMINGTON

THANKERTON

Leggatfoot (Down)

Pettinain (Up)
Water Troughs
Strawfrank Jc.(Down)
CARSTAIRS
Lanark Jc. (Down)
CLEGHORN

Craigenhill (Up)

BRAIDWOOD

CARLUKE
(Castlehill (Down))

LAW JC.

WISHAW SOUTH

Shieldmuir Jc. (Up)
FLEMINGTON
MOTHERWELL
Lesmahagow Jc. (Up)
Douglas Park (Up)
FALLSIDE
UDDINGSTON
(DIRECT)
Clyde Viaduct
NEWTON

CAMBUSLANG
Rutherglen Jc.(Up)
RUTHERGLEN

Polmadie Bridge
Tunnel (Up)
EGLINTON ST.
GLASGOW
(CENTRAL)

M.P. MILEAGE
ROUTE AND 55 M.P. MILEAGE

CONCLUDED ABOVE

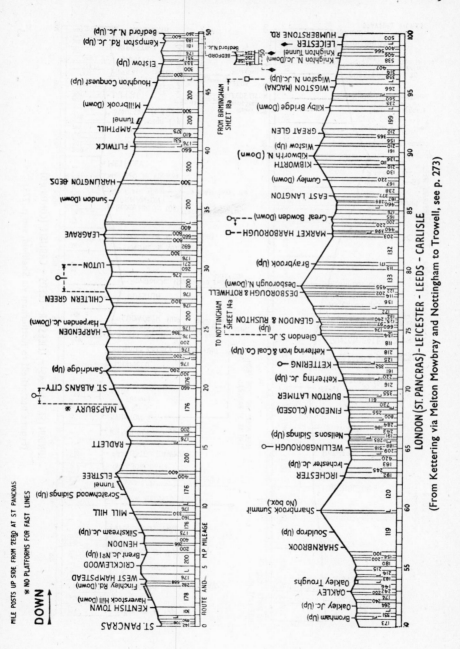

LONDON (ST. PANCRAS)-LEICESTER-LEEDS-CARLISLE

(From Kettering via Melton Mowbray and Nottingham to Trowell, see p. 273)

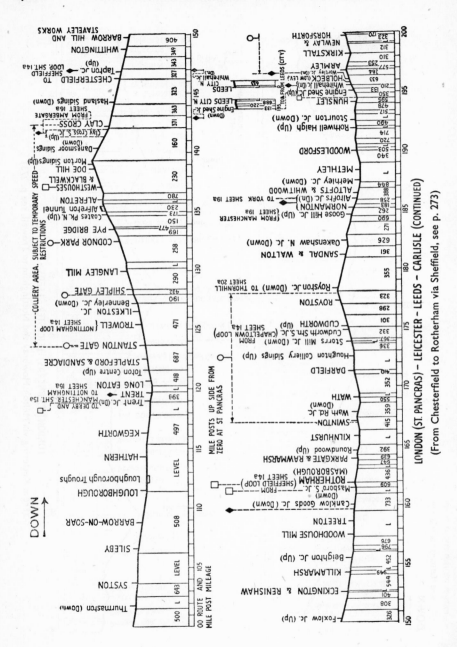

LONDON (ST. PANCRAS) – LEICESTER – LEEDS – CARLISLE (CONTINUED)

(From Chesterfield to Rotherham via Sheffield, see p. 273)

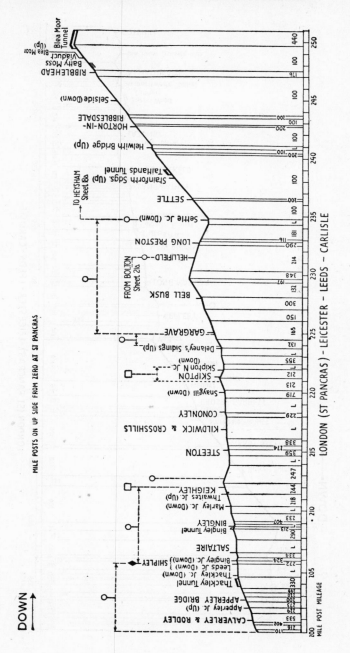

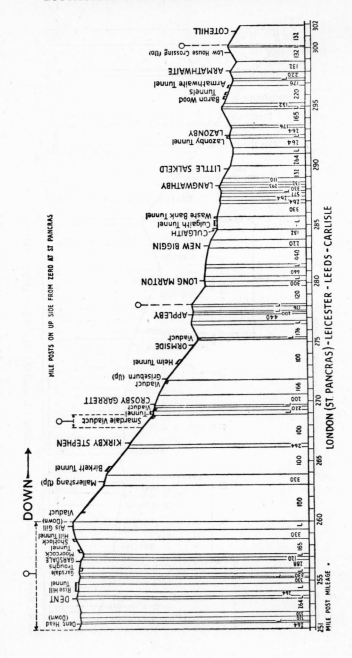

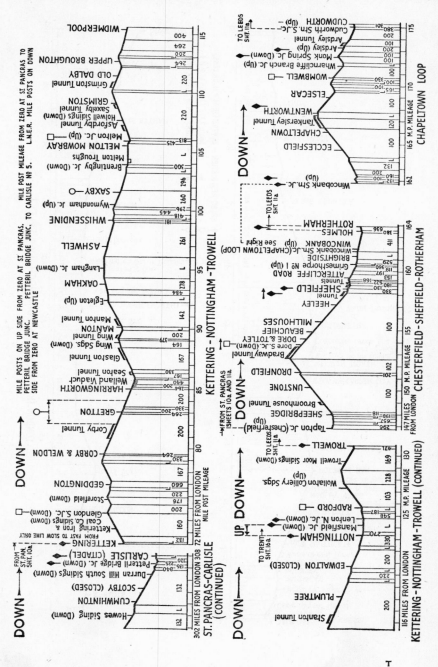

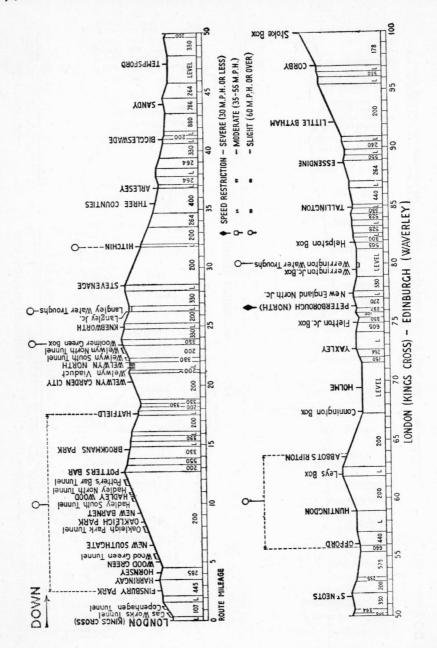

SPEED RESTRICTION — SEVERE (30 M.P.H. OR LESS)
— MODERATE (35-55 M.P.H.)
— SLIGHT (60 M.P.H. OR OVER)

LONDON (KINGS CROSS) – EDINBURGH (WAVERLEY)

DOWN

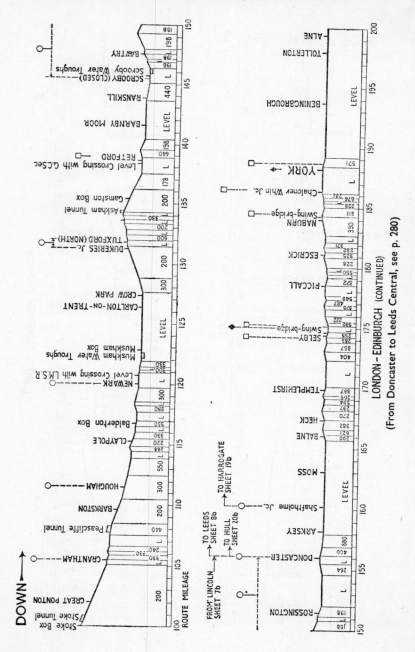

DOWN

ROUTE MILEAGE

Stoke Box
Stoke Tunnel
GREAT PONTON

GRANTHAM

Peascliffe Tunnel
BARKSTON

HOUGHAM

CLAYPOLE
Balderton Box

NEWARK
Level Crossing with L.M.S.R
Muskham Water Troughs
Muskham Box

CARLTON-on-TRENT
CROW PARK

DUKERIES Jc.
TUXFORD (NORTH)

Askham Tunnel
Gamston Box

Level Crossing with G.C.Sec.
RETFORD

BARNBY MOOR
RANSKILL

SCROOBY (CLOSED)
Scrooby Water Troughs

BAWTRY

FROM LINCOLN
SHEET 7b

TO LEEDS
SHEET 8b

TO HULL
SHEET 20b

TO HARROGATE
SHEET 19b

LONDON – EDINBURGH (CONTINUED)

(From Doncaster to Leeds Central, see p. 280)

ROSSINGTON

DONCASTER

ARKSEY

MOSS

Shaftholme Jc.

BALNE
HECK

TEMPLEHIRST

SELBY
Swing-bridge

PICCALL

ESCRICK

NABURN
Swing-bridge
Chaloner Whin Jc.

YORK

BENINGBROUGH

TOLLERTON
ALNE

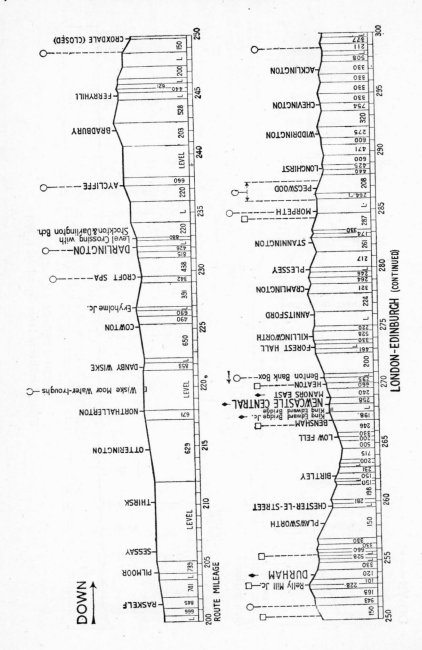

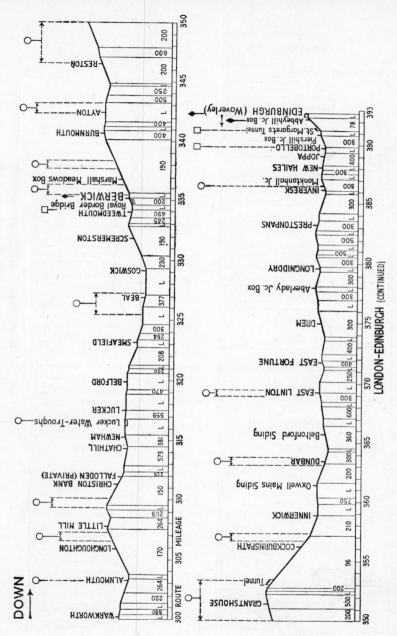

DOWN

LONDON–EDINBURGH (CONTINUED)

MILEAGE

ROUTE

WARKWORTH
ALNMOUTH
LONGHOUGHTON
LITTLE MILL
CHRISTON BANK
FALLODEN (PRIVATE)
CHATHILL
NEWHAM
Lucker Water-Troughs
LUCKER
BELFORD
SMEAFIELD
BEAL
GOSWICK
SCREMERSTON
TWEEDMOUTH
Royal Border Bridge
BERWICK
Marshall Meadows Box
BURNMOUTH
AYTON
RESTON

GRANTSHOUSE
Tunnel
COCKBURNSPATH
INNERWICK
Oxwell Mains Siding
DUNBAR
Beltonford Siding
EAST LINTON
EAST FORTUNE
DREM
Aberlady Jc. Box
LONGNIDDRY
PRESTONPANS
INVERESK
Monktonhall Jc.
NEW HAILES
JOPPA
PORTOBELLO
Piershill Jc. Box
St. Margarets Tunnel
Abbeyhill Jc. Box
EDINBURGH (Waverley)

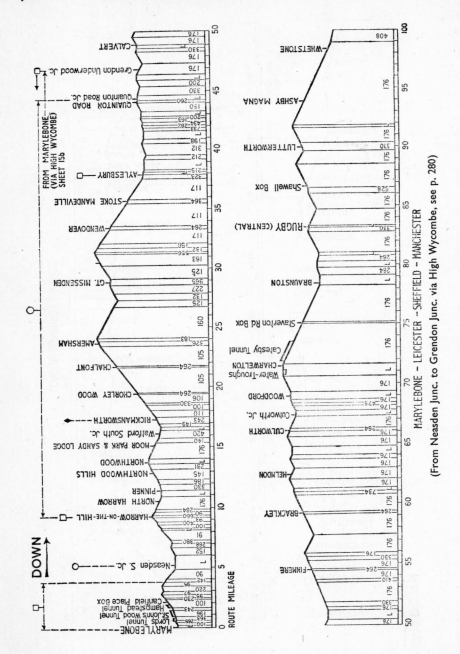

MARYLEBONE – LEICESTER – SHEFFIELD – MANCHESTER

(From Neasden Junc. to Grendon Junc. via High Wycombe, see p. 280)

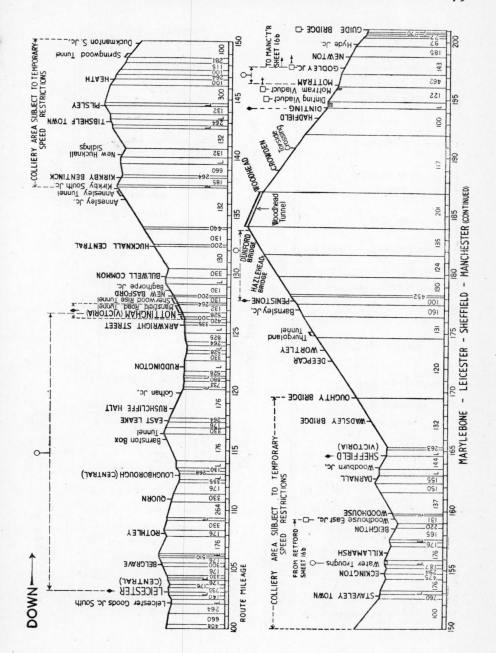

MARYLEBONE – LEICESTER – SHEFFIELD – MANCHESTER (CONTINUED)

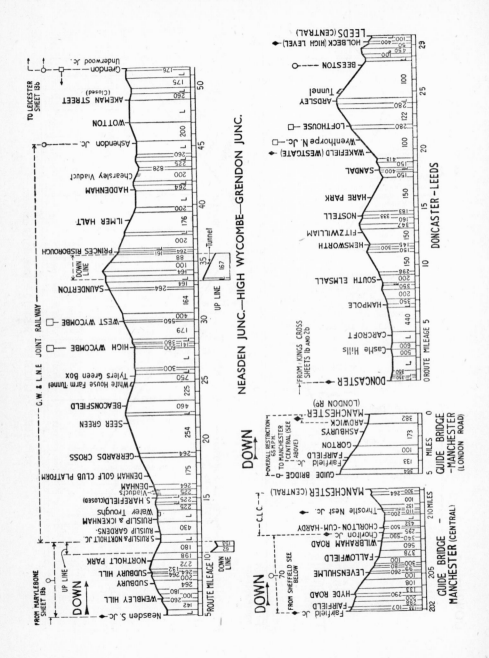

NEASDEN JUNC.—HIGH WYCOMBE—GRENDON JUNC.

DONCASTER—LEEDS

GUIDE BRIDGE—MANCHESTER (LONDON ROAD)

GUIDE BRIDGE—MANCHESTER (CENTRAL)

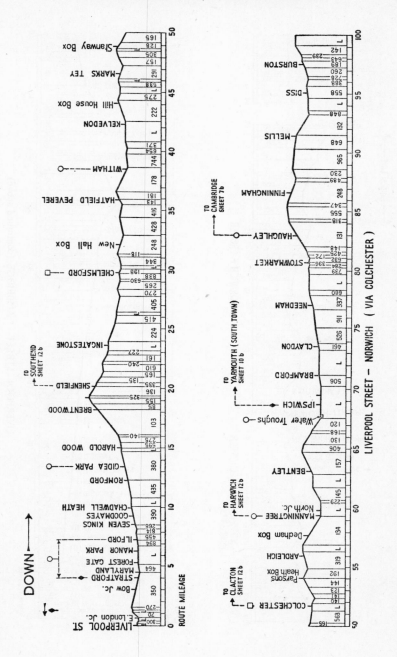

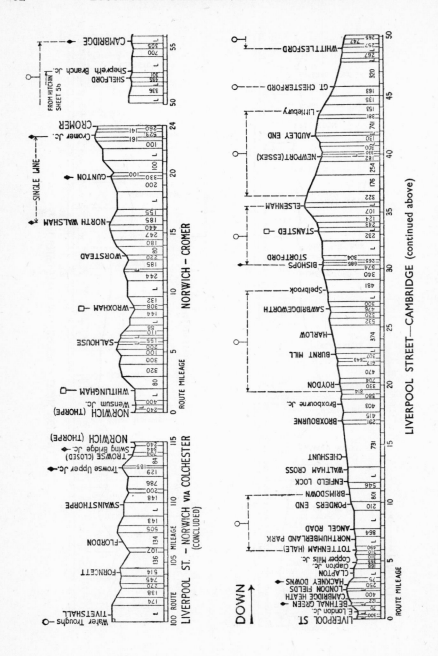

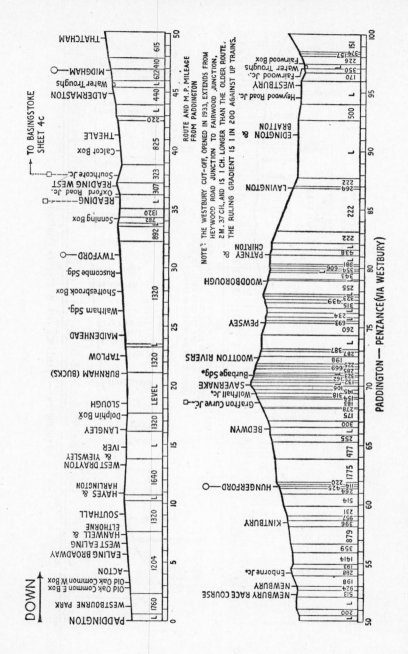

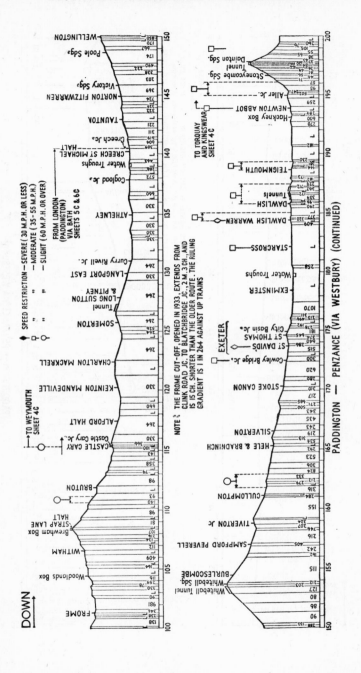

DOWN

PADDINGTON — PENZANCE (VIA WESTBURY) (CONTINUED)

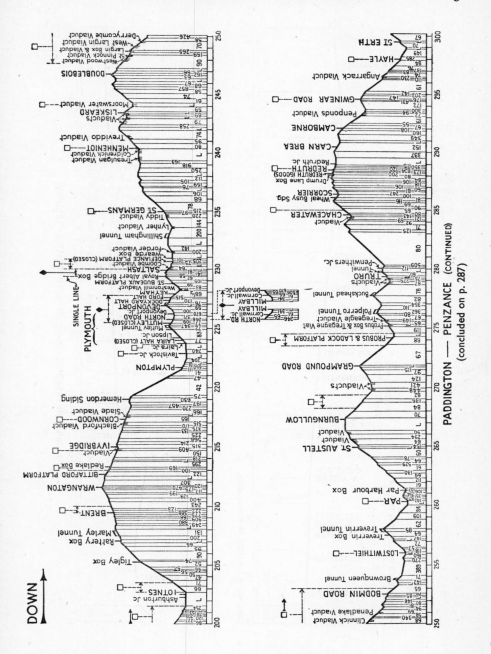

DOWN

PLYMOUTH

SINGLE LINE

PADDINGTON — PENZANCE (CONTINUED)

(concluded on p. 287)

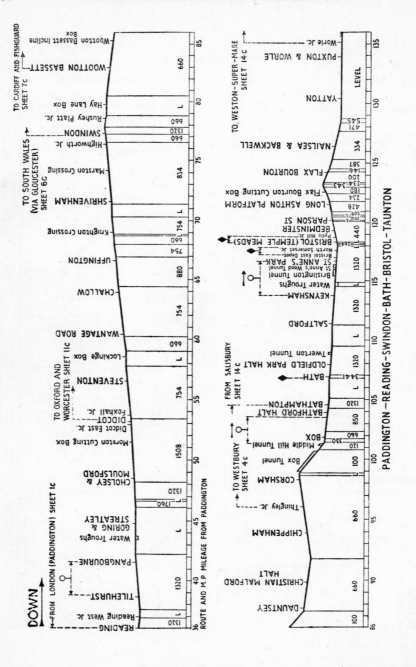

PADDINGTON – READING – SWINDON – BATH – BRISTOL – TAUNTON

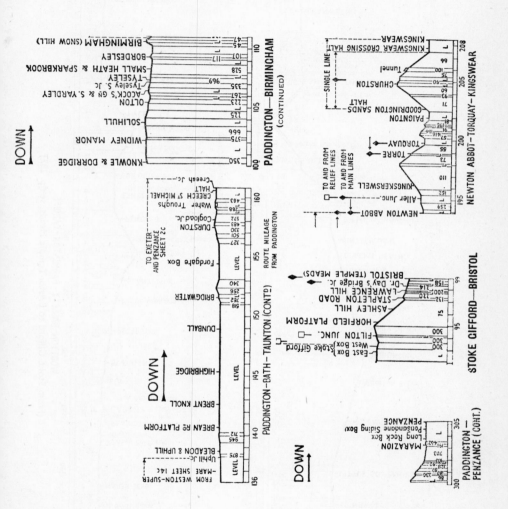

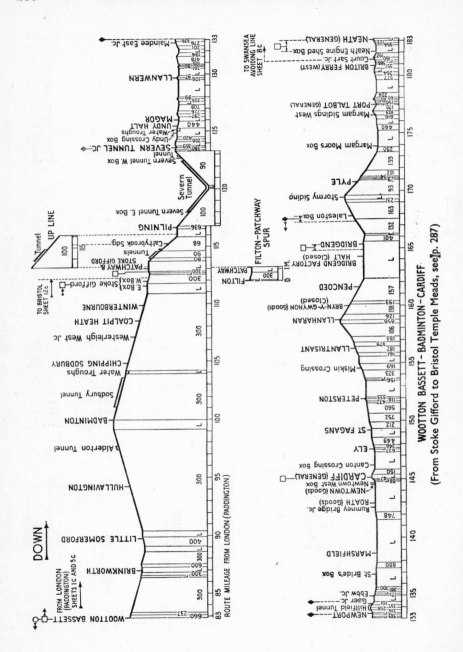

DOWN

FROM LONDON (PADDINGTON)
SHEETS 1C AND 5C

ROUTE MILEAGE FROM LONDON (PADDINGTON)

WOOTTON BASSETT–BADMINTON–CARDIFF
(From Stoke Gifford to Bristol Temple Meads, see p. 287)

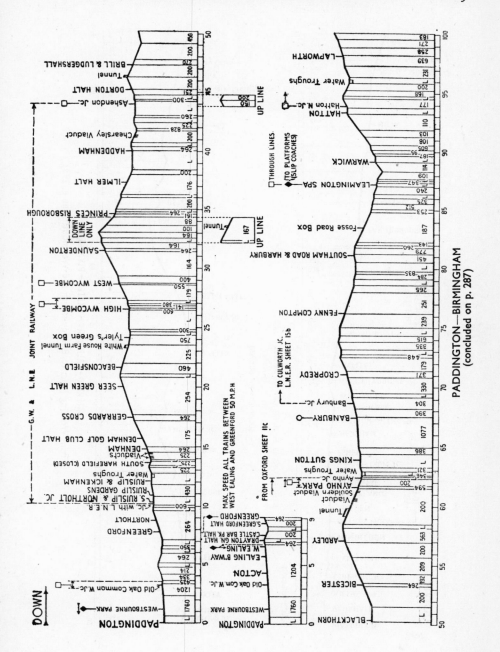

PADDINGTON—BIRMINGHAM
(concluded on p. 287)

V

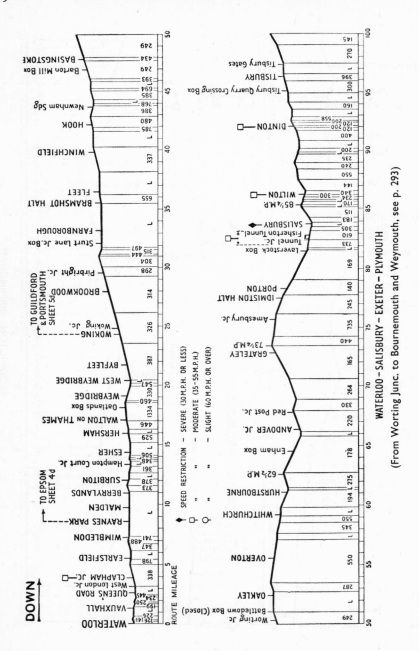

WATERLOO – SALISBURY – EXETER – PLYMOUTH

(From Worting Junc. to Bournemouth and Weymouth, see p. 293)

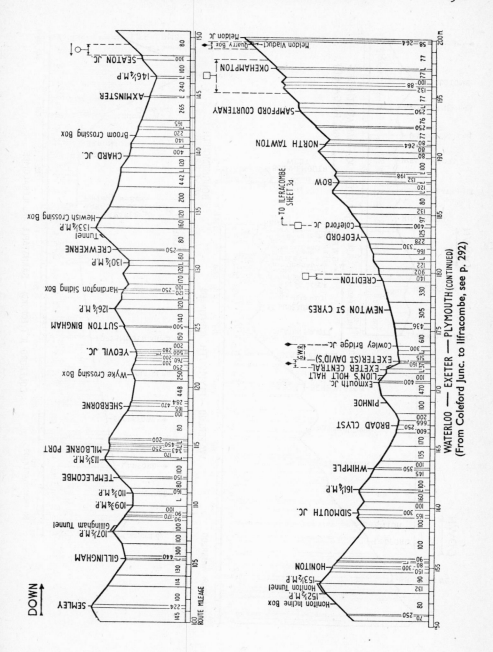

WATERLOO — EXETER — PLYMOUTH (CONTINUED)

(From Coleford Junc. to Ilfracombe, see p. 292)

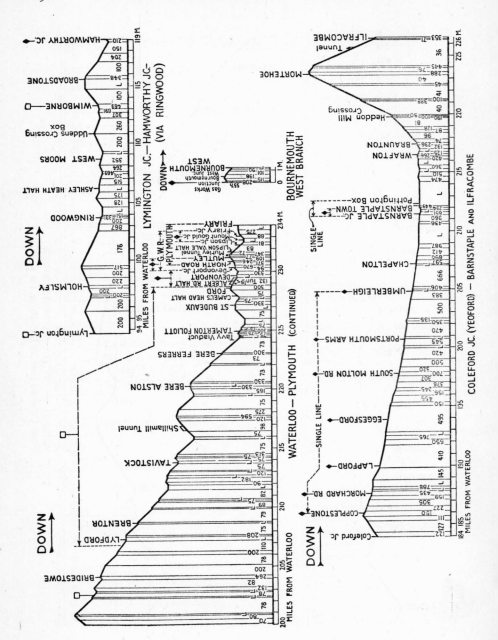

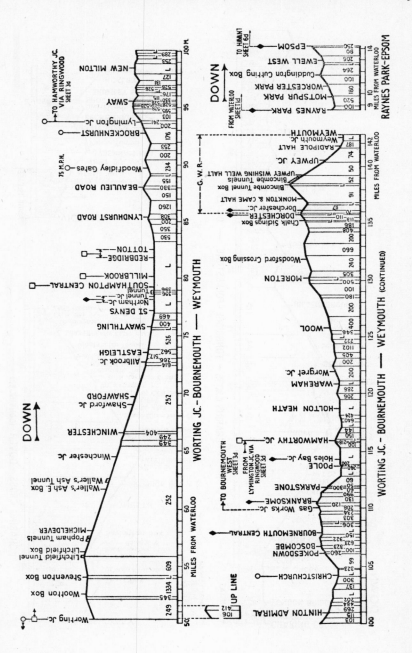

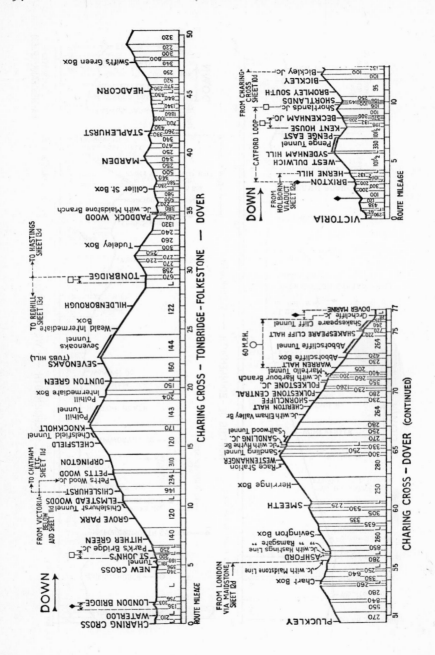

Index